INVESTIGATIONS GUIDE

Electromagnetic Force

Full Option Science System
Developed at the Lawrence Hall of Science, University of California, Berkeley
Published and Distributed by Delta Education

FOSS Lawrence Hall of Science Team
Larry Malone and Linda De Lucchi, FOSS Project Codirectors and Lead Developers
Kathy Long, FOSS Assessment Director; David Lippman, Program Manager; Carol Sevilla, Publications Design Coordinator;
Susan Stanley, Illustrator; John Quick, Photographer
FOSS Curriculum Developers: Brian Campbell, Teri Lawson, Alan Gould, Susan Kaschner Jagoda, Ann Moriarty, Jessica Penchos, Kimi Hosoume, Virginia Reid, Joanna Snyder, Erica Beck Spencer, Joanna Totino, Diana Velez, Natalie Yakushiji
Susan Ketchner, Technology Project Manager
FOSS Technology Team: Dan Bluestein Christopher Cianciarulo, Matthew Jacoby, Kate Jordan, Frank Kusiak, Nicole Medina, Jonathan Segal, Dave Stapley, Shan Tsai

Delta Education Team
Bonnie A. Piotrowski, Editorial Director, Elementary Science
Project Team: Jennifer Apt, Sandra Burke, Mary Connell, Joann Hoy, Kristen Mahoney, Jennifer McKenna, Angela Miccinello

Content Reviewer
Bryan J. Mendez
Astronomer & Public Education Specialist, Space Sciences Laboratory
University of California, Berkeley

Thank you to all FOSS Middle School Revision Trial Teachers and District Coordinators
Jonah Cohn, St. Anthony's School, Oakland, CA; Frances Amojioyi, Lincoln Middle School, Alameda, CA; Dean Anderson, Organized trials for Boston Public Schools, Boston, MA; Thomas Archer, Organized trials for ESD 112, Vancouver, WA; Lauresa Baker, Lincoln Middle School, Alameda, CA; Bobbi Anne Barnowsky, Canyon Middle School, Castro Valley, CA; Christine Bertko, St. Finn Barr Catholic School, San Francisco, CA; Stephanie Billinge, James P. Timilty Middle School, Roxbury, MA; Jerry Breton, Ingleside Middle School, Phoenix, AZ; Robert Cho, Timilty Middle School, Boston, MA; Susan Cohen, Cherokee Heights Middle School, Madison, WI; Malcolm Davis, Canyon Middle School, Castro Valley, CA; Marilyn Decker, Organized trials for Milton PS, Milton, MA; Jenny Ernst, Park Day School, Oakland, CA; Marianne Floyd, Spanaway Middle School, Spanaway, WA; Sarah Kathryn Gessford, Journeys School, Jackson, WY; Charles Hardin, Prairie Point Middle School, Cedar Rapids, IA; Jennifer Hartigan, Lincoln Middle School, Alameda, CA; Sheila Holland, TechBoston Academy, Boston, MA; Nicole Hoyceanyls, Charles S. Pierce Middle School, Milton, MA; Bruce Kamerer, Donald McKay K-8 School, East Boston, MA; Carmen Saele Kardokus, Reeves Middle School, Olympia, WA; Janey Kaufman, Organized trials for Scottsdale USD, Scottsdale, AZ; Erica Larson, Organized trials for Grant Wood AEA, Cedar Rapids, IA; Lindsay Lodholz, O'Keeffe Middle School, Madison, WI; Robert Mattisinko, Chaparral High School, Scottsdale, AZ; Brenda McGurk, Prairie Point Middle School, Cedar Rapids, IA; Tim Miller, Mountainside Middle School, Scottsdale, AZ; Thomas Miro, Lincoln Middle School, Alameda, CA; Spencer Nedved, Frontier Middle School, Vancouver, WA; Joslyn Olsen, Lincoln Middle School, Alameda, CA; Stephanie Ovechka, Cedarcrest Middle School, Spanaway, WA; Barbara Reinert, Copper Ridge School, Scottsdale, AZ; Stephen Ramos, Lincoln Middle School, Alameda, CA; Gina Rutenbeck, Prairie Point Middle School, Cedar Rapids, IA; John Sheridan, Boston Public Schools (Boston Schoolyard Initiative), Boston, MA; Barbara Simon, Timilty Middle School, Boston, MA; Lise Simpson, Alcott Middle School, Norman, OK; Autumn Stevick, Thurgood Marshall Middle School, Olympia, WA; Ted Stoeckley, Hall Middle School, Larkspur, CA; Lesli Taschwer, Organized trials for Madison SD, Madison, WI; Paula Warner, Alcott Middle School, Norman, OK; Darren T. Wells, James P. Timilty Middle School, Boston, MA; Kristin White, Frontier Middle School, Vancouver, WA

Photo Credits: © iStockphoto/Bosca78 (cover); © iStockphoto/Marcos Ribeiro de Cast; © Laurie Meyer/Delta Education; © Robert Nyholm/Shutterstock; © iStockphoto/Tommounsey; © Vasin Lee/Shutterstock; © anweber/Shutterstock; © Delta Education

Published and Distributed by Delta Education, a member of the School Specialty Family
The FOSS program was developed in part with the support of the National Science Foundation grant nos. ESI-9553600 and ESI-0242510. However, any opinions, findings, conclusions, statements, and recommendations expressed herein are those of the authors and do not necessarily reflect the views of NSF. FOSSmap was developed in collaboration between the BEAR Center at UC Berkeley and FOSS at the Lawrence Hall of Science.

Copyright © 2019 by The Regents of the University of California

All rights reserved. Any part of this work may not be reproduced or transmitted in any form or by any means, electronic or mechanical, including photocopying and recording, or by an information storage or retrieval system without prior written permission. For permission please write to: FOSS Project, Lawrence Hall of Science, University of California, Berkeley, CA 94720 or foss@berkeley.edu.

Electromagnetic Force
Investigations Guide, 1465681
978-1-62571-195-3
Printing 3 – 11/2017
Webcrafters, Madison, WI

INVESTIGATIONS GUIDE

Electromagnetic Force

TABLE OF CONTENTS

Overview 1
Framework and NGSS 33
Materials 61
Technology 71
Investigation 1: What Is Force? 81
Part 1: Push and Pull 94
Part 2: Friction 109
Part 3: Forces in Action 118

Investigation 2: The Force of Magnetism ... 137
Part 1: Properties of Magnets 150
Part 2: Magnetic Fields 160
Part 3: Force over Distance 178

Investigation 3: Electromagnetism 193
Part 1: Building a Circuit 206
Part 2: Building an Electromagnet 226
Part 3: Improving the Design 242

Investigation 4: Energy Transfer 257
Part 1: Electric Motors 270
Part 2: Electric Generators 281
Part 3: Force and Energy 303

Assessment 309

Welcome to FOSS® Next Generation™

Getting Started with FOSS Next Generation for Grades 6–8

Whether you're new to hands-on science or a FOSS veteran, you'll be up and running in no time and ready to lead your students on a fantastic voyage through the wonders of the natural and designed world.

Watch our short video series or browse the next few pages to get started!

Getting Started with FOSS: Meet Your Module video

Scan here or visit deltaeducation.com/goFOSS

Three-Dimensional Active Science

It's time to experience the three dimensions of the NGSS—**disciplinary core ideas**, **crosscutting concepts**, and **science and engineering practices**. Engage in rich investigations that immerse your students in real-world applications of important scientific phenomena, supported by just-in-time teaching tips and strategies.

Getting Started with Your Equipment Kit

Meet Your FOSS Course!

Your FOSS course includes one or more large boxes, called drawers, and two smaller boxes for the Teacher Toolkit, student books, and other equipment. Each drawer has a label on the front listing its contents.
Your packing list is always in Drawer 1.

Permanent Equipment

Your equipment kit includes enough permanent equipment for up to 8 groups (32 students). This equipment is classroom-tested and expected to last 7–10 years.

Consumable Equipment

Your kit also includes consumable materials for five class uses. Convenient refill kits provide materials for five additional uses and are available through Delta Education.

New Equipment Options for Middle Schools

We designed new, flexible equipment kit options to meet the unique needs of middle school classrooms. Whether you teach in a general education classroom or a well-stocked science lab, there's a FOSS Next Generation Middle School equipment kit option that's right for you:

	Full Kit	Lite Kit
Consumable items *(refill kits available)*	✓	✓
Unique, program-specific permanent items	✓	✓
Common science lab items *(beakers, graduated cylinders, etc.)* **or items found in multiple FOSS courses**	✓	

Live Organisms

Some investigations require live organisms. Schools are encouraged to purchase these organisms from a local biological supply company to minimize both transit time and the impact of adverse weather on the health of the organisms.

If living material cards are purchased from Delta Education, they will be shipped separately in a green and white envelope. Keep these cards in a safe place until it's time to redeem them for the investigation.

Call Delta Education at 800-258-1302 at least three weeks before you need your organisms.

Premium Student eBook Access

If your school purchased a premium class license for the *FOSS Science Resources* student eBook, your access codes will be shipped separately in a blue and white striped envelope. Use this access code on FOSSweb to unlock student eBook access.

Getting Started with Your Teacher Toolkit

The Teacher Toolkit is the most important part of the FOSS program. There are three parts of the Teacher Toolkit—the *Investigations Guide*, *Teacher Resources*, and the student *Science Resources* book. It's here that all the wisdom and experience from years of research and classroom development comes together to support teachers with lesson facilitation and in-depth strategies for taking investigations to the next level.

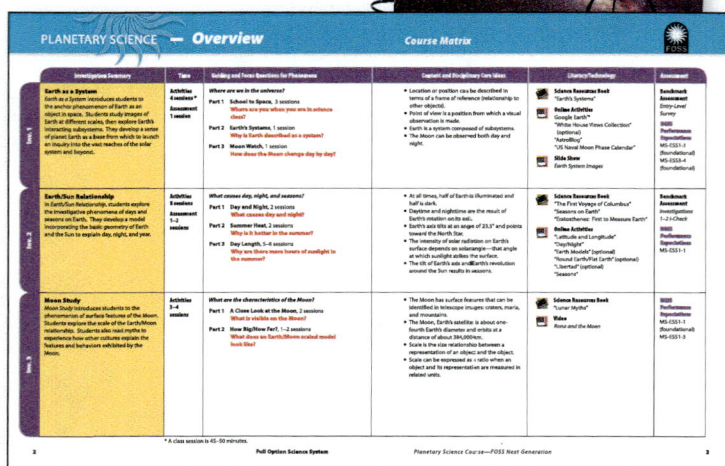

1. Investigations Guide

The *Investigations Guide* is your roadmap to prepare for and lead the FOSS investigations. Chapters are tabbed for easy access to important course information.

The course **Overview** gives you a high-level look at the 5–12 weeks of instruction in each course, including a summary matrix, schedule for the course, and product support contacts.

Framework and the NGSS provides a complete overview of NGSS connections, learning progressions, and background to support the conceptual framework for the course.

Course matrix

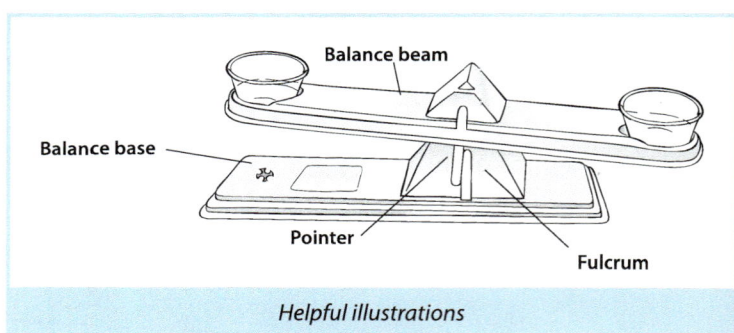

Helpful illustrations

The **Materials** chapter is a must-read resource that helps you get your student equipment ready for first-time use and shares helpful tips for getting your classroom ready for FOSS.

The **Technology** chapter provides an overview for each digital resource in the course and gets you up and running on FOSSweb.com, complete with technical support.

Each **Investigation** includes an At-a-Glance overview, science background content with NGSS connections, and in-depth guidance for preparing and facilitating instruction.

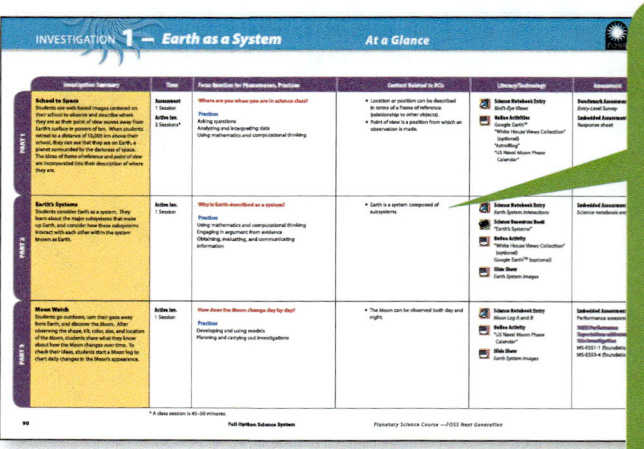

The At-a-Glance chart includes:
- Summaries and pacing for investigation scheduling
- Focus questions for investigative phenomena
- Connections to disciplinary core ideas
- Reading, writing, and technology integration opportunities
- Embedded and benchmark assessments

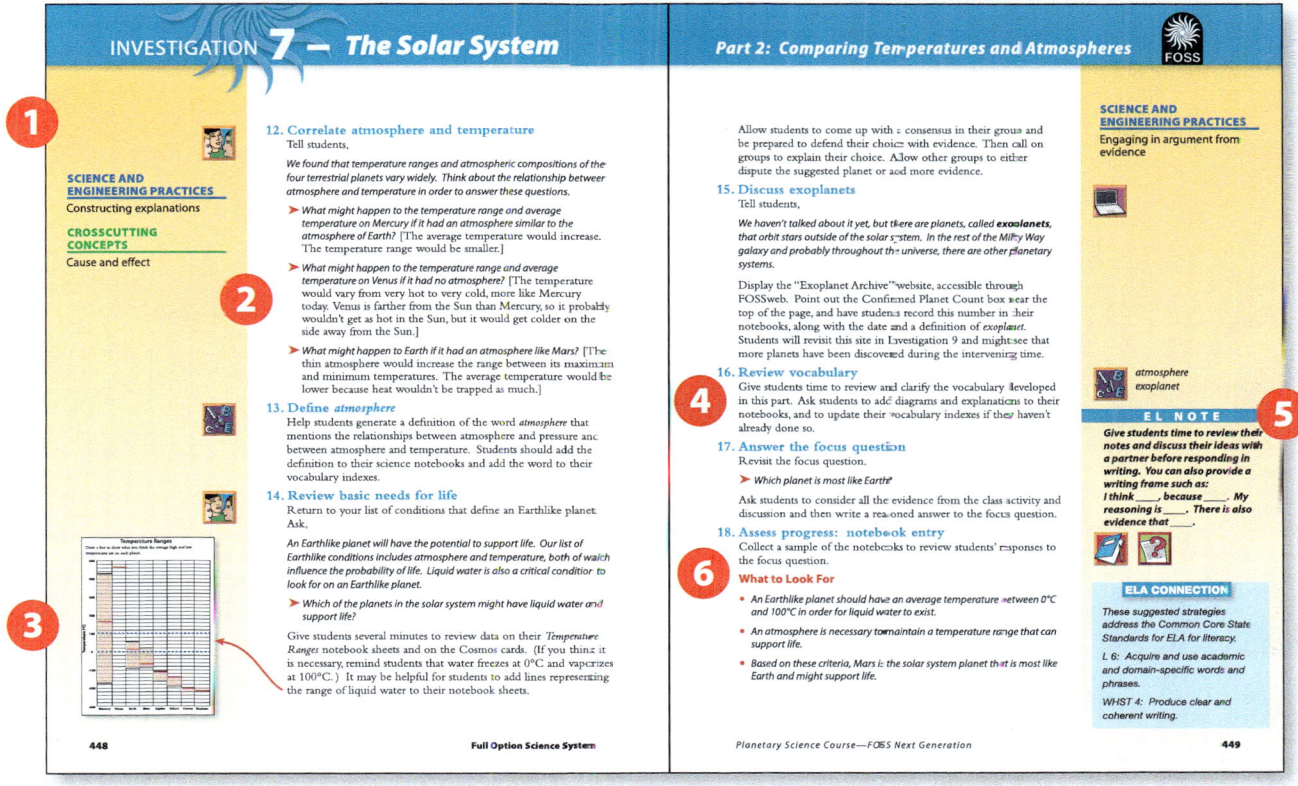

FOSS investigations provide the right support, when you need it with point-of-use guidance.

1. Key three-dimensional highlights
2. Guiding questions and expected responses
3. Helpful drawings and diagrams
4. Vocabulary review
5. Strategies to support English learners
6. Embedded assessment "What to Look For"

The **Assessment** chapter gives you an in-depth look at the research-based components of the FOSS Assessment System, guidance on assessing for the NGSS, and generalized next-step strategies to use in your classroom. Find duplication masters, assessment charts, coding guides, and specific next-step strategies on FOSSweb.com

Getting Started with Your Teacher Toolkit

2. Teacher Resources

Your *Investigations Guide* tells you how to facilitate each investigation of a course. The ***Teacher Resources*** provides guidance on how to do it at your grade level throughout the year with effective practices and strategies derived from extensive field-testing.

A grade-level **Planning Guide** provides an overview to your courses and an introduction to three-dimensional teaching and learning.

The **Science Notebooks** chapter provides age-appropriate methods to support students in developing productive science notebooks. Access powerful research-based next-step strategies to maximize the effectiveness of the notebook as a formative assessment tool.

Science-Centered Language Development is a collection of standards-aligned strategies to support and enhance literacy development in the context of science—reading, writing, speaking, listening, and vocabulary development.

Teacher Resources also includes:

- Elaborating science and engineering practices and crosscutting concepts as bridges to integrated instruction
- Information about access and equity and taking FOSS outdoors
- Grade level connections to Common Core ELA and Math standards
- Course-specific notebook, teacher, and assessment blackline masters.

Check FOSSweb for the latest updates to chapters in *Teacher Resources*.

3. FOSS Science Resources Student Book

The Teacher Toolkit includes one copy of the student book. Reading is an integral part of science learning. Reading informational text critically and effectively is an important component of today's ELA standards. Once students have engaged with phenomena first-hand, they go more in-depth with articles in *FOSS Science Resources*.

Articles from FOSS *Science Resources* complement and enhance the active investigations, giving students opportunities to:
- Ask and answer questions
- Use evidence to support their ideas
- Use text to acquire information
- Draw information from multiple sources
- Interpret illustrations to build understanding

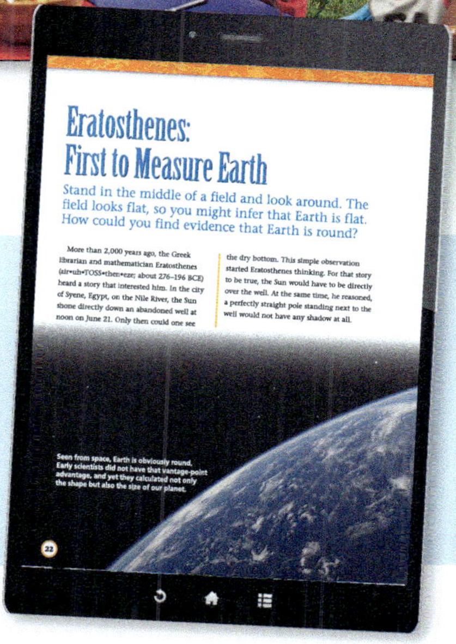

Interactive eBooks

FOSS Science Resources is available as a convenient, platform-neutral student eBook to support homework or out-of-school reading. Student access to eBooks is available as an additional purchase.

Getting Started with Technology

FOSSweb.com

Easy access to program support resources

FOSSweb.com is your home for accessing the complete portfolio of digital resources in the FOSS program. Easily manage each of your courses, create class pages for students, and keep helpful references at your fingertips.

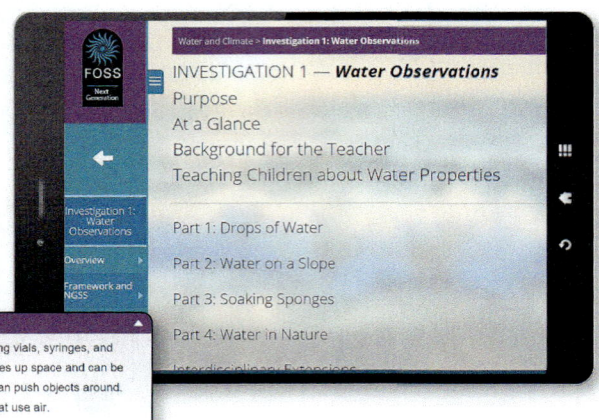

eInvestigations Guide

This easy-to-use interactive version of the *Investigations Guide* is mobile-friendly and offers simplified navigation, collapsible sections, and the ability to add customized notes. *(coming in 2018, PDF-based eBook available now)*

Resources by Investigation

Easily access the duplication masters, online activities, and streaming videos needed for the current investigation part.

Teacher Preparation Videos

Videos provide helpful equipment setup instructions, safety information, and a summary of what students will do and learn throughout a part.

Editable Teaching Slides

Access customizable teaching slides for each investigation part of middle school courses. Master slides are downloadable from FOSSweb and include focus questions, key investigation steps, student prompts, helpful illustrations, connections to integrated multimedia, and assessment.

Online Activities for Differentiating Instruction

FOSSweb digital resources provide engaging, interactive virtual investigations that offer additional content and skill support for students. These experiences also help students who were absent catch up with class.

Streaming Videos

Videos are available on FOSSweb to support many investigations and often take students "on location" around the world or showcase experiments that would be too messy, expensive, or dangerous for the classroom.

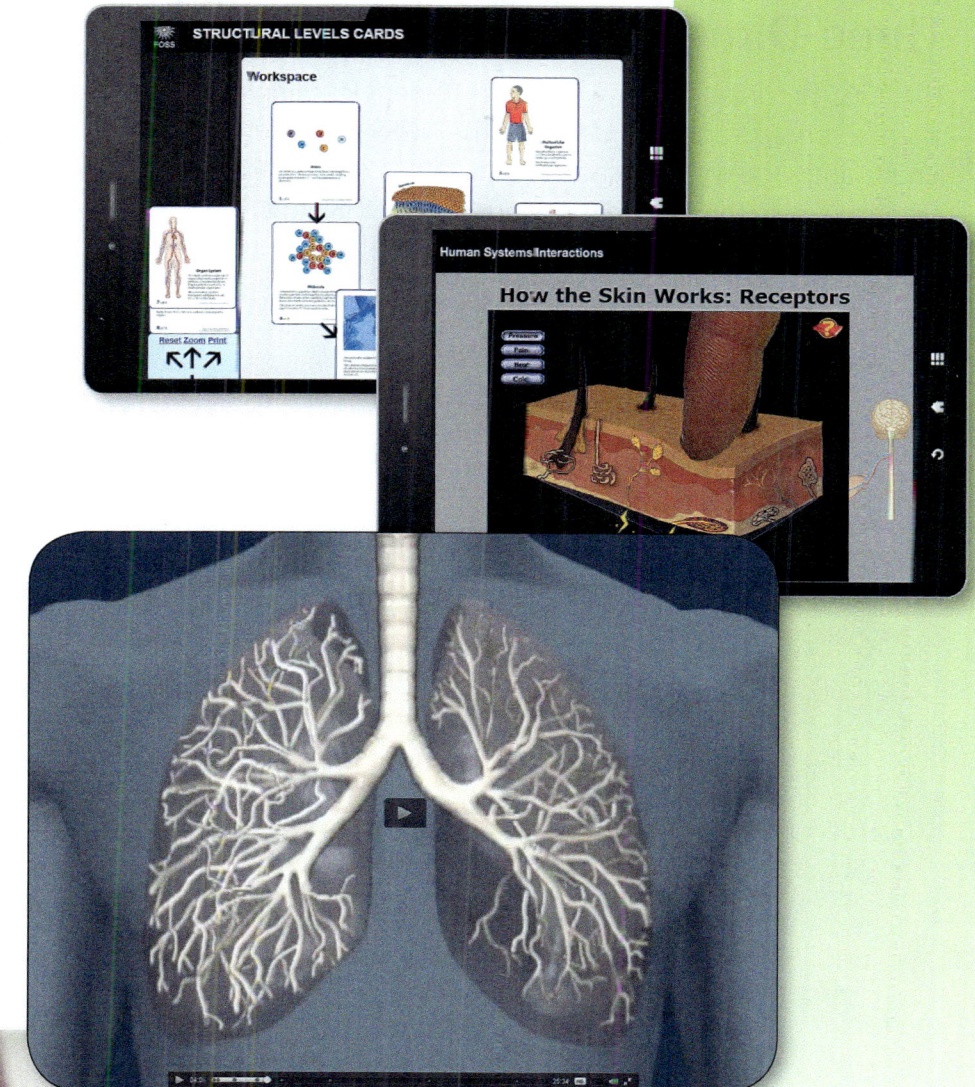

FOSSmap Online Assessment

Students in grades 6–8 can take benchmark assessments online with automatic coding of most responses to save you valuable time and provide instant feedback. A variety of student- and class-level reports help you identify where extra attention is needed and support communication with families and administration. FOSSmap is accessible through the FOSSweb portal.

Three-Dimensional Active Learning

The FOSS program has always placed student learning of science *practices* on equal footing with science *concepts* and *core ideas* and the NGSS and *Framework for K–12 Science Education* have provided a new language with which to articulate this. In each **FOSS Next Generation** investigation, students are engaged in the three dimensions of the NGSS to develop increasingly complex knowledge and understanding.

Science and engineering practices are the cognitive tools scientists and engineers use to answer questions and design solutions. FOSS students use these tools to gather evidence and to explain real-world phenomena.

Grade-level appropriate **disciplinary core ideas** are the concepts and established ideas of science. FOSS students develop these building blocks throughout investigations to make sense of phenomena.

Crosscutting concepts help students to connect the varied concepts and disciplines of science. FOSS students apply these concepts to different situations in order to make connections and develop comprehensive understanding.

FOSS Forward Thinking

The FOSS Vision

When the Full Option Science System (FOSS) began, the founders envisioned a science curriculum that was enjoyable, logical, and intuitive for teachers, and stimulating, provocative, and informative for students. Achieving this vision was informed by research in cognitive science, learning theory, and critical study of effective practice. The modular design of the FOSS product allowed users to select topics that aligned with district or state learning objectives, or simply resonated with their perception of comprehensive and reasonable science instruction. The original design of the FOSS Program was comprehensive in terms of coverage. FOSS was designed to provide real and meaningful student experience with important scientific ideas and to nurture developmentally appropriate knowledge of the objects, organisms, systems, and principles governing, the natural world.

The FOSS Next Generation Program

But the developers never envisioned FOSS to be a static curriculum, and now the Full Option Science System has evolved into a fully realized 21st century science program with authentic connection to the *Next Generation Science Standards (NGSS)*. The FOSS science curriculum is a comprehensive science program, featuring instructional guidance, student equipment, student reading materials, digital resources, and an embedded assessment system. The FOSS philosophy has always taken very seriously the teaching of good, comprehensive, accurate, science content using the methods of inquiry to advance that science knowledge. But the *Framework for K–12 Science Education*, on which the NGSS are based has allowed us to articulate our mission in a more coherent manner, using the vocabulary established by the authors of the *Framework*. The FOSS instructional design now strives to

a. communicate the disciplinary core ideas (content) of science, while

b. guiding and encouraging students to engage in or exercise the science and engineering practices (inquiry methods) to develop knowledge of the disciplinary core ideas, and

c. help students apprehend the crosscutting concepts (themes that unite core ideas, overarching concepts) that connect the learning experiences within a discipline and bridge meaningfully across disciplines as students gain more and more knowledge of the natural world.

The Full Option Science System has evolved into a fully realized 21st century science program with authentic connection to the Next Generation Science Standards (NGSS).

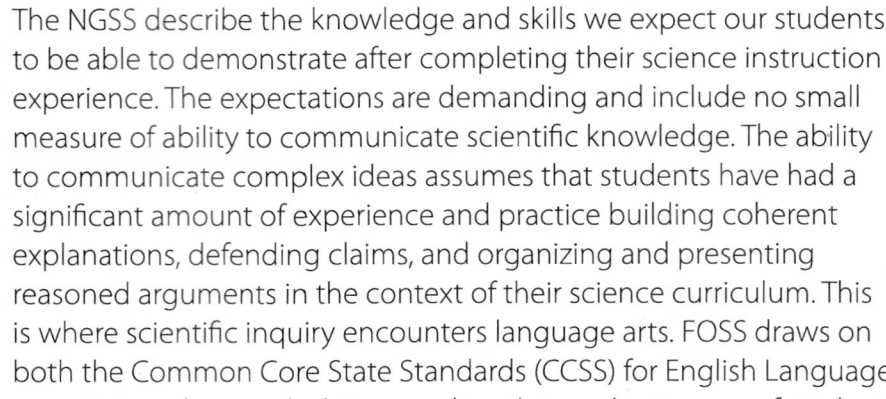

The NGSS describe the knowledge and skills we expect our students to be able to demonstrate after completing their science instruction experience. The expectations are demanding and include no small measure of ability to communicate scientific knowledge. The ability to communicate complex ideas assumes that students have had a significant amount of experience and practice building coherent explanations, defending claims, and organizing and presenting reasoned arguments in the context of their science curriculum. This is where scientific inquiry encounters language arts. FOSS draws on both the Common Core State Standards (CCSS) for English Language Arts and research data regarding the productive use of student science notebooks. FOSS developers realize that the most effective science program must seamlessly integrate science instruction goals and language arts skills. Science is one of the most engaging and productive arenas for introducing and exercising language arts skills: vocabulary, nonfiction (informational) reading, cause-and-effect relationships, on and on.

FOSS is strongly grounded in the realities of the classroom and the interests and experiences of the learners. The content in FOSS is teachable and learnable over multiple grade levels as students increase in their abilities to reason about and integrate complex ideas within and between disciplines.

FOSS is crafted with a structured, yet flexible, teaching philosophy that embraces the much-heralded 21st century skills; collaborative teamwork, critical thinking, and problem solving. The FOSS curriculum design promotes a classroom culture that allows both teachers and students to assume prominent roles in the management of the learning experience.

FOSS is built on the assumptions that understanding of core scientific knowledge and how science functions is essential for citizenship, that all teachers can teach science, and that all students can learn science. Formative assessment in FOSS creates a community of reflective practice. Teachers and students make up the community and establish norms of mutual support, trust, respect, and collaboration. The goal of the community is that everyone will demonstrate progress and will learn and grow.

Overview

ELECTROMAGNETIC FORCE — *Overview*

INTRODUCTION

Electricity and magnetism are some of the most fascinating physics phenomena to study in a middle school classroom. Students will measure the force of invisible magnetic fields, learn to build a circuit, design an electromagnet, and explain the energy transfers that make it all possible. The anchor phenomena for this course are force interactions and effects. The driving question for the course is what is the relationship between magnetic and electric forces?

In the **FOSS Electromagnetic Force Course**, students manipulate equipment to collect data about magnetic fields and electricity. They construct explanations based on observable patterns and develop models that define the cause-and-effect relationships of the forces and interactions they are measuring.

The culmination of the course leads students to consider accessible energy sources and the reliance of modern lifestyles on access to this energy, as well as the consequences of such energy use. Students leave this course with an understanding of force and energy that forms a solid foundation for high school and college physics.

FOSS Electromagnetic Force is a 6-week course.

Contents
Introduction 1
Course Matrix 2
FOSS Middle School Components 6
FOSS Instructional Design 10
Differentiated Instruction for Access and Equity 18
FOSS Investigation Organization 21
Classroom Organization 23
Establishing a Classroom Culture 28
Safety in the Classroom and Outdoors 31
FOSS Contacts 32

The NGSS Performance Expectations bundled in this course include:

Physical Sciences
MS-PS2-2
MS-PS2-3
MS-PS2-5
MS-PS3-2
MS-PS3-5

Earth and Space Sciences
MS-ESS3-4

Engineering Design
MS-ETS1-1
MS-ETS1-2
MS-ETS1-3
MS-ETS1-4

Full Option Science System

ELECTROMAGNETIC FORCE — Overview

	Investigation Summary	Time	Guiding and Focus Questions for Phenomena
Inv. 1	**What Is Force?** Students start their inquiry of force by using spring scales to push and pull objects, noting that some objects require more push or pull to put them into motion. Students are introduced to the idea of net force. They measure the force needed to move loads on different surfaces. Friction is developed as a force opposing motion, a force that changes depending on the two surfaces that are touching. Finally, students use net force to explain why force causes motion in some instances but not in others.	**Activities** 6 sessions * **Assessment** 2–3 sessions	*How are force and motion related?* Part 1 **Push and Pull**, 3 sessions What makes things move? Part 2 **Friction**, 1 session How does friction affect the force needed to move an object? Part 3 **Forces in Action**, 2 sessions How do multiple forces affect motion?
Inv. 2	**The Force of Magnetism** Students conduct an investigation to determine if like or opposite poles attract. They work with magnets and other objects to discover that magnetism acts through certain materials. They also discover that bringing a magnet close to a piece of iron induces magnetism in the iron. Students learn that these effects are manifestations of the invisible magnetic field that surrounds every magnet. Students use a spring balance to measure the force of attraction between magnets. They determine that the force of attraction between magnets decreases as the distance between them increases and that magnetic fields can overlap and add their forces together.	**Activities** 7 sessions **Assessment** 1–2 sessions	*How can we describe magnetic force?* Part 1 **Properties of Magnets**, 1 session What happens when magnets interact? Part 2 **Magnetic Fields**, 3 sessions How can we detect a magnetic field? Part 3 **Force over Distance**, 3 sessions What factors affect the force of attraction between magnets?

* A class session is 45–50 minutes.

Course Matrix

Content and Disciplinary Core Ideas	Literacy/Technology	Assessment
• A force is a push or a pull. • The metric unit for force is the newton (N). • Friction is a force that acts to oppose a force acting to put a mass in motion. • Net force is the sum of the forces acting on a mass.	**Science Resources Book** "The Force Is with You" "The Discovery of Friction" "Net Force" **Video** *Forces*	**Benchmark Assessment** *Entry-Level Survey* *Investigation 1 I-Check* **NGSS Performance Expectation** MS-PS2-2
• Magnets stick to (attract) objects that contain iron. • All magnets have two poles, a north pole on one side and a south pole on the other side. Like poles of magnets repel each other; opposite poles attract. • Magnets are surrounded by an invisible magnetic force field, which acts through space and through all nonmagnetic materials. • Magnetic materials may become temporary magnets when they interact with magnetic fields. • The magnitude of the magnetic force between two interacting magnetic fields decreases as the distance between them increases.	**Science Resources Book** "Magnetic Force" **Online Activity** "Adding Magnetic Fields" **Video** *Magnetism*	**Benchmark Assessment** *Investigation 2 I-Check* **NGSS Performance Expectations** MS-PS2-2 MS-PS2-3 MS-PS2-5 MS-PS3-2

Electromagnetic Force Course—FOSS Next Generation

ELECTROMAGNETIC FORCE — Overview

	Investigation Summary	Time	Guiding and Focus Questions for Phenomena
Inv. 3	**Electromagnetism** Students are introduced to electricity and energy. They discover how to make a complete circuit using a D-cell, wires, and a lightbulb. Students discuss the electricity's pathway in the circuit and the function of each of the system's components. Students discover that a steel core becomes a temporary magnet when current flows through an insulated wire wound around the steel core. They brainstorm different variables that might affect the strength of their electromagnet, and then test those variables. Working as a class, they combine their results to determine the best design for an electromagnet.	**Activities** 8 sessions * **Assessment** 1–2 sessions	*How are electricity and magnetism related?* Part 1 **Building a Circuit**, 3 sessions What is required to complete an electric circuit? Part 2 **Building an Electromagnet**, 3 sessions How does an electromagnet work? Part 3 **Improving the Design**, 3 sessions Student-generated question, e.g., How does (student-chosen process) affect the strength of an electromagnet?
Inv. 4	**Energy Transfer** Students operate an electric motor in a circuit, dissect a motor, and explain how it works after analyzing its components. They describe its design and function in terms of its components and energy transfers. They observe a generator and compare its components and function to a motor, explaining the interactions in terms of energy transfer. They consider energy sources for human electricity use and use solar cells to power an electric motor. Students read about human energy sources, including resource limitations and consequences. Finally, they consider key points from the entire course to prepare for the final benchmark assessment.	**Activities** 6 sessions **Assessment** 2–3 sessions	*How do humans use energy?* Part 1 **Electric Motors**, 2 sessions How does an electric motor work? Part 2 **Electric Generators**, 3 sessions How can we generate electrical energy? Part 3 **Force and Energy**, 1 session What is the relationship between magnetic and electrical forces?

* A class session is 45–50 minutes.

Course Matrix

Content and Disciplinary Core Ideas	Literacy/Technology	Assessment
• Energy transfers through an electric circuit from a source to components. • A magnetic field surrounds a wire through which electric current is flowing. • The magnetic field produced by a current-carrying wire can induce magnetism in a piece of iron or steel. • An electromagnet is made by sending electric current through an insulated wire wrapped around an iron core. • The strength of magnetism induced in the core of an electromagnet increases with the number of winds of wire, the amount of electric current flowing in the wire, and the iron content of the core.	**Science Resources Book** "Parts of an Incandescent Bulb" "Circuitry and Lightbulbs" "What Is Electricity?" "Electromagnetism" "Engineering Design Process" "Electromagnetic Engineering" **Online Activities** "Lighting a Bulb" "Kitchen Magnets" "Virtual Electromagnet"	**Benchmark Assessment** *Investigation 3 I-Check* **NGSS Performance Expectations** MS-PS2-2 MS-PS2-3 MS-PS2-5 MS-PS3-2 MS-ETS1-1 MS-ETS1-2 MS-ETS1-3 MS-ETS1-4

• An electric motor is designed with a commutator that acts as a switch turning on and off an electromagnet.
• Electric generators transfer energy from kinetic energy to electrical energy.
• Energy cannot be created or destroyed, only transferred.
• Every energy use can be described as a sequence of energy transfers.
• Energy sources can be categorized as renewable or nonrenewable.
	Science Resources Book
	"Motor Dissection A"
	"Motor Dissection B"
	"Generator Dissection"
	"The Rebirth of Electric Cars"
	"Where We Get Energy"
	Online Activity
	"Kitchen Magnets"
	Video
	Generator Dissection
		Benchmark Assessment
		Investigation 4 I-Check
		Posttest
		NGSS Performance Expectations
		MS-PS3-5
		MS-ESS3-3
		  (foundational)
		MS-ESS3-4
		  (foundational)

Electromagnetic Force Course—FOSS Next Generation

ELECTROMAGNETIC FORCE — *Overview*

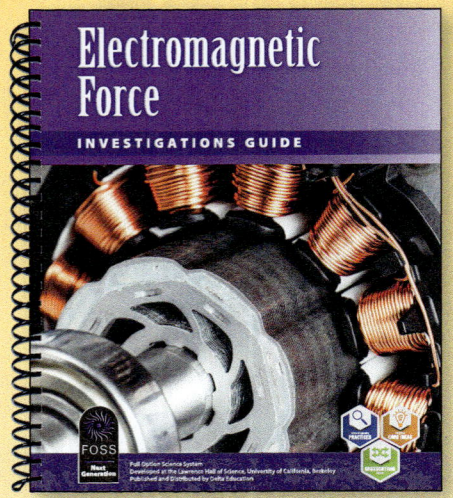

FOSS MIDDLE SCHOOL COMPONENTS

Teacher Toolkit for Each Module

Each course comes with a *Teacher Toolkit*. The *Teacher Toolkit* is the most important part of the FOSS Program. It is here that all the wisdom and experience contributed by hundreds of educators have been assembled. Everything we know about the content of the module, how to teach the subject, and the resources that will assist the effort are presented here. Each middle school toolkit has three parts.

Investigations Guide. This spiral-bound document contains these chapters.

- Overview
- Framework and NGSS
- Materials
- Technology
- Investigations (four in this course)
- Assessment

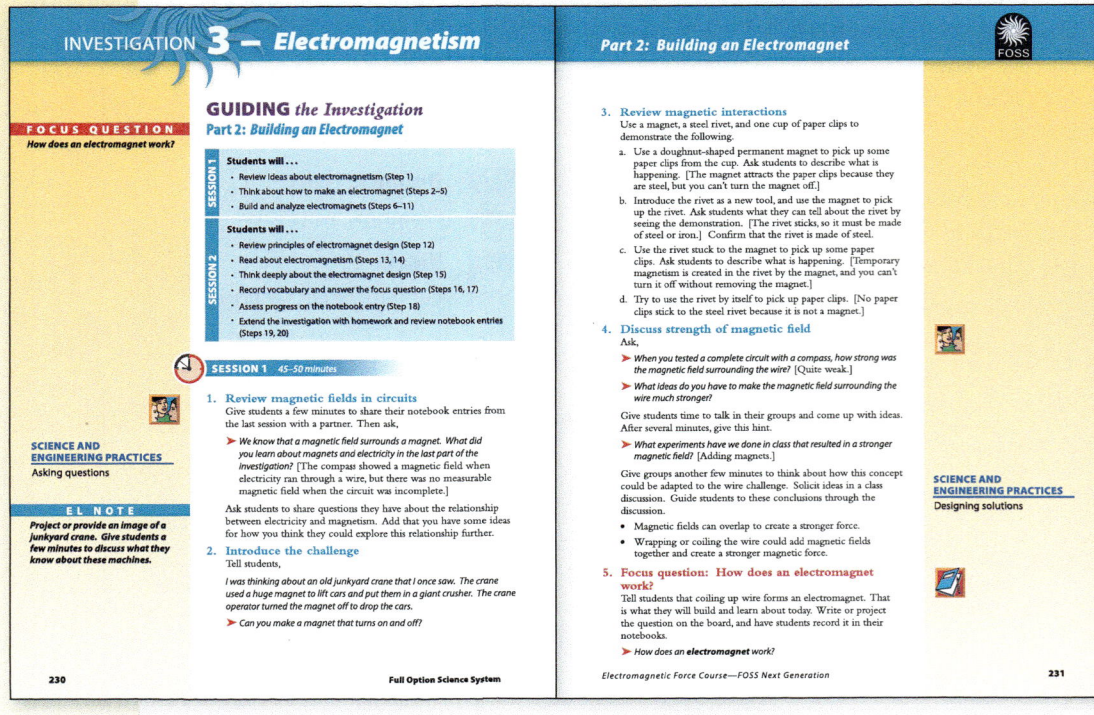

FOSS Middle School Components

FOSS Science Resources book. One copy of the student book of readings is included in the *Teacher Toolkit*.

Teacher Resources. These chapters can be downloaded from FOSSweb and most are also in the bound *Teacher Resources* book.

- FOSS Program Goals
- Grade-Level Planning Guide
- Science and Engineering Practices
- Crosscutting Concepts and Integration
- Sense-Making Disscussions for Three-Dimensional Learning
- Access and Equity
- Science Notebooks in Middle School
- Science-Centered Language Development in Middle School
- FOSS and Common Core ELA
- FOSS and Common Core Math
- Taking FOSS Outdoors
- Science Notebook Masters
- Teacher Masters
- Assessment Masters
- Notebook Answers

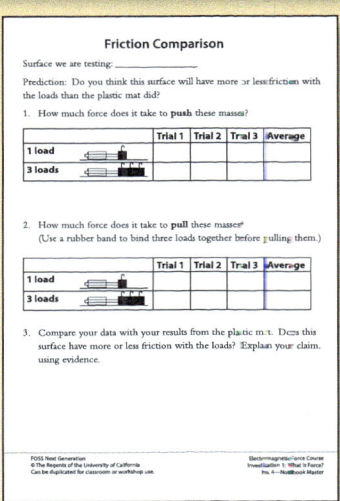

Equipment for Each Course

The FOSS Program provides the materials needed for the investigations in sturdy, front-opening drawer-and-sleeve cabinets. Inside, you will find high-quality materials packaged for a class of 32 students. Consumable materials are supplied for five sequential uses (five periods in one day) before you need to restock. You will need to supply some items usually available in middle school science classrooms, and they are listed separately in the materials lists.

The middle school equipment kits are divided into unique permanent items, common permanent items, and consumable items. Speak to your FOSS sales representative about custom configuration to best address your classroom needs.

Electromagnetic Force Course—FOSS Next Generation

ELECTROMAGNETIC FORCE — Overview

FOSS Science Resources Books

FOSS Science Resources: Electromagnetic Force is a book of original readings developed to accompany this course. The readings are referred to as articles in the *Investigations Guide*. Students read the articles in the book as they progress through the course. The articles cover specific concepts, usually after the concepts have been introduced in the active investigation.

The articles in *FOSS Science Resources* and the discussion questions provided in the *Investigations Guide* help students make connections to the science concepts introduced and explored during the active investigations. Concept development is most effective when students are allowed to experience organisms, objects, and phenomena firsthand before engaging the concepts in text. The text and illustrations help make connections between what students experience concretely and the ideas that explain their observations.

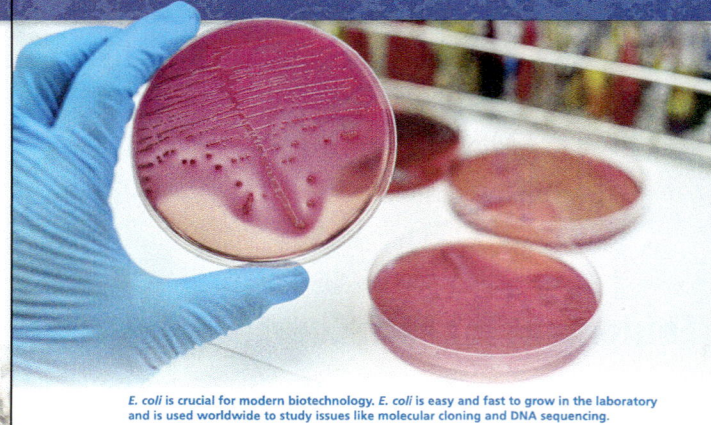

8   **Full Option Science System**

FOSS Middle School Components

Technology

The FOSS website opens new horizons for educators and students in the classroom or at home. Each course has digital resources for students—interactive simulations, resources for research, and online activities. For teachers, FOSSweb provides resources for materials management, general teaching tools for FOSS, purchasing links, contact information for the FOSS Program, and technical support.

For each course, registered FOSSweb users can view teacher preparation videos, download editable teacher slides for classroom instruction, print or display digital duplication masters in English or Spanish, and get reports from the online assessment system, FOSSmap.

As a registered FOSSweb educator, you can customize your homepage, set up easy access to the digital components of the courses you teach, and create class pages for your students with access to activities and online assessments.

▶ **NOTE**
To access all the teacher resources and to set up customized pages for using FOSS, log in to FOSSweb through an educator account. See the Technology chapter for more specifics.

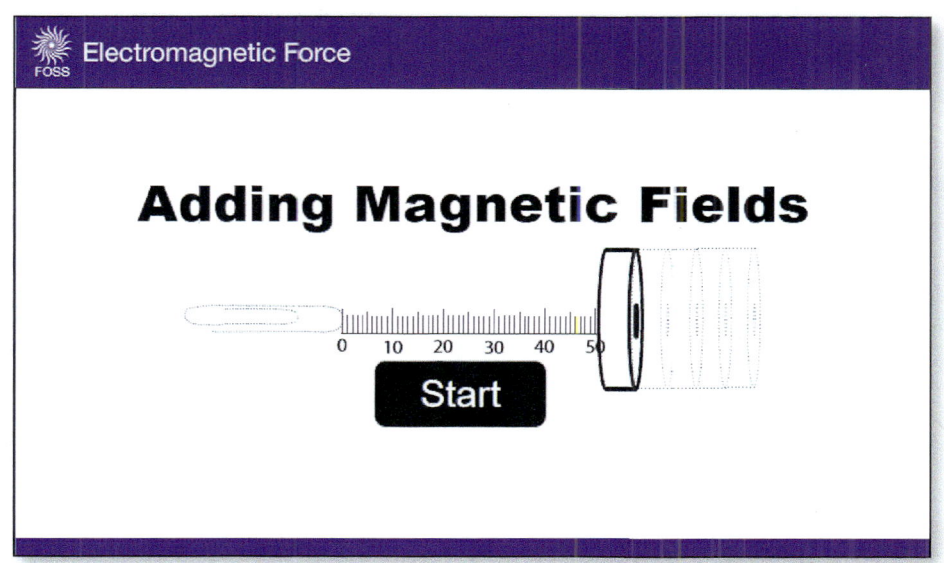

Ongoing Professional Learning

The Lawrence Hall of Science and Delta Education strive to develop long-term partnerships with districts and teachers through thoughtful planning, effective implementation, and ongoing teacher support. FOSS has a strong network of consultants who have rich and experienced backgrounds in diverse educational settings using FOSS.

▶ **NOTE**
Look for professional-development opportunities and online teaching resources on www.FOSSweb.com.

Electromagnetic Force Course—FOSS Next Generation

ELECTROMAGNETIC FORCE — *Overview*

FOSS INSTRUCTIONAL DESIGN

FOSS is designed around active investigation that provides engagement with science concepts and science and engineering practices. Surrounding and supporting those firsthand investigations are a wide range of experiences that help build student understanding of core science concepts and deepen scientific habits of mind.

The Elements of the FOSS Instructional Design

Using Formative Assessment

Integrating Science Notebooks

Active Investigation

Solving Real-World Problems and Engineering Challenges

Engaging in Science–Centered Language Development

Engaging with Technology

Reading FOSS Science Resources Books

FOSS Instructional Design

Each FOSS investigation follows a similar design to provide multiple exposures to science concepts. The design includes these pedagogies.

- Active investigation in collaborative groups: firsthand experiences with phenomena in the natural and designed worlds
- Recording in science notebooks to answer a focus question dealing with the scientific phenomenon under investigation
- Informational reading in *FOSS Science Resources* books
- Online activities to acquire data or information or to elaborate and extend the investigation
- Opportunities to apply knowledge to solve problems through the engineering design process or to address regional ecological issues
- Assessment to monitor progress and motivate student learning

In practice, these components are seamlessly integrated into a curriculum designed to maximize every student's opportunity to learn.

A **learning cycle** employs an instructional model based on a constructivist perspective that calls on students to be actively involved in their own learning. The model systematically describes both teacher and learner behaviors in a systematic approach to science instruction.

The most recent model employs a series of five phases of intellectual involvement known as the 5Es: engage, explore, explain, elaborate, and evaluate. The body of foundational knowledge that informs contemporary learning-cycle thinking has been incorporated seamlessly and invisibly into the FOSS curriculum design.

Engagement with real-world **phenomena** is at the heart of FOSS. In every part of every investigation, the central phenomenon is referenced implicitly in the focus question that guides instruction and frames the intellectual work. The focus question is a prominent part of each lesson and is called out for the teacher and student. The investigation Scientific and Historical Background section is organized by focus question—the teacher has the opportunity to read and reflect on the phenomenon in each part before in preparing for the lesson. Students record the focus question in their science notebooks, and after exploring the phenomenon thoroughly, explain their thinking in words and drawings.

In science a phenomenon is a natural occurrence, circumstance, or structure that is perceptible by the senses—an observable reality. Scientific phenomena are not necessarily phenomenal (although they may be)—most of the time they are pretty mundane and well within the everyday experience. What FOSS does to enact an effective engagement with the NGSS is thoughtful selection of phenomena for students to investigate.

> **NOTE**
> The anchor phenomena establish the storyline for the module. The investigative phenomena guide each investigation part. Related examples of everyday phenomena are incorporated into the readings, videos, discussions, formative assessments, outdoor experiences, and extensions.

ELECTROMAGNETIC FORCE — Overview

Active Investigation

Active investigation is a master pedagogy. Embedded within active learning are a number of pedagogical elements and practices that keep active investigation vigorous and productive. The enterprise of active investigation includes

- context: questioning and planning;
- activity: doing and observing;
- data management: recording, organizing, and processing;
- analysis: discussing and writing explanations.

Context: questioning and planning. Active investigation requires focus. The context of an inquiry can be established with a focus question about a phenomenon or challenge from you, or in some cases, from students—What is required to complete an electric circuit? At other times, students are asked to plan a method for investigation. This might include determining the important data to gather and the necessary tools. In either case, the field available for thought and interaction is limited. This clarification of context and purpose results in a more productive investigation.

Activity: doing and observing. In the practice of science, scientists put things together and take things apart, they observe systems and interactions, and they conduct experiments. This is the core of science—active, firsthand experience with objects, organisms, materials, and systems in the natural world. In FOSS, students engage in the same processes. Students often conduct investigations in collaborative groups of four, with each student taking a role to contribute to the effort.

The active investigations in FOSS are cohesive, and build on each other and the readings to lead students to a comprehensive understanding of concepts. Through the investigations, students gather meaningful data.

Online activities throughout the course provide students with opportunities to collect data, manipulate variables, and explore models and simulations beyond what can be done in the classroom. Seamless integration of the online activities forms an integral part of students' active investigations in FOSS.

Data management: recording, organizing, and processing. Data accrue from observation, both direct (through the senses) and indirect (mediated by instrumentation). Data are the raw material from which scientific knowledge and meaning are synthesized. During and after work with materials, students record data in their notebooks. Data recording is the first of several kinds of student writing.

FOSS Instructional Design

Students then organize data so that they will be easier to think about. Tables allow efficient comparison. Organizing data in a sequence (time) or series (size) can reveal patterns. Students process some data into graphs, providing visual display of numerical data. They also organize data and process them in the science notebook.

Analysis: discussing and writing explanations. The most important part of an active investigation is extracting its meaning. This constructive process involves logic, discourse, and existing knowledge. Students share their explanations for phenomena, using evidence generated during the investigation to support their ideas. They conclude the active investigation by writing in their notebooks a summary of their learning as well as questions raised during the activity.

Science Notebooks

Research and best practice have led us to place more emphasis on the student science notebook. Keeping a notebook helps students organize their observations and data, process their data, and maintain a record of their learning for future reference. The process of writing about their science experiences and communicating their thinking is a powerful learning device for students. And the student notebook entries stand as a credible and useful expression of learning. The artifacts in the notebooks form one of the core elements of the assessment system.

You will find the duplication masters for middle school presented in a notebook format. They are reduced in size (two copies to a standard sheet) for placement (glue or tape) in a bound composition book. Student work is entered partly in spaces provided on the notebook sheets and partly on adjacent blank sheets. Full-sized masters that can be filled in electronically and are suitable for projection are available on FOSSweb. Look to the chapter in *Teacher Resources* called Science Notebooks in Middle School for more details on how to use notebooks with FOSS.

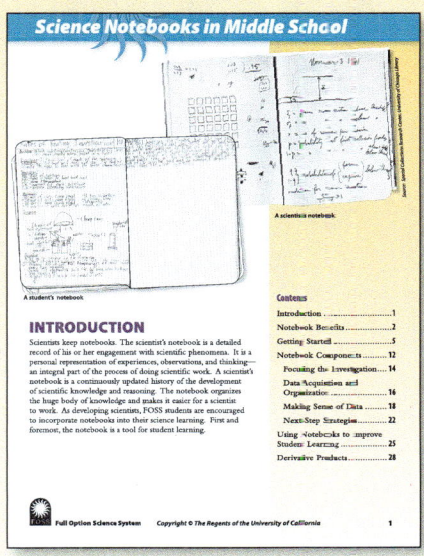

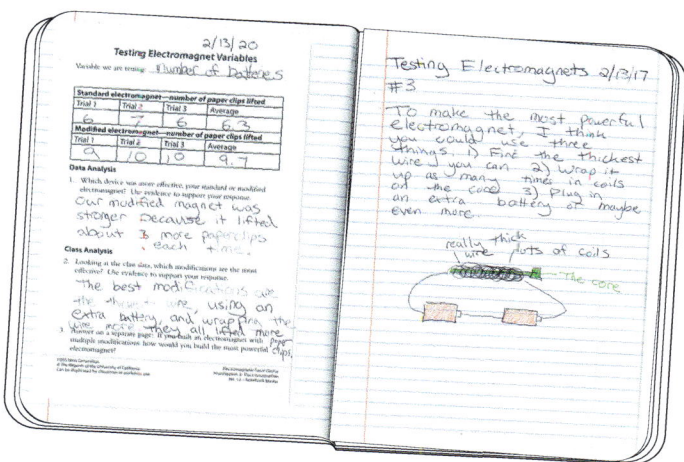

Electromagnetic Force Course—FOSS Next Generation

ELECTROMAGNETIC FORCE — *Overview*

Reading in *Science Resources*

Reading is a vital component of the FOSS Program. Reading enhances and extends information and concepts acquired through direct experience.

Readings are included in the **FOSS Science Resources: Electromagnetic Force** book. Students read articles as well as access data and information for use in investigations.

Some readings can be assigned as homework or extension activities, whereas other readings have been deemed important for all students to complete with a teacher's support in class.

Each in-class reading has a reading guide embedded in Guiding the Investigation. The reading guide suggests breakpoints with questions to help students connect the reading to their experiences from class, and recommends notebook entries. Each of these readings also includes one or more prompts that ask students to make additional notebook entries. These prompts should help students who missed the in-class reading to process the article in a more meaningful way. Some of the most essential articles are provided as notebook masters. Students can highlight the article as they read, add notes or questions, and add the article to their science notebooks.

The FOSS and Common Core ELA chapter in *Teacher Resources* shows how FOSS provides opportunities to develop and exercise the Common Core ELA practices through science. A detailed table identifies these opportunities in the FOSS courses for middle school.

Integrating Technology through FOSSweb

The simulations and online activities on FOSSweb are designed to support students' learning at specific times during instruction. Digital resources include streaming videos that can be viewed by the class or small groups.

The Technology chapter provides details about the online activities for students and the tools and resources for teachers to support and enrich instruction. There are many ways for students to engage with the digital resources—in class as individuals, in small groups, or as a whole class, and at home with family and friends.

FOSS Instructional Design

Assessing Progress

The FOSS assessment system includes both formative and summative assessments. Formative assessment monitors learning during the process of instruction. It measures progress, provides information about learning, and is predominantly diagnostic. Summative assessment looks at the learning after instruction is completed, and it measures achievement.

Formative assessment in FOSS, called **embedded assessment**, is an integral part of instruction, and occurs on a daily basis. You observe action during class in a performance assessment or review notebooks after class. Performance assessments look at students' engagement in science and engineering practices or their recognition of crosscutting concepts. Embedded assessment provides continuous monitoring of students' learning and helps you make decisions about whether to review, extend, or move on to the next idea to be covered.

The embedded assessments are based on authentic work produced by students during the course of participating in the FOSS activities. Students do their science, and you look at their notebook entries. Bullet points in Guiding the Investigation tell you specifically what students should know and be able to communicate.

Benchmark assessments are short summative assessments given after each investigation. These **I-Checks** are actually hybrid tools: they provide summative information about students' achievement, and because they occur soon after teaching each investigation, they can be used diagnostically as well. Reviewing specific items on an I-Check with the class provides additional opportunities for students to clarify their thinking.

If student work is incorrect or incomplete, you know that there has been a breakdown in learning or communications. The assessment system provides a menu of next-step strategies to resolve the situation. Embedded assessment is assessment *for* learning, not assessment *of* learning.

Assessment *of* learning is the domain of the benchmark assessments. Benchmark assessments are delivered at the beginning of the module (*Entry-Level Survey*) and at the end of the module (*Posttest*), and after each investigation (I-Checks). The benchmark tools are carefully crafted and thoroughly tested assessments composed of valid and reliable items. The assessment items do not simply identify whether a student knows a piece of science content. They also identify the depth to which students understand science concepts and principles and the extent to which they can apply that understanding.

▶ TECHNOLOGY COMPONENTS OF THE FOSS ASSESSMENT SYSTEM

FOSSmap for teachers and online assessment for students are the technology components of the FOSS assessment system. Students can take assessments online. FOSSmap provides the tools for you to review those assessments online so you can determine next steps for the class or differentiated instruction for individual students based on assessment performance. For updated information on FOSSmap, download the latest Assessment chapter and coding guides on FOSSweb.

ELECTROMAGNETIC FORCE — Overview

Solving Real-World Problems

FOSS investigations introduce science content in the context of real-world applications, so that students develop an understanding of how scientific principles explain natural phenomena. By middle school, students can begin to apply this understanding of science to develop solutions to real-world problems. We ask students to consider problem-solving and engineering challenges that are precise in scope, giving students a thorough understanding of the problem and potential solutions. Students have clear criteria and constraints (in the case of engineering design challenges) and focused topics of research (in the case of research projects).

In life science, students explore local environments, issues of biodiversity, medical technology applications, and human impact upon ecosystems. In earth science, students consider natural resource supplies and demands, technological advances in space exploration, and human effects on Earth's ocean and atmosphere. In physical science, students apply concepts of motion, kinetic energy, heat, and energy transfer in a series of engineering challenges where students develop and refine designs to meet solve an engineering problem.

Throughout all content areas, students have opportunities to collaborate and develop or select solutions to real-world issues. As described in the NRC *Framework* (2012, page 12), "engineering and technology provide a context in which students can test their own developing scientific knowledge and apply it to practical problems; doing so enhances their understanding of science—and, for many, their interest in science—as they recognize the interplay among science, engineering, and technology." By providing students with ongoing opportunities to understand and engage with the application of science, we help students develop an appreciation of and enthusiasm for science.

Taking FOSS Outdoors

The true value of science knowledge is its usefulness in the real world and not just in the classroom. When students are able to transfer knowledge of scientific principles to natural systems, they experience a sense of accomplishment.

FOSS middle school courses provide outdoor activities and extensions. Teaching outdoors is the same as teaching indoors—except for the space. Because of the different space, new management procedures are required. Students can get farther away. Materials have to be transported. The space has to be defined and honored. Time has to be budgeted for getting to, moving around in, and returning from the outdoor study site. All these and more issues and solutions are discussed in the Taking FOSS Outdoors chapter in *Teacher Resources* on FOSSweb.

FOSS Instructional Design

Science-Centered Language Development and Standards for Literacy in Science

The FOSS active investigations, science notebooks, *FOSS Science Resources* articles, and formative assessments provide rich contexts in which students develop and exercise thinking and communication. These elements are essential for effective instruction in both science and language arts—students experience the natural world in real and authentic ways and use language to inquire, process information, and communicate their thinking about scientific phenomena. FOSS refers to this development of language process and skills within the context of science as science-centered language development.

In the Science-Centered Language Development in Middle School chapter in *Teacher Resources*, we explore the intersection of science and language and the implications for effective science teaching and language development. Language plays two crucial roles in science learning: (1) it facilitates the communication of conceptual and procedural knowledge, questions, and propositions, and (2) it mediates thinking—a process necessary for understanding. Science provides a real and engaging context for developing literacy, and language-arts skills and strategies to support conceptual development and scientific practices. The skills and strategies used for enhancing reading comprehension, writing expository text, and exercising oral discourse are applied when students are recording their observations, making sense of science content, and communicating their ideas.

The most effective integration depends on the type of investigation, the experience of students, the language skills and needs of students, and the language objectives that you deem important at the time. The Science-Centered Language Development chapter is a library of resources and strategies for you to use. The chapter describes how literacy strategies are integrated purposefully into the FOSS investigations, gives suggestions for additional literacy strategies that both enhance students' learning in science and develop or exercise English-language literacy skills, and develops science vocabulary with scaffolding strategies for supporting all learners. We identify effective practices in language-arts instruction that support science learning and examine how learning science content and engaging in science and engineering practices support language development.

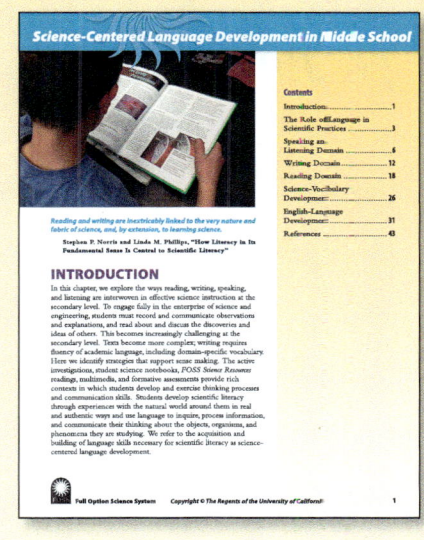

Specific methods to make connections to the Common Core State Standards for Literacy in Science are included in the flow of Guiding the Investigation. These recommended methods are linked through ELA Connection notes. In addition, the FOSS and the Common Core ELA chapter in *Teacher Resources* summarizes all of the connections to each standard at the given grade level.

ELECTROMAGNETIC FORCE — *Overview*

DIFFERENTIATED INSTRUCTION FOR ACCESS AND EQUITY

Learning from Experience

The roots of FOSS extend back to the mid-1970s and the Science Activities for the Visually Impaired and Science Enrichment for Learners with Physical Handicaps projects (SAVI/SELPH). As those special-education science programs expanded into fully integrated settings in the 1980s, hands-on science proved to be a powerful medium for bringing all students together. The subject matter is universally interesting, and the joy and satisfaction of discovery are shared by everyone. Active science by itself provides part of the solution to full inclusion and provides many opportunities at one time for differentiated instruction.

Many years later, FOSS began a collaboration with educators and researchers at the Center for Applied Special Technology (CAST), where principles of Universal Design for Learning (UDL) had been developed and applied. FOSS continues to learn from our colleagues about ways to use new media and technologies to improve instruction. Here are the UDL principles.

Principle 1. Provide multiple means of representation. Give learners various ways to acquire information and knowledge.

Principle 2. Provide multiple means of action and expression. Offer students alternatives for demonstrating what they know.

Principle 3. Provide multiple means of engagement. Help learners get interested, be challenged, and stay motivated.

FOSS for All Students

The FOSS Program has been designed to maximize the science learning opportunities for students with special needs and students from culturally and linguistically diverse origins. FOSS is rooted in a 35-year tradition of multisensory science education and informed by recent research on UDL. Procedures found effective with students with special needs and students who are learning English are incorporated into the materials and strategies used with all students. In addition, the **Access and Equity** chapter in *Teacher Resources* (or go to FOSSweb to download this chapter) provides strategies and suggestions for enhancing the science and engineering experiences for each of the specific groups noted above.

> *"Active science by itself provides part of the solution to full inclusion and provides many opportunities at the same time for differentiated instruction."*

Differentiated Instruction for Access and Equity

FOSS instruction allows students to express their understanding through a variety of modalities. Each student has multiple opportunities to demonstrate his or her strengths and needs. The challenge is then to provide appropriate follow-up experiences for each student. For some students, appropriate experience might mean more time with the active investigations or online activities. For other students, it might mean more experience building explanations of the science concepts orally or in writing or drawing. For some students, it might mean making vocabulary more explicit through new concrete experiences or through reading to students. For some students, it may be scaffolding their thinking through graphic organizers. For other students, it might be designing individual projects or small-group investigations. For some students, it might be more opportunities for experiencing science outside the classroom in more natural, outdoor environments.

Assessment and Extensions

The next-step strategies used during the self-assessment sessions after I-Checks provide many opportunities for differentiated instruction. For more on next-step strategies, see the Assessment chapter.

There are additional strategies for providing differentiated instruction. The FOSS Program provides tools and strategies so that you know what students are thinking throughout the module. Based on that knowledge, read through the extension activities for experiences that might be appropriate for students who need additional practice with the basic concepts as well as those ready for more advanced projects. Interdisciplinary extensions are listed at the end of each investigation. Use these ideas to meet the individual needs and interests of your students. In addition, online activities including tutorials and virtual investigations are effective tools to provide differentiated instruction.

English Learners

The FOSS multisensory program provides a rich laboratory for language development for English learners. The program uses a variety of techniques to make science concepts clear and concrete, including modeling, visuals, and active investigations in small groups at centers. Key vocabulary is usually developed within an activity context with frequent opportunities for interaction and discussion between teacher and student and among students. This provides practice and application of the new vocabulary. Instruction is guided and scaffolded through

ELECTROMAGNETIC FORCE — Overview

carefully designed lesson plans, and students are supported throughout. The learning is active and engaging for all students, including English learners.

Science vocabulary is introduced in authentic contexts while students engage in active learning. Strategies for helping all students read, write, speak, and listen are described in the Science-Centered Language Development chapter. There is a section on science-vocabulary development with scaffolding strategies for supporting English learners. These strategies are essential for English learners, and they are good teaching strategies for all learners.

FOSS Investigation Organization

FOSS INVESTIGATION ORGANIZATION

Courses are subdivided into **investigations** (four in this course). Investigations are further subdivided into two to four **parts**. Each investigation has a general guiding question for the phenomenon students investigate and each part of each investigation is driven by a **focus question**. The focus question, usually presented as the part begins, signals the challenge to be met, mystery to be solved, or principle to be uncovered. The focus question guides students' actions and thinking and makes the learning goal of each part explicit for teachers over several class sessions. Each part concludes with students recording an answer to the focus question in their notebooks.

The investigation is summarized for the teacher in the At a Glance chart at the beginning of each investigation.

Investigation-specific **scientific background** information for the teacher is presented in each investigation chapter organized by the focus questions.

The **Teaching and Learning about** section makes direct connections to the NGSS foundation boxes for the grade level—Disciplinary Core Ideas, Science and Engineering Practices, and Crosscutting Concepts. This information is later presented in color-coded sidebar notes to identify specific places in the flow of the investigation where connections to the three dimensions of science learning appear. The section ends with a conceptual-flow graphic of the content.

The **Materials** and **Getting Ready** sections provide scheduling information and detail exactly how to prepare the materials and resources for conducting the investigation. The **Quick Start** table lists planning and preparation steps.

Teaching Notes and **ELA Connections** appear in blue boxes in the sidebars. These notes compose a second voice in the curriculum—an educative element. The first (traditional) voice is the message you deliver to students. The second (educative) voice, shared as a teaching note, is designed to help you understand the science content and pedagogical rationale at work behind the instructional scene. ELA Connection boxes show the relevant Common Core State Standards for English Language Arts.

The **Getting Ready** and **Guiding the Investigation** sections have several features that are flagged in the sidebars. These include several icons to remind you when a particular pedagogical method is suggested, as well as concise bits of information in several categories.

FOCUS QUESTION
How can we generate electrical energy?

SCIENCE AND ENGINEERING PRACTICES
Using mathematics and computational thinking

DISCIPLINARY CORE IDEAS
PS3.C: Relationship between energy and forces

CROSSCUTTING CONCEPTS
Systems and system models

TEACHING NOTE
This focus question can be answered with a simple yes or no, but the question has power when students support their answers with evidence. Their answers should take the form "Yes, because _____."

ELECTROMAGNETIC FORCE — Overview

The **safety** icon alerts you to potential safety issues related to chemicals, allergic reactions, and the use of safety goggles.

The small-group **discussion** icon asks you to pause while students discuss data or construct explanations in their groups.

The **vocabulary** icon indicates where students should review recently introduced vocabulary.

The **recording** icon points out where students should make a science-notebook entry.

The **reading** icon signals when the class should read a specific article in the *FOSS Science Resources* book.

The **technology** icon signals when the class should use a digital resource on FOSSweb.

The **assessment** icons appear when there is an opportunity to assess student progress by using embedded or benchmark assessments. Some are performance assessments—observations of science and engineering practices, crosscutting concepts, and core ideas, indicated by an icon that includes a beaker and ruler.

The **engineering** icon indicates opportunities for an experience incorporating engineering practices.

The **math** icon indicates an opportunity to engage in numerical data analysis and mathematics practice.

The **crosscutting concepts** icon indicates a key opportunity to integrate content between courses by using supports from the Crosscutting Concepts and Integration chapter in *Teacher Resources*.

The **homework** icon indicates science learning experiences that extend beyond the classroom.

EL NOTE
The **EL note** provides a specific strategy to assist English learners in developing science concepts.

To help with scheduling, you will see icons for the start of a new **session** within an investigation part.

SESSION 2 *45–50 minutes*

CLASSROOM ORGANIZATION

FOSS has tried to anticipate the most likely learning environments in which science will be taught and designed the curriculum to be effective in those settings. The most common setting is the 1-hour period (45–55 minutes) every day, one teacher, in the science room. Students come in wave after wave, and they all learn the same thing. Some teachers may have two preps because they teach seventh-grade and eighth-grade classes. The **Electromagnetic Force Course** was designed to work effectively in this traditional hour-a-day format.

The 1-hour subdivisions of the course adapt nicely to the block-scheduling model. It is usually possible to conduct two of the 1-hour sessions in a 90-minute block because of the uninterrupted instructional period. A block allows students to set up an experiment and collect, organize, and process the data all in one sequence. Block scheduling is great for FOSS; students learn more, and teachers are responsible for fewer preps.

Interdisciplinary teams of teachers provide even more learning opportunities. Students will be using mathematics frequently and in complex ways to extract meaning from their inquiries. It has been our experience, however, that middle school students are not skilled at applying mathematics in science because they have had few opportunities to use these skills in context. In an interdisciplinary team, the math teacher can use student-generated data to teach and enhance math skills and application.

The integration of other subject areas, such as language arts, into the science curriculum is also enhanced when interdisciplinary teams are used.

Managing Time

Time is a precious commodity. It must be managed wisely in order to realize the full potential of your FOSS curriculum. The right amount of time should be allocated for preparation, instruction, discussion, assessment, research, and current events. Start from the premise that there will not be enough time to do everything, so you will have to budget selectively. Don't scrimp on the prep time, particularly the first time you use the curriculum. Spend enough time with *Investigations Guide* to become completely familiar with the lesson plans. Take extra time at the start of the course to set up your space efficiently; you will be repaid many times over later. As you become more familiar with the FOSS Program and the handling of the materials, the proportion of time devoted to each aspect of the program may shift, so that you are spending more and more time on instruction and enrichment activities.

ELECTROMAGNETIC FORCE — *Overview*

Effective use of time during the instructional period is one of the keys to a great experience with this course. *Investigations Guide* offers suggestions for keeping the activities moving along at a good pace, but our proposed timing will rarely exactly match yours. The best way we know for getting in stride with the curriculum is to start teaching it. Soon you will be able to judge where to break an activity or push in a little enrichment to fill your instructional period.

Managing Space

The **Electromagnetic Force Course** will work in the ideal setting: flat-topped tables where students work with materials in groups of four; theater seating for viewing online activities (darkened); technology available for accessing FOSSweb on the Internet for online activities, videos, and references. But we don't expect many teachers to have the privilege of working in such a space. So we designed FOSS courses to work effectively in a number of typical settings, including the science lab and regular classroom. We have described, however, the minimum space and resources needed to use FOSS. Here's the list, in order of importance.

- A computer with Internet access, and a large-screen display monitor or projector
- Tables or desks for students to work in groups of four
- A whiteboard, blackboard, or chart paper and marking pens
- A surface for materials distribution
- A place to clean and organize equipment
- A convenient place to store the kit
- A computer lab or multiple digital devices

Once the minimum resources are at hand, take a little time to set up your science area. This investment will pay handsome dividends later since everyone will be familiar with the learning setup.

- Organize your computer and projection system and be sure the Internet connection is working smoothly.
- Think about the best organization of furniture. This may change from investigation to investigation.
- Plan where to set up your materials stations.
- Know how students will keep notes and record data, and plan where students will keep their notebooks.

Classroom Organization

Managing Students

A typical class of middle school students is a wonderfully complex collection of personalities, including the clown, the athlete, the fashion statement, the worrier, the achiever, the pencil sharpener, the show-off, the reader, and the question-answerer. Notice there is no mention of the astrophysicist, but she could be in there, too. Management requires delicate coordination and flexibility—some days students take their places in an orderly fashion and sit up straight in their chairs, fully prepared to learn. Later in the week, they are just as likely to have the appearance of migrating waterfowl, unable to find their place, talkative, and constantly moving.

FOSS employs a number of strategies for managing students. Often a warm-up activity is a suitable transition from lunch or the excitement of changing rooms to the focused intellectual activities of the **Electromagnetic Force Course**. Warm-ups tend to be individual exercises that review what transpired yesterday with a segue to the next development in the curriculum. This gives students time to get out their notebooks, grind points on their pencils, settle into their space, and focus.

Students most often work in groups in this course. Groups of four are generally used, but at other times, students work in pairs.

Suggestions for guiding students' work in collaborative groups are described later in this chapter.

When Students Are Absent

When a student is absent for a session, another student can act as a peer tutor and share the science notebook entries made for that day. The science notebooks should be a valuable tool for students to share in order to catch up on missed classes. Also consider giving them a chance to spend some time with the materials.

Students can use the resources on FOSSweb at school or at home for the missed class. And finally, allow the student to bring home *FOSS Science Resources* to read any relevant articles. Each article has a few review items that the student can respond to verbally or in writing.

Electromagnetic Force Course—FOSS Next Generation

ELECTROMAGNETIC FORCE — *Overview*

Managing Technology

The **Electromagnetic Force Course** includes an online component. The online activities and materials are not optional. For this reason, it is essential that you have in your classroom at minimum one computer, a large-screen display monitor or projection system, and a connection to the Internet. Sometimes you will use multimedia to make presentations to the entire class. Sometimes small groups or individuals will use the online program to work simulations and representations, and to gather information. Plan on the students having access to computers or tablets for work in groups for these sessions.

- Investigation 2, Part 3, for online activity

Option 1: The computer lab. If you have access to a lab where all students can work simultaneously as individuals, pairs, or small groups, schedule time in the lab for your classes. If you have access to a cart with a class set of devices, schedule that for your classroom.

Option 2: Classroom computers or other digital devices. With multiple devices for groups in the science classroom, you can set up a multitasking environment with half the students working with Internet resources and half engaged in reading or small-group discussions. Then swap roles. If every student or pair has access to a device, you are all set.

Option 3: Home access. Students can access FOSSweb from home by visiting www.FOSSweb.com and accessing the class pages with the account information you provide for student use. You must set up a class page for students to have home access to the multimedia.

Classroom Organization

Managing Materials

The Materials section lists the items in the equipment kit and any teacher-supplied materials. It also describes things to do to prepare a new kit and how to check and prepare the kit for your classroom. Individual photos of each piece of FOSS equipment are available for printing from FOSSweb, and can help students and you identify each item.

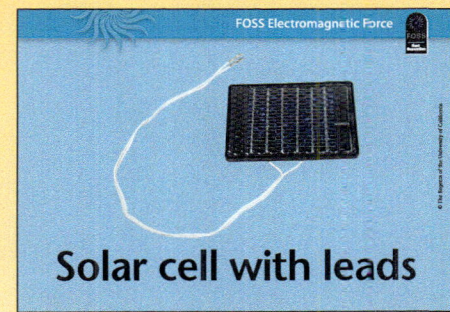

The FOSS Program designers suggest using a central materials distribution system. You organize all the materials for an investigation at a single location called the materials station. As the investigation progresses, one member of each group gets materials as they are needed, and another returns the materials when the investigation is complete. You place the equipment and resources at the station, and students do the rest. Students can also be involved in cleaning and organizing the materials at the end of a session.

The Materials list for each investigation is divided into these categories.

- Equipment provided in the FOSS kit
- Teacher-supplied items
- FOSSweb resources to be downloaded or projected

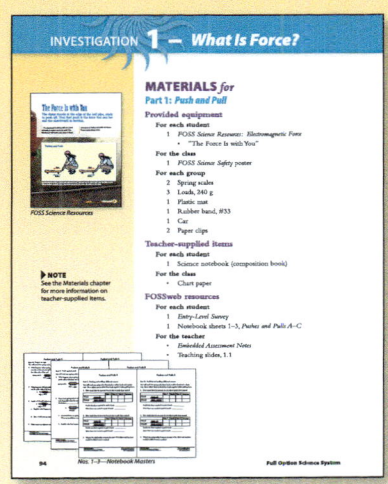

Each category is further subdivided by need.

- For each student
- For each group
- For the class
- For the teacher

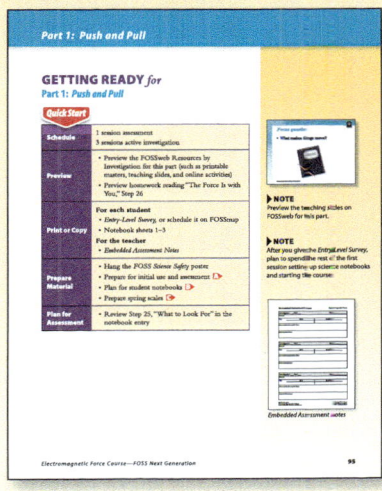

The Getting Ready section begins with the Quick Start table to help the teacher immediately know the schedule, what to preview, print, what materials to prepare; and what to plan for assessment. Preparation details linked to the Quick Start provide specific information.

Electromagnetic Force Course—FOSS Next Generation

ELECTROMAGNETIC FORCE — *Overview*

ESTABLISHING A CLASSROOM CULTURE

Working in Collaborative Groups

Collaboration is important in science. Scientists usually collaborate on research enterprises. Groups of researchers often contribute to the collection of data, the analysis of findings, and the preparation of the results for publication.

Collaboration is expected in the science classroom, too. Some tasks call for everyone to have the same experience, either taking turns or doing the same things simultaneously. At other times, group members may have different experiences that they later bring together.

Research has shown that students learn better and are more successful when they collaborate. Working together promotes student interest, participation, learning, and self-confidence. FOSS investigations use collaborative groups extensively.

No single model for collaborative learning is promoted by FOSS. We can suggest, however, a few general guidelines that have proven successful over the years.

For most activities in middle school, collaborative groups of four in which students take turns assuming specific responsibilities work best. Groups can be identified completely randomly (first four names drawn from a hat constitute group 1), or you can assemble groups to ensure diversity. Thoughtfully constituted groups tend to work better.

Groups can be maintained for extended periods of time, or they can be reconfigured more frequently. For a short course, you might keep students in the same groups for the entire course.

Functional roles within groups can be determined by the members themselves, or they can be assigned in one of several ways. Each member in a collaborative group can be assigned a number or a color. Then you need only announce which color or number will perform a certain task for the group at a certain time. Compass points can also be used: the person seated on the east side of the table will be the Reporter for this investigation.

The functional roles used in the investigations follow. If you already use other names for functional roles in your class, use those in place of these in the investigations.

Establishing a Classroom Culture

Getters are responsible for materials. One person from each group gets equipment from the materials station, and another person later returns the equipment.

One person is the **Starter** for each task. This person makes sure that everyone gets a turn and that everyone has an opportunity to contribute ideas to the investigation.

The **Recorder** collects data as it happens and makes sure that everyone has recorded information on his or her science notebook sheets.

The **Reporter** shares group data with the class or transcribes it to the board or class chart.

Getting started with collaborative groups requires patience, but the rewards are great. Once collaborative groups are in place, you will be able to engage students more in meaningful conversations about science content. You are free to "cruise" the groups, to observe and listen to students as they work, and to interact with individuals and small groups as needed.

Norms for Sense-Making Discussions

Setting up norms for discussion and holding yourself and your students accountable is the first step towards creating a culture of productive talk in the classroom that supports engagement in the science and engineering practices. Students need to feel free to express their ideas, and to provide and receive criticism from others as they work toward understanding of the disciplinary core ideas of science and methods of engineering.

Establish norms at the beginning of the school year. It is recommended that this be done together as a class activity. However, presenting a poster of norms to students and asking them to discuss why each one is important can also be effective. Before each sense-making discussion, review the norms. Review what it will look like, sound like, and feel like when everyone is following the agreements. You might have students work on one or two at a time as they are developing their oral discourse skills. After discussion, save a few minutes for reflection on how well the group or the class adhered to the norms and what they can do better next time. More strategies for supporting academic discourse can be found in the Sense-Making Discussions for Three-Dimensional Learning and Science-Centered Language Development in Middle School chapters in *Teacher Resources* (also available as downloadable PDFs on FOSSweb).

This poster is an example of student responsibilities that the class discussed and adopted as their norms.

Electromagnetic Force Course—FOSS Next Generation

ELECTROMAGNETIC FORCE — *Overview*

Collaborative Teaching and Learning

Collaborative learning requires a collective as well as individual growth mindset. A growth mindset is when people believe that their most basic abilities can be developed through dedication and hard work (see the research of Carol Dweck and her book *Mindset: The Psychology of Success*). As students work together to make sense of phenomena and develop their inquiry and discourse skills, it's important to recognize and value their efforts to try new approaches and their willingness to make their thinking visible. Remind students that everyone in the classroom, including you the teacher, will be learning new ideas and ways to think about the world. Where there is productive struggle, there is learning. Here are a few ways to help students develop a growth mind-set for science and engineering.

- **Praise effort, not right answers.** When students are successful at a task, provide positive feedback about their level of engagement and effort in the practices, e.g., the efforts they put into careful observations, how well they organized and interpreted their data, the relevancy of their questions, how well they connected or applied new concepts, and their use of precise vocabulary, etc. Also, try to provide feedback that encourages students to continue to improve their learning and exploring, e.g., is there another way to approach this question? Have you thought about _____ ? What evidence is there to support _____ ?

- **Foster and validate divergent thinking.** During sense-making discussions, continually emphasize how important it is to share emerging ideas and to be open to the ideas of others in order to build understanding. Model for students how you refine and revise your thinking based on new information. Make it clear to students that the point is not for them to show they have the right answer, but rather to help each other arrive at new understandings. Point out positive examples of students expressing and revising their ideas.

Establishing a classroom culture that supports three-dimensional teaching and learning centers on collaboration. Collaborative groupings, materials management, and norms are structures you can put into place to foster collaboration. These structures along with the expectations that students will be negotiating meaning together as a community of learners, creates a learning environment where students are compelled to work, think, and communicate like scientists and engineers to help one another learn.

Safety in the Classroom and Outdoors

SAFETY IN THE CLASSROOM AND OUTDOORS

Following the procedures described in each investigation will make for a very safe experience in the classroom. You should also review your district safety guidelines and make sure that everything that you do is consistent with those guidelines. Two posters are included in the kit, *FOSS Science Safety* and *FOSS Outdoor Safety*, for classroom use. The safety guidelines are in the *FOSS Science Resources* book for student reference.

Look for the safety icon in the Getting Ready and Guiding the Investigation sections, which will alert you to safety considerations throughout the course.

Safety Data Sheets (SDS) for materials used in the FOSS Program can be found on FOSSweb. If you have questions regarding any SDS, call Delta Education at 1-800-258-1302 (Monday–Friday, 8 a.m. to 5 p.m. ET).

General classroom safety rules to share with students are listed here.

1. Always follow the safety procedures outlined by your teacher Follow directions, and ask questions if you're unsure of what to do.
2. Never put any material in your mouth. Do not taste any material or chemical unless your teacher specifically tells you to do so.
3. Do not smell any unknown material. If your teacher tells you to smell a material, wave a hand over it to bring the scent toward your nose.
4. Avoid touching your face, mouth, ears, eyes, or nose while working with chemicals, plants, or animals. Tell your teacher if you have any allergies.
5. Always wash your hands with soap and warm water immediately after using chemicals (including common chemicals, such as salt and dyes) and handling natural materials or organisms.
6. Do not mix unknown chemicals just to see what might happen.
7. Always wear safety goggles when working with liquids, chemicals, and sharp or pointed tools. Tell your teacher if you wear contact lenses.
8. Clean up spills immediately. Report all spills, accidents, and injuries to your teacher.
9. Treat animals with respect, caution, and consideration.
10. Never use the mirror of a microscope to reflect direct sunlight. The bright light can cause permanent eye damage.

Electromagnetic Force Course—FOSS Next Generation

ELECTROMAGNETIC FORCE — Overview

FOSS CONTACTS

General FOSS Program information

www.FOSSweb.com

www.DeltaEducation.com/FOSS

Developers at the Lawrence Hall of Science

FOSS@berkeley.edu

Customer Service at Delta Education

www.DeltaEducation.com/contact.aspx

Phone: 1-800-258-1302, 8:00 a.m.–5:00 p.m. ET

FOSSmap (online component of FOSS assessment system)

http://FOSSmap.com/

FOSSweb account questions/access codes/help logging in

techsupport.science@schoolspecialty.com

Phone: 1-800-258-1302, 8:00 a.m.–5:00 p.m. ET

School Specialty online support

loginhelp@schoolspecialty.com

Phone: 1-800-513-2465, 8:30 a.m. –6:00 p.m. ET

FOSSweb tech support

support@fossweb.com

Professional development

www.FOSSweb.com/Professional-Development

Safety issues

www.DeltaEducation.com/SDS

Phone: 1-800-258-1302, 8:00 a.m.–5:00 p.m. ET

For chemical emergencies, contact Chemtrec 24 hours a day.

Phone: 1-800-424-9300

Sales and replacement parts

www.DeltaEducation.com/FOSS/buy

Phone: 1-800-338-5270, 8:00 a.m.–5:00 p.m. ET

Framework and NGSS

ELECTROMAGNETIC FORCE — *Framework and NGSS*

INTRODUCTION TO PERFORMANCE EXPECTATIONS

This chapter provides details about how this FOSS middle school course fits into the matrix of the FOSS Program. Each FOSS module K–5 and middle school course 6–8 has a functional role in the FOSS conceptual frameworks that were developed based on a decade of research on science education and the influence of *A Framework for K–12 Science Education* (2012) and *Next Generation Science Standards* (NGSS, 2013).

The FOSS curriculum provides a coherent vision of science teaching and learning in the three ways described by the *Framework*. First, FOSS is designed around learning as a developmental progression, providing experiences that allow students to continually build on their initial notions and develop more complex scientific and engineering knowledge. Students develop understanding over time by building on foundational elements or intermediate knowledge. Those elements are detailed in the conceptual frameworks.

Second, FOSS limits the number of core ideas, choosing depth of knowledge over comprehensive shallow coverage. Those core ideas are addressed at multiple grade levels in ever greater complexity. FOSS investigations at each grade level focus on elements of core ideas that are teachable and learnable at that grade level.

Third, FOSS investigations integrate engagement with scientific ideas (content) with the practices of science and engineering by providing students with firsthand experiences.

If this is your first time teaching a FOSS middle school course, you should review this conceptual design material but save an in-depth study of it until after you have experienced the course in the classroom with students. Teach the course with the confidence that the developers have carefully considered the latest research and have integrated into each investigation the three dimensions of the *Framework* and *NGSS*, and have designed powerful connections to the Common Core State Standards for English Language Arts.

Contents

Introduction to Performance Expectations 33

FOSS Conceptual Framework 44

Background for the Conceptual Framework in Electromagnetic Force 46

Connections to NGSS by Investigation 52

Recommended FOSS Next Generation K–8 Scope and Sequence 60

▶ REFERENCES

National Research Council. *A Framework for K–12 Science Education: Practices, Crosscutting Concepts, and Core Ideas.* Washington, DC: The National Academies Press, 2012.

NGSS Lead States. *Next Generation Science Standards: For States, by States.* Washington, DC: National Academies Press, 2013.

National Governors Association Center for Best Practices and Council of Chief States School Officers. *Common Core State Standards for English Language Arts and Literacy in History/Social Studies, Science, and Technical Subjects.* Washington, DC: authors, 2010.

Full Option Science System

ELECTROMAGNETIC FORCE — Framework and NGSS

DISCIPLINARY CORE IDEAS

A Framework for K–12 Science Education has four core ideas in physical sciences.

- PS1: Matter and its interactions
- PS2: Motion and stability: Forces and Interactions
- PS3: Energy
- PS4: Waves and their applications in technologies for information transfer

The questions and descriptions of the core ideas in the text on these pages are taken from the NRC Framework for the middle school grade band to keep the core ideas in a rich and useful context.

The performance expectations related to each core idea are primarily taken from the NGSS for middle school.

Disciplinary Core Ideas Addressed

The **Electromagnetic Force Course** connects with the NRC *Framework* and the NGSS performance expectations for middle school. The course focuses on core ideas for physical sciences and engineering design, with a connection to earth sciences.

Physical Sciences

Core idea PS2: Motion and Stability: Forces and Interactions—How can one explain and predict interactions between objects and within systems of objects?

- **PS2.A: Forces and motion**
  How can one predict an object's continued motion, changes in motion, or stability? [For any pair of interacting objects, the force exerted by the first object on the second object is equal in strength to the force that the second object exerts on the first but in the opposite direction (Newton's third law). The motion of an object is determined by the sum of the forces acting on it; if the total force on the object is not zero, its motion will change. The greater the mass of the object, the greater the force needed to achieve the same change in motion. For any given object, a larger force causes a larger change in motion. Forces on an object can also change its shape or orientation. All positions of objects and the directions of forces and motions must be described in an arbitrarily chosen reference frame and arbitrarily chosen units of size. In order to share information with other people, these choices must also be shared.]

- **PS2.B: Types of interactions**
  What underlying forces explain the variety of interactions observed? [Electric and magnetic (electromagnetic) forces can be attractive or repulsive, and their sizes depend on the magnitudes of the charges, currents, or magnetic strengths involved and on the distances between the interacting objects.

  Forces that act at a distance (gravitational, electric, and magnetic) can be explained by force fields that extend through space and can be mapped by their effect on a test object (a ball, a charged object, or a magnet, respectively).]

The following NGSS grades 6–8 performance expectations for PS2 are derived from the Framework disciplinary core ideas above.

- **MS-PS2-2.** Plan an investigation to provide evidence that the change in an object's motion depends on the sum of the forces on the object and the mass of the object.

Introduction to Performance Expectations

- **MS-PS2-3.** Ask questions about data to determine the factors that affect the strength of electric and magnetic forces.
- **MS-PS2-5.** Conduct an investigation and evaluate the experimental design to provide evidence that fields exist between objects exerting forces on each other even though the objects are not in contact.

Core idea PS3: Energy—How is energy transferred and conserved?

- **PS3.A: Definitions of energy**
  What is energy? [Motion energy is properly called kinetic energy; it is proportional to the mass of the moving object and grows with the square of its speed. A system of objects may also contain stored (potential) energy, depending on their relative positions. For example, energy is stored—in gravitational interaction with Earth—when an object is raised, and energy is released when the object falls or is lowered. Energy is also stored in the electric fields between charged particles and the magnetic fields between magnets, and it changes when these objects are moved relative to one another. Stored energy is decreased in some chemical reactions and increased in others.]

- **PS3.B: Conservation of energy and energy transfer**
  What is meant by conservation of energy? How is energy transferred between objects or systems? [When the motion energy of an object changes, there is inevitably some other change in energy at the same time. For example, the friction that causes a moving object to stop also results in an increase in the thermal energy in both surfaces; eventually heat energy is transferred to the surrounding environment as the surfaces cool. Similarly, to make an object start moving or to keep it moving when friction forces transfer energy away from it, energy must be provided from, say, chemical (e.g., burning fuel) or electrical (e.g., an electric motor and a battery) processes.]

- **PS3.C: Relationship between energy and forces**
  How are forces related to energy? [When two objects interact, each one exerts a force on the other that can cause energy to be transferred to or from the object. For example, when energy is transferred to an Earth-object system as an object is raised, the gravitational field energy of the system increases. This energy is released as the object falls; the mechanism of this release is the gravitational force. Likewise, two magnetic and electrically charged objects interacting at a distance exert forces on each other that can transfer energy between the interacting objects.]

Electromagnetic Force Course—FOSS Next Generation

ELECTROMAGNETIC FORCE — Framework and NGSS

The following NGSS grades 6–8 performance expectations for PS3 are derived from the Framework disciplinary core ideas above.

- **MS-PS3-2.** Develop a model to describe that when the arrangement of objects interacting at a distance changes, different amounts of potential energy are stored in the system.

- **MS-PS3-5.** Construct, use, and present arguments to support the claim that when the motion energy of an object changes, energy is transferred to or from the object.

Earth Sciences
Core idea ESS3: Earth and Human Activity—How do Earth's surface processes and human activities affect each other?

- **ESS3.A: Natural resources**
  How do humans depend on Earth's resources? [Humans depend on Earth's land, ocean, atmosphere, and biosphere for many different resources. Minerals, fresh water, and biosphere resources are limited, and many are not renewable or replaceable over human lifetimes. These resources are distributed unevenly around the planet as a result of past geological processes. Renewable energy resources, and the technologies to exploit them, are being rapidly developed.]

- **ESS3.C: Human impacts on earth systems**
  How do humans change the planet? [Human activities have significantly altered the biosphere, sometimes damaging or destroying natural habitats and causing the extinction of many other species. But changes to Earth's environments can have different impacts (negative and positive) for different living things. Typically, as human populations and per-capita consumption of natural resources increase, so do the negative impacts on Earth unless the activities and technologies involved are engineered otherwise.]

The following NGSS grades 6–8 performance expectations for ESS3 are derived from the Framework disciplinary core ideas above.

- **MS-ESS3-4.** Construct an argument supported by evidence for how increases in human population and per-capita consumption of natural resources impact Earth's systems.

Introduction to Performance Expectations

Engineering, Technology, and Applications of Science
Framework core idea ETS1: Engineering design—How do engineers solve problems?

- **ETS1.A: Defining and delimiting an engineering problem**
  What is a design for? What are the criteria and constraints of a successful solution? [The more precisely a design task's criteria and constraints can be defined, the more likely it is that the designed solution will be successful. Specification of constraints includes consideration of scientific principles and other relevant knowledge that are likely to limit possible solutions (e.g., familiarity with the local climate may rule out certain plants for the school garden).]

- **ETS1.B: Developing possible solutions**
  What is the process for developing potential design solutions? [A solution needs to be tested, and then modified on the basis of the test results, in order to improve it. There are systematic processes for evaluating solutions with respect to how well they meet the criteria and constraints of a problem. Sometimes parts of different solutions can be combined to create a solution that is better than any of its predecessors. In any case, it is important to be able to communicate and explain solutions to others. Models of all kinds are important for testing solutions, and computers are a valuable tool for simulating systems. Simulations are useful for predicting what would happen if various parameters of the model were changed, as well as for making improvements to the model based on peer and leader (e.g., teacher) feedback.]

- **ETS1.C: Optimizing the design solution**
  How can the various proposed design solutions be compared and improved? [There are systematic processes for evaluating solutions with respect to how well they meet the criteria and constraints of a problem. Comparing different designs could involve running them through the same kinds of tests and systematically recording the results to determine which design performs best. Although one design may not perform the best across all tests, identifying the characteristics of the design that performed the best in each test can provide useful information for the redesign process—that is, some of those characteristics may be incorporated into the new design. This iterative process of testing the most promising solutions and modifying what is proposed on the basis of the test results leads to greater refinement and ultimately to an optimal solution. Once such a suitable solution is determined, it is important to describe that solution, explain how it was developed, and describe the features that make it successful.]

Electromagnetic Force Course—FOSS Next Generation

ELECTROMAGNETIC FORCE — *Framework and NGSS*

The following NGSS grades 6–8 performance expectations for ETS1 are derived from the Framework disciplinary core ideas above.

- **MS-ETS1-1.** Define the criteria and constraints of a design problem with sufficient precision to ensure a successful solution, taking into account relevant scientific principles and potential impacts on people and the natural environment that may limit possible solutions.

- **MS-ETS1-2.** Evaluate competing design solutions using a systematic process to determine how well they meet the criteria and constraints of the problem.

- **MS-ETS1-3.** Analyze data from tests to determine similarities and differences among several design solutions to identify the solution to better meet the criteria for success.

- **MS-ETS1-4.** Develop a model to generate data for iterative testing and modification of a proposed object, tool, or process such that an optimal design can be achieved.

Introduction to Performance Expectations

Science and Engineering Practices Addressed

1. Asking questions and defining problems

- Ask questions that arise from careful observation of phenomena, models, or unexpected results; to clarify and/or seek additional information.
- Ask questions to identify and/or clarify evidence and/or the premise(s) of an argument.
- Ask questions that can be investigated within the scope of the classroom, outdoor environment, and museums and other public facilities with available resources and, when appropriate, frame a hypothesis based on observations and scientific principles.
- Define a design problem that can be solved through the development of an object, tool, process, or system and includes multiple criteria and constraints, including scientific knowledge that may limit possible solutions.

2. Developing and using models

- Develop and/or use a model to predict and/or describe phenomena.
- Develop a model to describe unobservable mechanisms.

3. Planning and carrying out investigations

- Plan an investigation individually and collaboratively, and in the design: identify independent and dependent variables and controls, what tools are needed to do the gathering, how measurements will be recorded, and how many data are needed to support a claim.
- Conduct an investigation and/or evaluate and/or revise the experimental design to produce data to serve as the basis for evidence that meet the goals of the investigation.
- Collect data to serve as the basis for evidence to answer scientific questions or test design solutions under a range of conditions.

4. Analyzing and interpreting data

- Construct, analyze, and/or interpret graphical displays of data and/or large data sets to identify linear and nonlinear relationships.
- Analyze and interpret data to provide evidence for phenomena.
- Analyze and interpret data to determine similarities and differences in findings.

SCIENCE AND ENGINEERING PRACTICES

A Framework for K–12 Science Education (National Research Council, 2012) describes eight science and engineering practices as essential elements of a K–12 science and engineering curriculum. All of these practices are incorporated into the learning experiences in the **Electromagnetic Force Course**.

The learning progression for this dimension of the framework is addressed in *Next Generation Science Standards* (National Academies Press, 2013, volume 2, appendix F). Elements of the learning progression for practices recommended for grades 6–8 as described in the performance expectations appear in bullets below each practice.

ELECTROMAGNETIC FORCE — Framework and NGSS

- Analyze data to define an optimal operational range for a proposed object, tool, process, or system that best meets criteria for success.

5. Using mathematics and computational thinking

- Apply mathematical concepts and/or processes (e.g., ratio, rate, percent, basic operations, simple algebra) to scientific and engineering questions and problems.
- Use digital tools and/or mathematical concepts and arguments to test and compare proposed solutions to an engineering design problem.

6. Constructing explanations and designing solutions

- Construct an explanation that includes qualitative or quantitative relationships between variables that predict(s) and/or describe(s) phenomena.
- Construct an explanation using models or representations.
- Construct a scientific explanation based on valid and reliable evidence obtained from sources (including the students' own experiments) and the assumption that theories and laws that describe the natural world operate today as they did in the past and will continue to do so in the future.
- Apply scientific reasoning to show why the data or evidence is adequate for the explanation or conclusion.
- Apply scientific ideas or principles to design, construct, and/or test a design of an object, tool, process, or system.
- Undertake a design project, engaging in the design cycle, to construct and/or implement a solution that meets specific design criteria and constraints.

7. Engaging in argument from evidence

- Respectfully provide and receive critiques about one's explanations, procedures, models, and questions by citing relevant evidence and posing and responding to questions that elicit pertinent elaboration and detail.
- Construct, use, and/or present an oral and written argument supported by empirical evidence and scientific reasoning to support or refute an explanation or a model for a phenomenon or a solution to a problem.
- Evaluate competing design solutions based on jointly developed and agreed-upon design criteria.

Introduction to Performance Expectations

8. Obtaining, evaluating, and communicating information
- Critically read scientific texts adapted for classroom use to determine the central ideas and/or obtain scientific and/or technical information to describe patterns in and/or evidence about the natural and designed world(s).
- Integrate qualitative and/or quantitative scientific and/or technical information in written text with that contained in media and visual displays to clarify claims and findings.
- Communicate scientific and/or technical information (e.g., about a proposed object, tool, process, system) in writing and/or through oral presentations.

Crosscutting Concepts Addressed

Patterns: *Observed patterns in nature guide organization and classification and prompt questions about relationships and causes underlying them.*
- Macroscopic patterns are related to the nature of microscopic and atomic-level structure.
- Patterns in rates of change and other numerical relationships can provide information about natural and human-designed systems.
- Patterns can be used to identify cause-and-effect relationships.

Cause and effect: *Events have causes, sometimes simple, sometimes multifaceted. Deciphering causal relationships, and the mechanisms by which they are mediated, is a major activity of science and engineering.*
- Cause-and-effect relationships may be used to predict phenomena in natural or designed systems.

Scale, proportion, and quantity: *In considering phenomena, it is critical to recognize what is relevant at different size, time, and energy scales, and to recognize proportional relationships between different quantities as scales change.*
- Time, space, and energy phenomena can be observed at various scales using models to study systems that are too large or too small.

Systems and system models: *A system is an organized group of related objects or components; models can be used for understanding and predicting the behavior of systems.*
- Systems may interact with other systems; they may have subsystems and be a part of larger complex systems.
- Models can be used to represent systems and their interactions—such as inputs, processes, and outputs—and energy, matter, and information flows within systems.

> **CROSSCUTTING CONCEPTS**
>
> *A Framework for K–12 Science Education* describes seven crosscutting concepts as essential elements of a K–12 science and engineering curriculum. The learning progression for this dimension of the framework is addressed in volume 2, appendix G, of the NGSS. Elements of the learning progression for crosscutting concepts recommended for grades 6–8, as described in the performance expectations, appear after bullets below each concept.

Electromagnetic Force Course—FOSS Next Generation

ELECTROMAGNETIC FORCE — Framework and NGSS

Energy and matter: *Tracking energy and matter flows into, out of, and within systems helps to understand the system's behavior.*

- Energy may take different forms (e.g., energy in fields, thermal energy, energy of motion).
- The transfer of energy can be tracked as energy flows through a designed or natural system.

Structure and function: *The way an object is shaped or structured determines many of its properties and its functions.*

- Structures can be designed to serve particular functions by taking into account properties of different materials, and how materials can be shaped and used.

Stability and change: *For both designed and natural systems, conditions that affect stability and factors that control rates of change are critical elements to consider and understand.*

- Small changes in one part of a system might cause large changes in another part.
- Stability might be disturbed either by sudden events or gradual changes that accumulate over time.

Connections to the Nature of Science

- **Scientific knowledge is based on empirical evidence.** Scientific knowledge is based on logical and conceptual connections between evidence and explanations. Science disciplines share common rules of obtaining and evaluating empirical evidence.

- **Scientific knowledge assumes an order and consistency in natural systems.** Science assumes that objects and events in natural systems occur in consistent patterns that are understandable through measurement and observation. Science carefully considers and evaluates anomalies in data and evidence.

- **Science addresses questions about the natural and material world.** Scientific knowledge is constrained by human capacity, technology, and materials. Science limits its explanations to systems that lend themselves to observation and empirical evidence. Scientific knowledge can describe consequences of actions but is not responsible for society's decisions.

- **Science is a human endeavor.** Men and women from different social, cultural, and ethnic backgrounds work as scientists and engineers. Scientists and engineers rely on human qualities such as persistence, precision, reasoning, logic, imagination, and creativity. Scientists and engineers are guided by habits of mind, such as intellectual honesty, tolerance of ambiguity, skepticism, and openness to new ideas. Advances in technology influence the progress of science, and science has influenced advances in technology.

CONNECTIONS

See volume 2, appendix H and appendix J, in the NGSS for more on these connections.

Introduction to Performance Expectations

Connections to Engineering, Technology, and Applications of Science

- **Interdependence of science, engineering, and technology.** Engineering advances have led to important discoveries in virtually every field of science, and scientific discoveries have led to the development of entire industries and engineered systems. Science and technology drive each other forward.

- **Influence of science, engineering, and technology on society and the natural world.** The uses of technologies are driven by people's needs, desires, and values; by the findings of scientific research; and by differences in such factors as climate, natural resources, and economic conditions. Technology use varies over time and from region to region.

- **Influence of science, engineering, and technology on society and the natural world.** All human activity draws on natural resources and has both short- and long-term consequences, positive as well as negative, for the health of people and the natural environment. The uses of technologies are driven by people's needs, desires, and values; by the findings of scientific research; and by differences in such factors as climate, natural resources, and economic conditions. Technology use varies over time and from region to region.

ELECTROMAGNETIC FORCE — Framework and NGSS

FOSS CONCEPTUAL FRAMEWORK

FOSS has conceptual structure at the course level. The concepts are carefully selected and organized in a sequence that makes sense to students when presented as intended. In the last half decade, research has focused on learning progressions. The idea behind a learning progression is that **core ideas** in science are complex and wide-reaching—ideas such as the structure of matter or the relationship between the distribution and function of organisms. From the age of awareness throughout life, matter and organisms are important to us. There are things we can and should understand about them in our primary school years, and progressively more complex and sophisticated things we should know about them as we gain experience and develop our cognitive abilities. When we as educators can determine those logical progressions, we can develop meaningful and effective curriculum.

FOSS has elaborated learning progressions for core ideas in science for kindergarten through grade 8. Developing the learning progressions involves identifying successively more sophisticated ways of thinking about core ideas over multiple years. "If mastery of a core idea in a science discipline is the ultimate educational destination, then well-designed learning progressions provide a map of the routes that can be taken to reach that destination" (National Research Council, *A Framework for K–12 Science Education*, 2012, page 26).

The FOSS modules (grades K–5) and courses (grades 6–8) are organized into three domains: physical science, earth science, and life science. Each domain is subdivided into two strands, each representing a core scientific idea, as shown in the columns in the table: matter/energy and change, atmosphere and Earth/rocks and landforms, structure and function/complex systems. The sequence of modules and courses in each strand relates to the core ideas described in the national framework. Modules at the bottom of the table form the foundation in the primary grades. The core ideas develop in complexity as they proceed up the columns.

In addition to the science content framework, every course provides opportunities for students to engage in and understand science practices, and many courses explore issues related to engineering practices and the use of natural resources.

FOSS Conceptual Framework

The science content used to develop the FOSS courses describes what we want students to learn; the science and engineering practices describe how we want students to learn; and crosscutting concepts stitch the whole effort into a coherent fabric describing the whole natural world. Practices involve a number of habits of mind and philosophical orientations, and these, too, will develop in richness and complexity as students advance through their science studies. Science and engineering practices involve behaviors, so they can be best assessed while in progress. Thus, assessment of practices is based on teacher observation. The indicators of progress include students involved in the many aspects of active thinking, students motivated to learn, and students taking responsibility for their own learning.

FOSS Next Generation—K–8 Sequence

	PHYSICAL SCIENCE		EARTH SCIENCE		LIFE SCIENCE	
	MATTER	ENERGY AND CHANGE	ATMOSPHERE AND EARTH	ROCKS AND LANDFORMS	STRUCTURE/ FUNCTION	COMPLEX SYSTEMS
6–8	Waves; Gravity and Kinetic Energy; Chemical Interactions; Electromagnetic Force		Planetary Science; Earth History; Weather and Water		Heredity and Adaptation; Populations and Ecosystems; Diversity of Life; Human Systems Interactions	
5	Mixtures and Solutions		Earth and Sun		Living Systems	
4		Energy		Soils, Rocks, and Landforms	Environments	
3	Motion and Matter		Water and Climate		Structures of Life	
2	Solids and Liquids			Pebbles, Sand, and Silt	Insects and Plants	
1		Sound and Light	Air and Weather		Plants and Animals	
K		Materials and Motion	Trees and Weather		Animals Two by Two	

Electromagnetic Force Course—FOSS Next Generation

45

ELECTROMAGNETIC FORCE — Framework and NGSS

BACKGROUND FOR THE CONCEPTUAL FRAMEWORK
in Electromagnetic Force

Force and Motion

A force is an interaction, a push or pull, between two objects. These objects can be large, like students playing a game of tug-of-war, or tiny, like subatomic particles. The principle remains the same: nothing changes in motion (kinetic energy) unless a force is applied. Not just any force will make an object move. The forces acting on an object are summative, including invisible forces like friction and gravity. If the net force on an object is greater than zero, its motion will change. The greater the object's mass, the more force needed to achieve the same change in motion.

Magnets are fascinating because they apply an invisible force. When a magnet is placed near another magnet, it attracts or repels, and it can do this even when it does not touch the other magnet. This is because a magnet exerts force through a field that extends from its poles. As you extend further from the magnet throughout the field, its force grows weaker.

Electric current running through a circuit also exerts a force. This force can make things happen in various electric components, such as light or heat from a lightbulb, or the rotation of a motor. Light, heat, and motion are evidence of energy. Electrical energy has transferred to another part of the system.

As electricity runs through a wire, it produces a small magnetic field around the wire. This is evidence of the electromagnetic force, one of the four fundamental forces that govern everything we know about the physical world. The relationship between electricity and magnetism can be manipulated by engineers to create electromagnets that are used to start car engines, run washing machines, move high-speed trains, and for medical scanning of internal organs.

As electricity and magnetism interact to move objects or give off light, energy transfers. Energy always comes from somewhere; it cannot be created or destroyed. Potential energy stored in systems, like the chemical potential energy of a battery, provides an energy source, but the energy must originate somewhere. Most human energy use relies on renewable systems like wind (kinetic energy), the Sun (solar energy), and hydroelectricity (kinetic energy), or nonrenewable resources like fossil

FOSS Conceptual Framework

fuels (chemical potential energy). Because human energy use continues to increase, it is increasingly important to develop new energy-efficient technologies and ways to maximize renewable energy sources.

CONCEPTUAL FRAMEWORK
Physical Sciences, Energy and Change: Electromagnetic Force

Motion and Stability: Forces and Interactions

Concept A The motion of an object is determined by the sum of the forces (pushes and pulls) acting on it.
- A force is a push or a pull. Net force is the sum of all the forces acting on a mass.
- The magnitude of the magnetic force between two interacting magnetic fields decreases as the distance between them increases.

Concept B All interactions between objects arise from a few types of forces, primarily gravity and electromagnetism.
- Magnets are surrounded by an invisible magnetic field. Magnetic materials may become temporary magnets when they interact with magnetic fields.
- The magnetic field produced by a current-carrying wire can induce magnetism in a piece of iron or steel, forming an electromagnet.

Energy Transfer and Conservation

Concept A Energy is a quantitative property (condition) of a system that depends on the motion and interactions of matter and radiation within the system.
- Kinetic energy is energy of motion; potential energy is dependent on the position of an object within a system.
- Changing the position of an object in an electric or magnetic field changes the potential energy.
- Energy sources can be categorized as renewable or non-renewable.

Concept B The total change of energy in any system is always equal to the total energy transferred into or out of the system. When two objects interact, each one exerts a force on the other, and these forces can transfer energy.
- Energy cannot be created or destroyed, only transferred.
- Every energy use can be described as a sequence of energy transfers.

Electromagnetic Force Course—FOSS Next Generation

ELECTROMAGNETIC FORCE — Framework and NGSS

Engineering Design

Science is a discovery activity, a process for producing new knowledge. Scientific knowledge advances when scientists observe objects and events, think about how their observations relate to what is known, test their ideas in logical ways, and generate explanations that integrate the new information into their understanding of the natural world. Thus, the scientific enterprise is both what we know (content knowledge) and how we come to know it (practices). Scientists engage in a set of practices as they do their work and these are the same practices students use in their science investigations.

Engineers apply that understanding of the natural world to solve real-world problems. Engineering is the systematic approach to finding solutions to problems identified by people in societies. The fields of science and engineering are mutually supportive, and scientists and engineers collaborate in their work. Often, acquiring scientific data requires designing and producing new technologies—tools, instruments, machines, and processes—to perform specific functions. The practices that engineers use are very similar to science practices but also involve defining problems and designing solutions.

The process of engineering design, while it involves engineering practices, is considered a separate set of disciplinary core ideas in the *Framework* and in the NGSS. There are three basic ideas of engineering design: defining the problem, developing possible solutions, and improving the design.

Defining the problem "with precision" means having a clear understanding of specific criteria and constraints in a complex problem that might have a broader societal or environmental impact.

Developing possible solutions at middle school focuses not only on generating design ideas, but also on a process of evaluating different ideas that have been proposed in a systematic way such as a trade-off matrix to determine the most promising designs. Those most promising designs would be tested and results would be combined into a new solution.

Optimizing the design involves an iterative process of testing the best design, systematically analyzing the results, modifying the design while controlling variables, retesting, comparing results, and again modifying the design. Students may go through this cycle several times in order to optimize the design. Students need to know that "failure" is not only OK, but expected in engineering design. Having something fail drives you to improve the system and make progress. Collaboration is an important aspect of engineering design; learning from the successes and

FOSS Conceptual Framework

failures of other design groups can be very productive. Students can engage in engineering practices without fully engaging in the iterative process of design.

In this course, there is one investigation in which students explore the disciplinary core ideas of engineering design in the context of force and energy. But students engage in engineering practices in other investigations without engaging in the full engineering design process. FOSS has a continuum of engagements in the engineering practices and process from short experiences to more in-depth experiences where students reflect on the core ideas about the design process.

CONCEPTUAL FRAMEWORK
Engineering Design: Electromagnetic Force

Concept A   **Defining and delimiting engineering problems**

- The more precisely a design task's criteria and constraints can be defined, the more likely it is that the designed solution will be successful. Specification of constraints includes consideration of scientific principles and other relevant knowledge likely to limit possible solutions.

Concept B   **Developing possible solutions**

- A solution needs to be tested and then modified on the basis of the test results in order to improve it.
- There are systematic processes for evaluating solutions with respect to how well they meet the criteria and constraints of a problem.
- Sometimes parts of different solutions can be combined to create a solution that is better than any of its predecessors.
- Models of all kinds are important for testing solutions.

Concept C   **Optimizing the design solution**

- Although one design may not perform the best across all tests, identifying the characteristics of the design that performed the best in each test can provide useful information for the redesign process—that is, some of those characteristics may be incorporated into the new design.
- The iterative process of testing the most promising solutions and modifying what is proposed on the basis of the test results leads to greater refinement and ultimately to an optimal solution.

Electromagnetic Force Course—FOSS Next Generation

ELECTROMAGNETIC FORCE — Framework and NGSS

Physical Science Content Sequence

This table shows all the modules and courses for grades 3–8 in the FOSS content sequence for physical science, with an emphasis on the modules that inform the Energy and Change strand. The supporting elements in these modules (somewhat abbreviated) are listed. The elements for the **Electromagnetic Force Course** are expanded to show how they fit into the sequence.

Module or course	ENERGY AND CHANGE	
	Motion and Stability: Forces and Interactions	**Energy Transfer and Conservation**
Electromagnetic Force (middle school)		
Waves (middle school)		• A simple wave has a repeating pattern related to the energy of the wave. • Waves interacting with a medium can be absorbed, reflected, or transmitted through the medium. • A wave model can be used to explain the properties of light. • Electromagnetic waves form a spectrum of different wavelengths. • Information technologies are instruments that produce and detect waves to encode and transmit information.
Gravity and Kinetic Energy (middle school)	• Gravity is an attractive force between two objects; a falling object increases speed with a constant acceleration due to gravity. • An object in motion will stay in motion (or an object at rest will stay at rest) unless acted on by an external force. • The greater the object's mass, the greater the force needed to change motion. • For interacting objects, the force exerted by one on the second is equal in strength to the force that the second object exerts on the first, but in the opposite direction.	• Kinetic energy is energy of moving things; potential energy is energy dependent on the position of an object within a system. • Kinetic energy is transferred in a collision. • Kinetic energy is proportional to the mass of a moving object. Increasing the speed of an object increases its kinetic energy by the same factor squared.
Energy (grade 4)	• Magnets interact with each other and with materials that contain iron. • Like poles of magnets repel each other; opposite poles attract. The magnetic force declines as the distance between the magnets increases. • Conductors are materials through which electric current can flow; all metals are conductors. • Any change of motion requires a force. • Gravity is a pulling force that acts between all masses.	• Energy can be generated by burning fossil fuels or harnessing renewable energy. • Electric current transfers energy that can produce heat, light, sound, and motion. • A circuit is a system that includes a pathway through which electric current flows. • Motion of one object can transfer to motion of other objects in a collision. • Waves are a repeating pattern of motion that transfer energy. • An object is seen when light from an object enters and is detected by the eye.
Motion and Matter (grade 3)	• Magnetic forces between a pair of objects do not require that the objects be in contact. The strength of the force depends on the properties of the objects and their distance apart. • Gravity is the force that pulls masses toward the center of Earth. • Any change of motion requires a force. Each force has a strength and direction.	

FOSS Conceptual Framework

	Motion and Stability: Forces and Interactions	Energy Transfer and Conservation
Electromagnetic Force	• A force is a push or a pull. Net force is the sum of all the forces acting on a mass. • The magnitude of the magnetic force between two interacting magnetic fields decreases as the distance between them increases. • Magnets are surrounded by an invisible magnetic field. Magnetic materials may become temporary magnets when they interact with magnetic fields. • The magnetic field produced by a current-carrying wire can induce magnetism in a piece of iron or steel, forming an electromagnet.	• Kinetic energy is energy of motion; potential energy is dependent on the position of an object within a system. • Changing the position of an object in an electric or magnetic field changes the potential energy. • Energy sources can be categorized as renewable or nonrenewable. • Energy cannot be created or destroyed, only transferred. • Every energy use can be described as a sequence of energy transfers.

> **NOTE**
> See the Assessment chapter in this *Investigations Guide* for more details on how the FOSS embedded and benchmark assessment opportunities align with the conceptual frameworks and the learning progressions. In addition, the Assessment chapter describes specific connections between the FOSS assessments and the NGSS Performance Expectations.

The NGSS Performance Expectations addressed in this course include

Physical Sciences
MS-PS2-2
MS-PS2-3
MS-PS2-5
MS-PS3-2
MS-PS3-5

Earth and Space Sciences
MS-ESS3-4

Engineering Design
MS–ETS1-1
MS–ETS1-2
MS–ETS1-3
MS–ETS1-4

See pages 34–38 in this chapter for more details on the grades 6–8 NGSS Performance Expectations.

ELECTROMAGNETIC FORCE — Framework and NGSS

CONNECTIONS TO NGSS BY INVESTIGATION

Inv. 1: What Is Force?

Science and Engineering Practices	Connections to Common Core State Standards—ELA
Asking questions Developing and using models Planning and carrying out investigations Analyzing and interpreting data Using mathematics and computational thinking Constructing explanations Engaging in an argument from evidence Obtaining, evaluating, and communicating information	**Reading—Literacy in Science and Technical Subjects** 1. Cite specific textual evidence to support analysis of science and technical texts. 2. Determine the central ideas or conclusions of a text; provide an accurate summary of the text distinct from prior knowledge or opinions. 5. Analyze the structure an author uses to organize a text, including how the major sections contribute to the whole and to an understanding of the topic. 7. Integrate quantitative or technical information expressed in words in a text with a version of that information expressed visually (e.g., in a flowchart, diagram, model, graph, or table). 10. Read and comprehend science/technical texts in the grades 6–8 text complexity band independently and proficiently. **Writing—Literacy in Science and Technical Subjects** 5. With some guidance and support from peers and adults, develop and strengthen writing as needed by planning, revising, editing, rewriting, or trying a new approach, focusing on how well purpose and audience have been addressed. 8. Gather relevant information from multiple print and digital sources, using search terms effectively. **Speaking and Listening** 5. Integrate multimedia and visual displays into presentations to clarify information, strengthen claims and evidence, and add interest. 6. Analyze the author's purpose in providing an explanation, describing a procedure, or discussing an experiment in a text. **Language** 4. Determine or clarify the meaning of unknown words or phrases. 5. Demonstrate understanding of word relationships and nuances in word meaning.

Connections to NGSS by Investigation

Disciplinary Core Ideas		Crosscutting Concepts
PS2.A: Forces and motion • For any pair of interacting objects, the force exerted by the first object on the second object is equal in strength to the force that the second object exerts on the first, but in the opposite direction (Newton's third law). **(MS-PS2-1)** • The motion of an object is determined by the sum of the forces acting on it; if the total force on the object is not zero, its motion will change. The greater the mass of the object, the greater the force needed to achieve the same change in motion. For any given object, a larger force causes a larger change in motion. **(MS-PS2-2)** • All positions of objects and the directions of forces and motions must be described in an arbitrarily chosen reference frame and arbitrarily chosen units of size. In order to share information with other people, these choices must also be shared. **(MS-PS2-2)**		Patterns Cause and effect Systems and system models Energy and matter Stability and change

ELECTROMAGNETIC FORCE — *Framework and NGSS*

Inv. 2: The Force of Magnetism

Science and Engineering Practices

Asking questions
Developing and using models
Planning and carrying out investigations
Analyzing and interpreting data
Using mathematics and computational thinking
Constructing explanations
Engaging in argument from evidence
Obtaining, evaluating, and communicating information

Connections to Common Core State Standards—ELA

Reading—Literacy in Science and Technical Subjects
2. Determine the central ideas or conclusions of a text; provide an accurate summary of the text distinct.
4. Determine the meaning of symbols, key terms, and domain-specific words and phrases as used in the text.
5. Analyze the structure an author uses to organize a text, including how the major sections contribute to the whole and to an understanding of the topic.
7. Integrate quantitative or technical information expressed in words in a text with a version of that information expressed visually.
9. Compare and contrast the information gained from experiments, simulations, video, or multimedia sources with that gained from reading a text.
10. Read and comprehend science texts in the grades 6–8 text complexity independently and proficiently.

Writing—Literacy in Science and Technical Subjects
8. Gather relevant information from multiple print and digital sources, using search terms effectively.

Speaking and Listening
6. Adapt speech to a variety of contexts and tasks, demonstrating command of formal English.

Language
5. Demonstrate understanding of word relationships.
6. Acquire and use academic and domain-specific words and phrases.

Connections to NGSS by Investigation

Disciplinary Core Ideas

PS2.A: Forces and motion
- The motion of an object is determined by the sum of the forces acting on it; if the total force on the object is not zero, its motion will change. The greater the mass of the object, the greater the force needed to achieve the same change in motion. For any given object, a larger force causes a larger change in motion. **(MS-PS2-2)**

PS2.B: Types of interactions
- Electric and magnetic (electromagnetic) forces can be attractive or repulsive, and their sizes depend on the magnitudes of the charges, currents, or magnetic strengths involved and on the distances between the interacting objects. **(MS-PS2-3)**
- Forces that act at a distance (electric and magnetic) can be explained by fields that extend through space and can be mapped by their effect on a test object (a ball, a charged object, or a magnet, respectively). **(MS-PS2-5)**

PS3.A: Definitions of energy
- A system of objects may also contain stored (potential) energy, depending on their relative positions. **(MS-PS3-2)**

PS3.C: Relationship between energy and forces
- When two objects interact, each one exerts a force on the other that can cause energy to be transferred to or from the object. **(MS-PS3-2)**

Crosscutting Concepts

Patterns
Cause and effect
Systems and system models
Energy and matter

Electromagnetic Force Course—FOSS Next Generation

ELECTROMAGNETIC FORCE — Framework and NGSS

Inv. 3: Electromagnetism

Science and Engineering Practices

Asking questions and defining problems
Developing and using models
Planning and carrying out investigations
Analyzing and interpreting data
Using mathematics and computational thinking
Constructing explanations and designing solutions
Engaging in argument from evidence
Obtaining, evaluating, and communicating information

Connections to Common Core State Standards—ELA

Reading—Literacy in Science and Technical Subjects
1. Cite specific textual evidence to support analysis of science and technical texts.
2. Determine the central ideas or conclusions of a text; provide an accurate summary of the text distinct from prior knowledge or opinions.
3. Follow precisely a multistep procedure when carrying out experiments, taking measurements, or performing technical tasks.
5. Analyze the structure an author uses to organize a text, including how the major sections contribute to the whole and to an understanding of the topic.
6. Analyze the author's purpose in providing an explanation or discussing an experiment in a text.
7. Integrate quantitative or technical information expressed in words in a text with a version of that information expressed visually.
8. Distinguish among facts, reasoned judgment based on research findings, and speculation in a text.
9. Compare and contrast the information gained from experiments, simulations, video, or multimedia sources with that gained from reading a text.

Writing—Literacy in Science and Technical Subjects
8. Gather relevant information from multiple print and digital sources, using search terms effectively.

Speaking and Listening
1. Engage effectively in a range of collaborative discussions.
4. Present claims and findings, emphasizing salient points in a focused, coherent manner with relevant evidence, valid reasoning, and well-chosen details.

Connections to NGSS by Investigation

Disciplinary Core Ideas

PS2.B: Types of interactions
- Electric and magnetic (electromagnetic) forces can be attractive or repulsive, and their sizes depend on the magnitudes of the charges, currents, or magnetic strengths involved and on the distances between the interacting objects. **(MS-PS2-3)**
- Forces that act at a distance (electric and magnetic) can be explained by fields that extend through space and can be mapped by their effect on a test object (a ball, a charged object, or a magnet, respectively). **(MS-PS2-5)**

PS3.A: Definitions of energy
- A system of objects may also contain stored (potential) energy, depending on their relative positions. **(MS-PS3-2)**

ETS1.A: Defining and delimiting engineering problems
- The more precisely a design task's criteria and constraints can be defined, the more likely it is that the designed solution will be successful. Specification of constraints includes consideration of scientific principles and other relevant knowledge that are likely to limit possible solutions. **(secondary to MS-PS3-3)**

ETS1.B: Developing possible solutions
- A solution needs to be tested, and then modified on the basis of the test results, in order to improve it. There are systematic processes for evaluating solutions with respect to how well they meet the criteria and constraints of a problem. **(secondary to MS-PS3-3)**
- Sometimes parts of different solutions can be combined to create a solution that is better than any of its predecessors. **(MS-ETS1-3)**
- Models of all kinds are important for testing solutions. **(MS-ETS1-4)**

ETS1.C: Optimizing the design solution
- Although one design may not perform the best across all tests, identifying the characteristics of the design that performed the best in each test can provide useful information for the redesign process—that is, some of those characteristics may be incorporated into the new design. The iterative process of testing the most promising solutions and modifying what is proposed on the basis of the test results leads to greater refinement and ultimately to an optimal solution. **(MS-ETS1-3, MS-ETS1-4)**

Crosscutting Concepts

Patterns
Cause and effect
Systems and system models
Energy and matter
Structure and function

ELECTROMAGNETIC FORCE — *Framework and NGSS*

Inv. 4: Energy Transfer

Science and Engineering Practices

Asking questions
Developing and using models
Planning and carrying out investigations
Analyzing and interpreting data
Constructing explanations
Engaging in argument from evidence
Obtaining, evaluating, and communicating information

Connections to Common Core State Standards—ELA

Reading—Literacy in Science and Technical Subjects
1. Cite specific textual evidence to support analysis of science and technical texts.
2. Determine the central ideas or conclusions of a text; provide an accurate summary of the text distinct.
3. Follow precisely a multistep procedure when carrying out experiments, taking measurements, or performing technical tasks.
4. Determine the meaning of symbols, key terms, and other domain-specific words and phrases as they are used in a specific scientific or technical context relevant to grades 6–8 texts and topics.
6. Analyze the author's purpose in providing an explanation, describing a procedure, or discussing an experiment in a text.
7. Integrate quantitative or technical information expressed in words in a text with a version of that information expressed visually.
9. Compare and contrast the information gained from experiments, simulations, video, or multimedia sources with that gained from reading a text on the same topic.
10. Read and comprehend science/technical texts in the grades 6–8 text complexity band independently and proficiently.

Writing—Literacy in Science and Technical Subjects
9. Draw evidence from informational texts to support analysis, reflection, and research.

Speaking and Listening
5. Integrate multimedia and visual displays into presentations to clarify information, strengthen claims and evidence, and add interest.

Language
5. Demonstrate understanding of word relationships and nuances in word meaning.
6. Acquire and use academic and domain-specific words and phrases.

Connections to NGSS by Investigation

Disciplinary Core Ideas		Crosscutting Concepts
PS3.B: Conservation of energy and energy transfer • When the motion energy of an object changes, there is inevitably some other change in energy at the same time. (MS-PS3-5) **PS3.C: Relationship between energy and forces** • When two objects interact, each one exerts a force on the other that can cause energy to be transferred to or from the object. (MS-PS3-2)	**ESS3.A: Natural resources** • Humans depend on Earth's land, ocean, atmosphere, and biosphere for many different resources. Minerals, fresh water, and biosphere resources are limited, and many are not renewable or replaceable over human lifetimes. (MS-ESS3-1) **ESS3.C: Human impacts on Earth systems** • Typically as human populations and per-capita consumption of natural resources increase, so do the negative impacts on Earth unless the activities and technologies involved are engineered otherwise. (MS-ESS3-3, MS-ESS3-4)	Patterns Cause and effect Scale, proportion, and quantity Systems and system models Energy and matter Structure and function Stability and change

ELECTROMAGNETIC FORCE — *Framework and NGSS*

RECOMMENDED FOSS NEXT GENERATION K–8 SCOPE AND SEQUENCE

Grade	Integrated Middle Grades				
6–8	Heredity and Adaptation*	Electromagnetic Force*	Gravity and Kinetic Energy*	Waves*	Planetary Science
	Chemical Interactions		Earth History		Populations and Ecosystems
	Weather and Water		Diversity of Life		Human Systems Interactions*

*Half-length courses 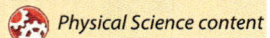 Physical Science content  Earth Science content  Life Science content   Engineering content

Grade	Physical Science	Earth Science	Life Science
5	Mixtures and Solutions	Earth and Sun	Living Systems
4	Energy	Soils, Rocks, and Landforms	Environments
3	Motion and Matter	Water and Climate	Structures of Life
2	Solids and Liquids	Pebbles, Sand, and Silt	Insects and Plants
1	Sound and Light	Air and Weather	Plants and Animals
K	Materials and Motion	Trees and Weather	Animals Two by Two

Full Option Science System

Materials

ELECTROMAGNETIC FORCE — *Materials*

Contents

Introduction 61
Kit Inventory List 62
Materials Supplied by the Teacher 63
Important Information for First-Time FOSS Users 65
Preparing the Kit for Your Classroom 68
Care, Reuse, and Recycling 70

INTRODUCTION

The Electromagnetic Force kit contains

- *Teacher Toolkit: Electromagnetic Force*
  1 *Investigations Guide: Electromagnetic Force*
  1 *Teacher Resources: Electromagnetic Force*
  1 *FOSS Science Resources: Electromagnetic Force*

- *FOSS Science Resources: Electromagnetic Force* (class set of student books)

- Equipment for 5 classes of 32 students

Each investigation in this course is divided into three parts. Each part has a Materials section that details the materials in the kit and the materials supplied by the teacher that will be used by each group of students and the class. The kit includes most of the learning equipment needed by students. There are enough consumable materials in the kit for 5 classes of 32 students each. Some of the teacher-supplied items can also be ordered through Delta Education.

For each investigation, you will need one computer with Internet access that can be displayed to the class, either by an LCD projector, interactive whiteboard, or large screen.

For updates to information on materials used in this course and to access the Safety Data Sheets (SDS), go to www.FOSSweb.com. Links to replacement-part lists and customer service are also available on FOSSweb.

▶ **NOTE**
Delta Education Customer Service can be reached at 1-800-258-1302.

FOSS Full Option Science System

ELECTROMAGNETIC FORCE — *Materials*

KIT INVENTORY List

Drawer 1—permanent equipment

★ The student books are shipped separately in two boxes of 16 hardbound books each.

▶ **NOTE**
The teacher toolkit is shipped separately. However, there is space in drawer 1 to store your toolkit.

✪ These items might occasionally need replacement.

Quantity	Item	Equipment condition
1	Teacher Toolkit: Electromagnetic Force (1 Investigations Guide, 1 Teacher Resources, and 1 FOSS Science Resources: Electromagnetic Force)	
32	FOSS Science Resources: Electromagnetic Force, student books ★	
8	Car, toy	
16	Cell holders	
8	Compasses, magnetic	
20	Cups, plastic, 250 mL	
16	D-cells, alkaline ✪	
32	Force markers	
36	Magnets, doughnut-shaped	
1	Masking tape, 2.5 cm (1"), roll ✪	
8	Mats, plastic	
400	Paper clips, regular ✪	
1	Poster, FOSS Outdoor Safety	
1	Poster, FOSS Science Safety	
100	Rubber bands, #33	
16	Spring scales, 500 g/5 N	
1	Wire, 20-gauge, insulated, roll, 16 m/roll (53') ✪	

Drawer 2—permanent equipment

Quantity	Item	Equipment condition
8	Box, cardboard ✪	
16	Bulb holders	
1	Generator, hand-crank, with two bulbs	
1	Iron filings, 150 g	
20	Lightbulbs, #222	
24	Loads, 240 g	
20	Magnets, bar	
8	Magnets-on-a-post	
18	Motors, electric, with leads	
8	Paper plates, small	
8	Rivets, with rubber washers	
9	Solar cells, with leads	
50	Spacers, plastic	
1	String, ball ✪	
16	Switches	
1	Wire, 24-gauge, insulated, roll, 16 m/roll (53') ✪	
1	Wire stripper	
25	Zip bags, 1 L	

Full Option Science System

MATERIALS *Supplied by the Teacher*

Each part of each investigation has a Materials section that describes the materials required for that part. It lists materials needed for each student or group of students and for the class.

Be aware that you must supply some items. These appear in the materials list for each part of the investigation. Here is a summary list of those items. Some of the supplies and tools are available from Delta Education. Check the replacement-part list for the course on the Delta Education website.

Technology equipment
- Computers with Internet access
- 1 Document camera or overhead projector
- 1 Projection system
- Extension cords with multiple outlets (optional)

Measuring tools
- 1 Ruler or measuring tape, metric
- 1 Teaspoon, 1/4

Paper
- Chart paper
- Index cards (optional)
- Science notebooks (composition books)
- Self-stick notes
- White paper, 22 × 28 cm (8.5" × 11")

Supplies
- 1 Bag, paper or plastic (optional)
- Friction test surfaces (newspaper, blanket, sandpaper, etc.)
- 1–2 Incandescent lightbulbs (optional)
- 2 Nails, 5 cm or longer
- 1 Rolling cart, rolling chair, or small desk
- Talc or flour (optional)

> **NOTE**
> Throughout the *Investigations Guide*, we refer to materials not provided in the kit as "teacher-supplied." These materials are generally common or consumable items that schools and/or classrooms already have, such as rulers, paper towels, and computers. If your school/classroom does not have these items, they can be provided by teachers, schools, districts, or materials centers (if applicable). You can also borrow the items from other departments or classrooms, or request these items as community donations.

ELECTROMAGNETIC FORCE — Materials

Other tools

- Colored pencils, marking pens, and highlighters
- 1 Craft knife (optional)
- 1 Craft stick (optional)
- 1 Lamp (optional)
- 32 Mini-whiteboards, (optional)
- 32 Scissors
- 1 Screwdriver, approximately 3 mm blade
- 8 Whiteboard erasers (optional)
- 8 Whiteboard marking pens (optional)
- 1 Work gloves

IMPORTANT *Information for First-Time FOSS Users*

If this is your first time using a FOSS middle school course, you should become familiar with a few items before beginning instruction. These steps will also prepare you to teach any other FOSS middle school course.

1. Plan for student notebooks

In FOSS, students keep science notebooks both as organized records of their scientific investigations and as places to reflect about their thinking. Notebook opportunities appear in each part of each investigation.

Students will need their own notebooks dedicated for use in science class, in which they can record focus questions, observations, data, conclusions, their own questions, and so on. These notebooks are typically bound composition books in which students make entries and glue or tape photocopied notebook sheets or other artifacts.

In preparation for each part of each investigation, you will make copies of the specified notebook masters. You can print or copy the preprinted notebook masters from *Teacher Resources* or download digital versions from www.FOSSweb.com. Each notebook master consists of two copies of a notebook sheet, so each photocopied page will need to be cut in half. Sometimes you might prefer to project a notebook master and have students copy some information from the notebook sheet into their notebooks, adding their own data and responses.

> **TEACHING NOTE**
>
> Notebook sheets are available on FOSSweb in several formats. For each notebook sheet, you can select "to photocopy," which will be identical to the printed notebook masters in **Teacher Resources**, or "to project," which is rotated and zoomed for easier display. You can also type into these notebook sheets while projecting them.

In the first investigation, make sure students have prepared their notebooks by setting up a table of contents, creating an index for vocabulary words, and numbering the pages. For more information on notebook use in FOSS, see the Science Notebooks in Middle School chapter.

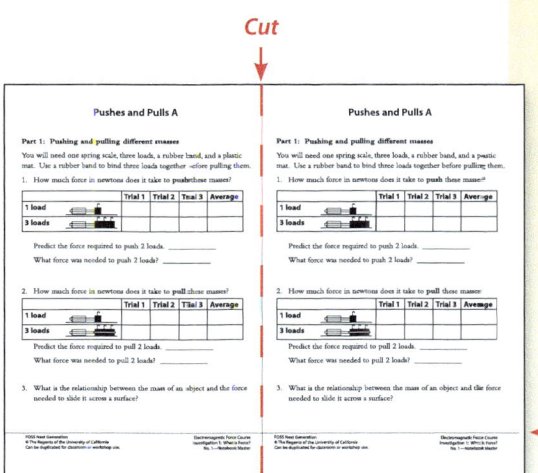

Notebook master

Electromagnetic Force Course—FOSS Next Generation

65

ELECTROMAGNETIC FORCE — *Materials*

2. Plan for online activities and projection

Throughout this course, you will need to project digital components through your computer for the class to see. The Getting Ready section for each part will indicate what to prepare.

In general, you will need regular access to a computer with Internet access, a document camera, and either an LCD projector or a large-screen display. If regular projection is difficult given your classroom setup, you could use the notebook masters and teacher masters to make transparencies for use with a document camera or an overhead projector.

For other projection needs, such as displaying a FOSSweb program, you will need to make sure students can see the computer display.

3. Become familiar with FOSSweb

If you have never logged into FOSSweb before, visit the site to set up your account. The site is used throughout the course to project teacher masters and notebook sheets, display digital components, such as animations and simulations, and provide student access to course resources and assignments that you create. For more information on how to set up an account and to access the digital resources, see the Technology chapter.

Once you've logged in, familiarize yourself with the layout of the site and the additional resources available to you there. The easiest way to access resources is by clicking the icon for the course and going to Resources by Investigation.

4. Review teaching slides

Available on FOSSweb is a series of editable slides for you to use with your class as an instructional tool. There is one set of slides for each part of each investigation. Look for the teaching slides under Digital-Only Resources on FOSSweb.

5. Plan for groups

Plan to organize students into groups of four around lab benches or tables. Seating should facilitate students' working together and sharing observations and ideas. The "for each group" section of the materials list will always describe the materials needed by a group of four students.

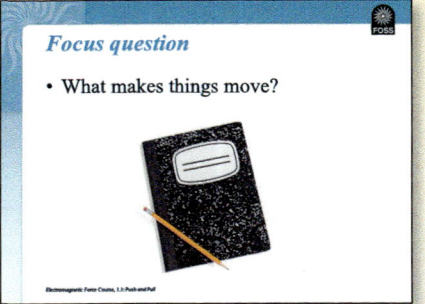

66 Full Option Science System

6. Display safety posters
Display the *FOSS Science Safety* and *FOSS Outdoor Safety* posters in prominent locations in the classroom.

7. Set up a materials station
Plan to establish a materials station where students will always pick up and return materials. Select a location that minimizes congestion and provides easy supervision as needed.

8. Assess progress throughout the course
Embedded (formative) assessments provide a variety of ways to gather information about students' thinking while their ideas are developing. These assessments are designed to be diagnostic. They provide you with information about student learning so that you know if you need to plan a next step to clarify understanding before going on to the next part of the investigation. Each Getting Ready section describes an embedded-assessment strategy you may find useful in that part. Two assessment masters, *Embedded Assessment Notes* and *Performance Assessment Checklist*, are provided as tools to help you analyze students' data (see the Assessment chapter for more on how to use these tools).

At the end of most investigations, there is an I-Check benchmark assessment. The questions on these assessments are summative—they examine all the concepts students have learned up to that point in the curriculum. You can find out more about I-Check assessments in the Assessment chapter and in Investigation 1.

Use the *Assessment Record* to record results. Check FOSSweb for downloadable spreadsheets for the *Performance Assessment Checklist* and *Assessment Record*.

Embedded Assessment Notes

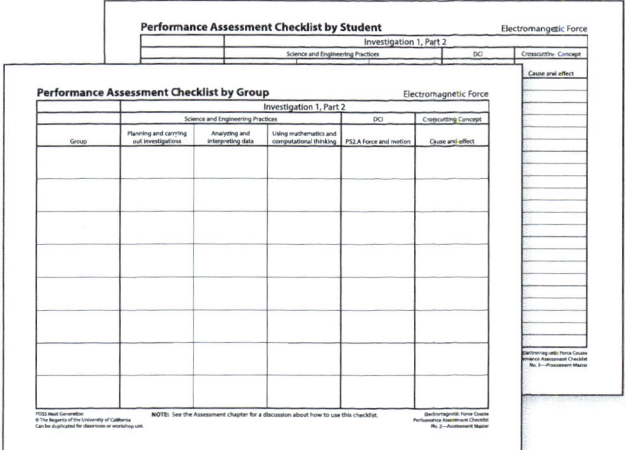

Performance Assessment Checklists

Assessment Record

Electromagnetic Force Course—FOSS Next Generation

ELECTROMAGNETIC FORCE — Materials

PREPARING the Kit for Your Classroom

Some preparation is required each time you use the kit. Doing things before beginning the course will make daily setup quicker and easier.

Each part of each investigation includes a section called Getting Ready, which describes what you need to do or consider to be prepared to conduct the part.

Note that a few items are consumable, but there should be enough in the kit for at least five classes before you need to restock.

One-Time Preparation

Some of the preparation will need to be done only once. Here are things that require one-time preparation.

Investigation 1, Part 1

Prepare spring scales by placing one plastic force marker on the rod end of each device. Calibrate the scales so that when they sit at rest, the wide green marker in the barrel rests at 0 N (0 g).

Investigation 2, Part 2

Prepare iron filings by placing about a quarter teaspoon of filings on a paper plate. Keeping it positioned horizontally, slide the plate into the plastic bag. Seal the bag. Prepare the cardboard magnet boxes by assembling each box, place a piece of reusable masking tape to seal the lid, and label the outside of the box lids with numbers 1–8.

Investigation 2, Part 3

Tie strings with loops to the end of the magnets-on-a-post.

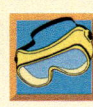

Investigation 3, Part 1

Cut 48 connecting wires using the 20-gauge red insulated wire. Each connector should be 15 cm long. Strip about 1 cm of red plastic insulation from each end of the wire.

Investigation 3, Part 2

Cut eight 150 cm electromagnet wires from the thinner 24-gauge insulated wire, usually yellow in this kit. Strip about 2 cm of plastic insulation from each end of the wires.

Investigation 3, Part 3

Cut one 150 cm electromagnet wires from the thicker 20-gauge insulated wire, usually red in this kit. Strip about 2 cm of plastic insulation from each end of the wires.

Investigation 4, Part 1

Dissect eight motors for inspection of their internal components. Preview teacher master I, *Dissected Motor in Three Parts*, and look at the three parts of the motor after dissection. Reassemble the casing and slide the casing back onto the plastic head for distribution in class

Investigation 4, Part 2

The solar cells come with two sets of wires. Use the set that has two different ends: one end has a metal ring, and the other end has a flat connector. Unscrew the wing nuts that are on the screws on the back of the solar cell. Place the metal rings of the positive wire over the positive screw, and tighten the wing nut. Place the metal rings of the negative wire over the negative screw, and tighten the wing nut.

Review Safety Guidelines

There is a safety poster in the kit. Consider how to introduce the class rules so that everyone has a safe science experience.

Students build electric circuits in this kit. Be alert for short circuits. If students complain that the wire or D-cell is getting hot, tell them to disconnect all their wires immediately and try something else. The heat is evidence of a short circuit.

Reserve Computers

Students should have access to computers or tablets in pairs or groups throughout the course. This is especially important in this part:

- Investigation 2, Part 3, for online activity

Plan ahead to use multiple computers at those times.

Sequential Classes

The materials are designed to be used with sequential classes. Organize a materials station in a central location in the classroom. Organize the materials at the station before first period. Each period, the appropriate materials are picked up for each group by a Getter, used for the investigation, inventoried by students at the end of the period, and returned to the materials station by a Getter. You can quickly review the materials station to ensure that all the materials came back (and take appropriate action if they didn't) and that the materials are ready for the next class.

Electromagnetic Force Course—FOSS Next Generation

ELECTROMAGNETIC FORCE — *Materials*

CARE, *Reuse, and Recycling*

When you finish teaching the course, inventory the kit carefully. Note the items that were used up, lost, or broken, and immediately arrange to replace the items. Use a photocopy of the *Kit Inventory List*, and put your marks in the "Equipment condition" column. Replacement parts are available for FOSS by calling Delta Education at 1-800-258-1302 or by using the online replacement-part catalog (www.DeltaEducation.com/FOSS/buy).

The items in the kit have been selected for their ease of use and durability. Make sure that items are clean and dry before putting them back in the kit. Small items should be inventoried (a good job for students under your supervision) and put into zip bags for storage. Any items that are no longer useful for science should be properly recycled.

Technology

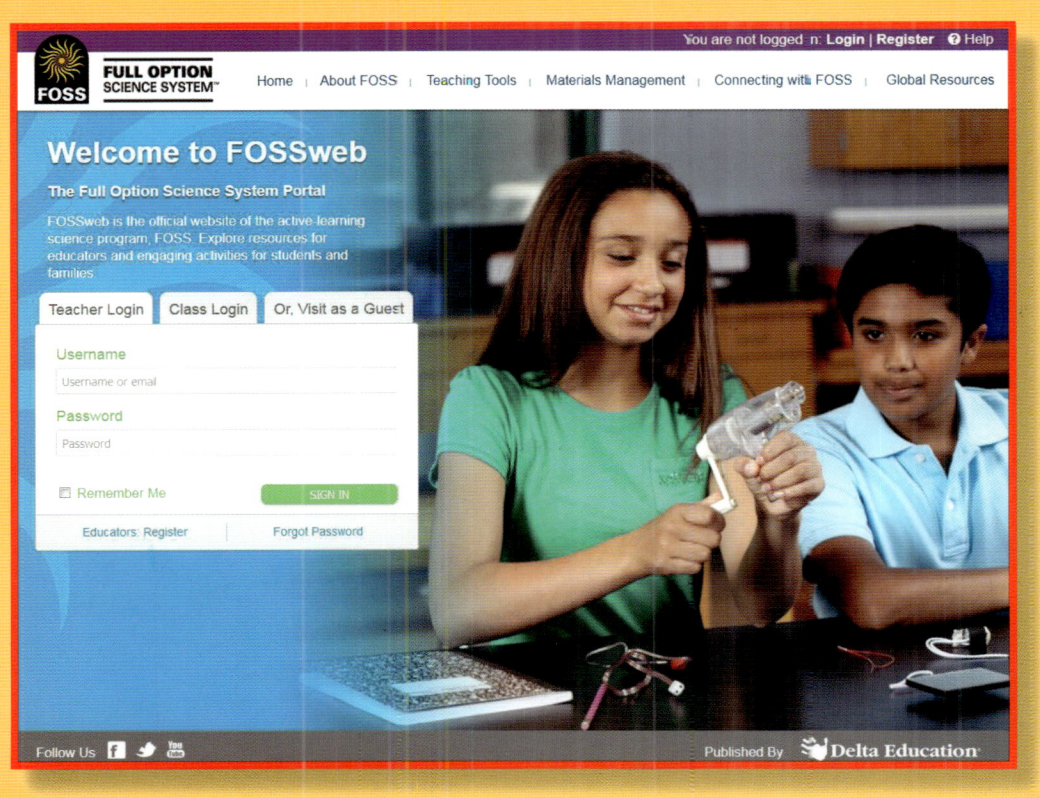

ELECTROMAGNETIC FORCE – *Technology*

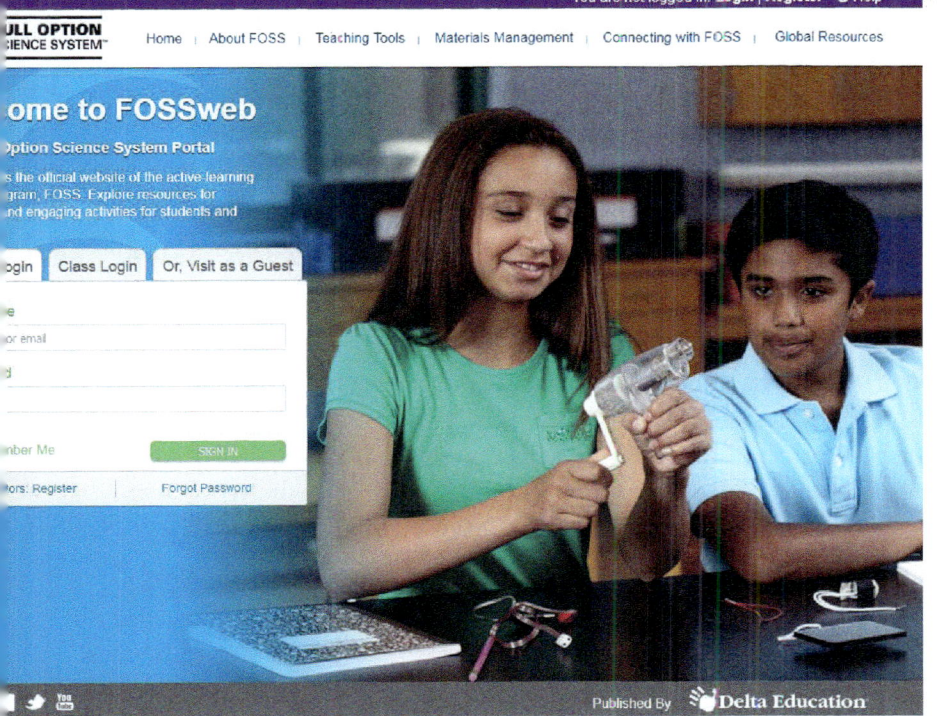

Contents

Introduction	71
Technology for Students	72
Technology for Teachers	73
Requirements for Accessing FOSSweb	78
Troubleshooting and Technical Support	80

INTRODUCTION

FOSSweb technology is an integral part of the **Electromagnetic Force Course**. It provides students with the opportunity to access and interact with simulations, images, video, and text—digital resources that can enhance their understanding of life science concepts. Different sections of digital resources are incorporated into each investigation during the course. Each use is marked with the technology icon in the *Investigations Guide*. You will sometimes use the digital resources to make presentations to the class. At other times, individuals or small groups of students will work with the digital resources to review concepts or reinforce their understanding.

The FOSSweb components are not optional. To prepare to use these digital resources, you should have at a minimum one device with Internet access that can be displayed to the class by an LCD projector with an interactive whiteboard or a large screen arranged for class viewing. Access to a computer lab or to enough computers in your classroom for students to work in small groups is also required during one investigation, and recommended during others.

The digital resources are available online at www.FOSSweb.com for teachers and students. We recommend you access FOSSweb well in advance of starting the course to set up your teacher-user account and become familiar with the resources.

▶ **NOTE**
To get the most current information, download the latest Technology chapter on FOSSweb.

ELECTROMAGNETIC FORCE — *Technology*

TECHNOLOGY *for Students*

FOSS is committed to providing a rich, accessible technology experience for all FOSS students. Students access FOSSweb using a class login that you set up. Here are brief descriptions of selected resources for students on FOSSweb.

Online activities. The online simulations and activities are designed to support students' learning and extend it beyond classroom experimentation. They include activities and resources that review or supplement active investigations and support students who have difficulties with the materials or who have been absent.

FOSS Science Resources—eBooks. As premium content, *FOSS Science Resources* is available as an eBook on computer or tablet, either as a read-only PDF or in an interactive format that allows text to be read and provides points of interactivity. The eBook can also be projected for guided reading with the whole class.

Media library. A variety of media enhances students' learning and provides them with opportunities to obtain, evaluate, and communicate information. FOSS has reviewed print books and digital resources that are appropriate for students and prepared a list of these resources with links to content websites. There is also a list of regional resources for virtual and actual field trips for students to use in gathering information for projects, and a database of science and engineering careers. Other resources include vocabulary lists to promote use of academic language.

Class pages. Teachers with a FOSSweb account can easily set up class pages with notes and assignments for each class. Students and families can then access this class information online, using the teacher-assigned class login.

▶ **NOTE**
The following student-facing resources are available in Spanish on FOSSweb using a teacher's class page.

- Vocabulary
- Equipment photo cards
- eBooks
- Select streaming videos
- Audio books

Technology for Teachers

TECHNOLOGY *for Teachers*

The teacher side of FOSSweb provides access to all the student resources plus those designed for teaching FOSS. By creating a FOSSweb user account and activating your modules, you can personalize FOSSweb for easy access to your instructional materials. You can also set up a class login for students and their families.

Creating a FOSSweb Teacher Account

Setting up an account. Set up a teacher account on FOSSweb before you begin teaching a module. Go to FOSSweb and register for an account with your school e-mail address. Complete registration instructions are available online. If you have a problem, go to the Connecting with FOSS pull-down menu, and look at Technical Help and Access Codes. You can also access online tutorials for getting started with FOSSweb at www.FOSSweb.com/fossweb-walkthrough-videos.

Entering your access code. Once your account is set up, go to FOSSweb and log in. To gain access to all the teacher resources for your module, you will need to enter your access code. Your access code should be printed on the inside cover of your *Investigations Guide*. If you cannot find your FOSSweb access code, contact your school administrator, your district science coordinator, or the purchasing agent for your school or district.

Familiarize yourself with the layout of the site and the additional resources available when you log in to your account. From the module page, you will be able to access teacher masters, science notebook masters, assessment masters, the FOSSmap online assessment component, and other digital resources not available to "guests."

Explore the Resources by Investigation, as this will help you plan. This page makes it simple to select the investigation you are teaching, and view all the digital resources organized by part. Resources by Investigation provides immediate access to the streaming videos, online activities, science notebook masters, teacher masters, and other digital resources for each investigation part.

Setting up class pages and student accounts. To enable your students to log in to FOSSweb to see class assignments and student-facing digital resources, set up a class page and generate a username and password for the class. To do this, log in to FOSSweb and go to your teacher page. Under "My Class Pages," follow the instructions to create a new class page and to leave notes for students. Note: student access to the student eBook from your class page requires premium content.

▶ **NOTE**
For more information about FOSS premium content, including pricing and ordering, contact your local Delta sales representative by visiting www.DeltaEducation.com or by calling 1-800-258-1302.

ELECTROMAGNETIC FORCE — *Technology*

Support for Teaching FOSS

FOSSweb is designed to support teachers using FOSS. FOSSweb is your portal to instructional tools to make teaching efficient and effective. Here are some of the tools available to teachers.

- **Grade-level Planning Guide.** The Planning Guide provides strategies for three-dimensional teaching and learning.

- **Resources by Investigation.** The Resources by Investigation organizes in one place all the print and online instructional materials you need for each part of each investigation.

- **Investigations eGuide.** The eGuide is the complete *Investigations Guide* component of the *Teacher Toolkit*, in an electronic web-based format for computers or tablets. If your district rotates modules among several teachers, this option allows all teachers easy access to *Investigations Guide* at all times.

- **Teacher preparation videos.** Videos present information to help you prepare for a module, including detailed investigation information, equipment setup and use, safety, and what students do and learn in each part of the investigation.

- **Teaching slides.** These slides (available as PDFs or PowerPoint) provide an outline for your classroom instruction, featuring key questions, instructions, and vocabulary. You can download the slides and modify them for your classes.

- **Focus questions.** The focus questions address the phenomenon for each part of each investigation, and are formatted for classroom projection and for printing, so that students can glue each focus question into their science notebooks.

- **Important course updates.** Important updates cover teacher materials, student equipment, and safety considerations.

- **Course teaching notes.** These notes include teaching suggestions and enhancements to the module, sent in by experienced FOSS users.

- **State and regional resources.** Listings of resources for your geographic region are provided for virtual and actual field trips and for students to use as individual or class projects.

- **Access to FOSS developers.** Through FOSSweb, teachers have a connection to the FOSS developers and expert FOSS teachers.

▶ **NOTE**
There are two versions of the eGuide, a PDF-based eGuide that mimics the hard copy guide, and an HTML interactive eGuide that allows you to write instructional notes and to interface with online resources from the guide.

▶ **NOTE**
The following resources are available on FOSSweb in Spanish.

Teacher-facing resources:
- Science notebook masters
- Teacher masters
- Assessment masters
- Focus questions
- Teaching slides

Student-facing resources:
- Vocabulary
- Equipment photo cards
- eBooks
- Select streaming videos
- Audio books

Technology for Teachers

Technology Components of FOSS Assessment System

FOSSmap for teachers and online assessments for students are the technology components of the FOSS assessment system.

For teachers. FOSSmap is where you set up your class, to schedule online assessments, review/record codes, and run reports. The reports are diagnostic and help you know what students understand and what they still need help with individually and as a class.

The teacher page of FOSSweb has a direct link to FOSSmap. Once you have a login and password for FOSSweb, use the same login and password to access FOSSmap. FOSSmap is a secure site that only you can see. FOSSmap tutorials will get you started with these technology components.

For students. FOSSmap.com/icheck is the URL for students who take the assessments online (*Survey/Posttest*, I-Checks, and interim assessments). Students can access this site only when you have scheduled an assessment for them to take. Access codes are generated for each student in the FOSSmap program and can be printed out on mailing labels. Each access code is good for all the assessments taken in one module. When you change modules, students get new access codes.

For more information about the FOSS assessment system and the technology components, see the Assessment chapter.

Technology for Differentiated Instruction

Some resources are for differentiated instruction. They can be used by students at home or by you as part of classroom instruction.

- **Online activities.** The online simulations and activities described earlier in this chapter are designed to support student learning and are often used during instruction. They extend opportunities to explore beyond what can be tested in the classroom, including advanced simulations and models that represent real-world phenomena. They can also be used as nextstep strategies to support students who have difficulties with the materials or who have been absent.
- **Vocabulary.** The online word list has science-related vocabulary and definitions used in the module (in both English and Spanish).
- **Equipment photo cards.** Equipment cards provide labeled photos of equipment that students use in the investigations. Cards can be printed and posted on the word wall as part of instruction.

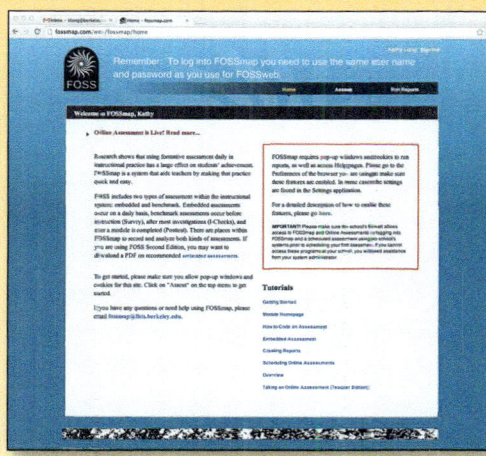

▶ **NOTE**
FOSSmap has a number of short online tutorials to get you started. Titles include:

- Overview
- Getting Started
- Module Homepage
- Embedded Assessment
- Scheduling Online Assessments
- Taking an Online Assessment (Teacher Edition)
- How to Code an Assessment
- Creating Reports

Electromagnetic Force Course—FOSS Next Generation

ELECTROMAGNETIC FORCE — *Technology*

> **NOTE**
> The eBook is premium content for students.

- **Student eBooks.** With premium content, students can access the books from any Internet-enabled device. The eBooks are available in PDF and interactive versions. The PDF version mimics the hard copy book. The interactive eBook reads the text to students—highlighting the text as it is read—and provides students with video clips and online activities.

- **Streaming videos used for extensions.** Some videos are part of the instruction in the investigation and are in Resources by Investigation for each part. Those videos also appear again in the digital resources under "Streaming Videos" along with other videos that extend concepts presented in a module.

- **Recommended books, websites, and careers database.** FOSS-recommended books, websites, and a Science and Engineering Careers Database that introduces students to a variety of career options and diversity of individuals engaged in those careers are provided.

- **Regional resources.** This list provides local resources that can be used to enhance instruction. The list includes website links and PDF documents from local sources.

Support for Classroom Materials Management

- **Materials chapter.** A PDF of the Materials chapter in *Investigations Guide* is available to help you prepare for teaching. A list, organized by drawer, shows the materials included in the FOSS kit for a given module. You can print and use this list for inventory and to monitor equipment condition.

- **Safety Data Sheets (SDS).** A link takes you to the latest safety sheets, with information from materials manufacturers on the safe handling and disposal of materials.

- **Plant and animal care.** This section includes information on caring for organisms used in the investigations.

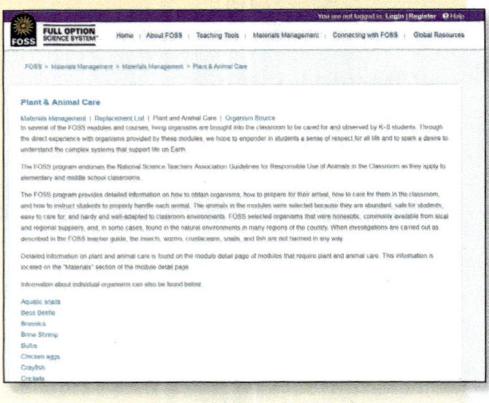

Technology for Teachers

Professional Learning Connections

FOSSweb provides PDF files of professional development chapters, mostly from *Teacher Resources*, that explain how to integrate instruction to improve learning. Some of them are

- Grade-Level Planning Guide
- Science and Engineering Practices
- Crosscutting Concepts and Integration
- Sense-Making Discussions for Three-Dimensional Learning
- Science Notebooks in Middle School
- Science-Centered Language Development in Middle School
- FOSS and Common Core English Language Arts and Math
- Access and Equity
- Taking FOSS Outdoors

ELECTROMAGNETIC FORCE — Technology

REQUIREMENTS *for Accessing* FOSSweb

FOSSweb Technical Requirements

To use FOSSweb, your computer must meet minimum system requirements and have a compatible browser and recent versions of Flash Player, QuickTime, and Adobe Reader. Many online activities have been updated to an HTML5 version compatible with all devices. (Those designated with "Flash" after the title require Flash Player.) The system requirements are subject to change. It is strongly recommended that you visit FOSSweb to review the most recent minimum system requirements and any plug-in requirements. There, you can access the "Tech Specs and Info" page to confirm that your browser has the minimum requirements to support the online activities.

Preparing your browser. FOSSweb requires a supported browser for Windows or Mac OS with a current version of the Flash Player plug-in, the QuickTime plug-in, and Adobe Reader or an equivalent PDF reader program. You may need administrator privileges on your computer in order to install the required programs and/or help from your school's technology coordinator.

By accessing the "Tech Specs and Info" page on FOSSweb, you can check compatibility for each computer you will use to access FOSSweb, including your classroom computer, computers in a school computer lab, and a home computer. The information on FOSSweb contains the most up-to-date technical requirements for all devices, including tablets and mobile devices.

Support for plug-ins and reader. Flash Player and Adobe Reader are available on www.adobe.com as free downloads. QuickTime is available for free from www.apple.com. FOSS does not support these programs. Please go to the program's website for troubleshooting information.

▶ **NOTE**
It is strongly recommended that you visit FOSSweb to review the most recent minimum system requirements.

Requirements for Accessing FOSSweb

Other FOSSweb Considerations

Firewall or proxy settings. If your school has a firewall or proxy server, contact your IT administrator to add explicit exceptions in your proxy server and firewall for FOSSweb, FOSSmap, and FOSSweb Akamai video servers. For more specific information on servers for firewalls, refer to "Tech Specs and Info" on FOSSweb.

Classroom technology setup. FOSS has a number of digital resources and makes every effort to accommodate users with different levels of access to technology. The digital resources can be used in a variety of ways and can be adapted to a number of classroom setups.

Teachers with classroom computers and an LCD projector, interactive whiteboard, or a large screen will be able to show online materials to the class. If you have access to a computer lab, or enough computers in your classroom for students to work in small groups, you can set up time for students to use the FOSSweb digital resources during the school day. Teachers who have access to only a single computer will find a variety of resources on FOSSweb that can be used to assist with teacher preparation and materials management.

Teachers who have tablets available for student use and have premium content can download the FOSS eBook app onto devices for easy student access to the FOSS eBooks. Instructions for downloading the app can be found on FOSSweb on the Module Detail Page for any course. You'll find them under the Digital-Only Resources section and then under the tab for Student eBooks.

Displaying online content. Throughout each module, you may occasionally want to project online components for instruction through your computer. To do this, you will need a computer with Internet access and either an LCD projector and a large screen, an interactive whiteboard, or a document camera arranged for the class to see.

You might want to display the notebook and teacher masters to the class. In Resources by Investigation, you'll have the option of downloading the masters to project or to copy. Choose "for Display" if you plan on projecting to the class. These masters are optimized for a projection system and allow text entry directly onto the sheet from the computer. The "for Print" versions are sized to minimize paper use when photocopying for the class. In Resources by Investigation the print versions of the master are typically unlabeled.

▶ **NOTE**
FOSSweb activities are designed for a minimum screen size of 1024 × 768. It is recommended that you adjust your screen resolution to 1024 × 768 or higher.

ELECTROMAGNETIC FORCE — *Technology*

> **NOTE**
> The FOSS digital resources are available online on FOSSweb. You can always access the most up-to-date technology information, including help and troubleshooting, on FOSSweb.

TROUBLESHOOTING *and Technical Support*

If you experience trouble with FOSSweb, you can troubleshoot in a variety of ways.

1. Test your browser to make sure you have the correct plug-in and browser versions. Even if you have the necessary plug-ins installed on your computer, they may not be recent enough to run FOSSweb correctly. Go to FOSSweb, and select the "Tech Specs and Info" page to review the most recent system requirements and check your browser.
2. Check the FAQs on FOSSweb for additional information that may help resolve the problem.
3. Empty the cache from your browser and/or quit and relaunch.
4. Restart your computer, and make sure all computer hardware turns on and is connected correctly.

If you are still experiencing problems after taking these steps, send FOSS Technical Support an e-mail to support@FOSSweb.com. In addition to describing the problem you are experiencing, include the following information about your computer: Mac or PC, operating system, browser name and version, plug-in names and versions. This will help us troubleshoot the problem.

Where to Get Help

For further questions about FOSSweb, please don't hesitate to contact our technical support team.

Account questions/help logging in

School Specialty Online Support
techsupport.science@schoolspecialty.com
loginhelp@schoolspecialty.com

Phone: 1-800-513-2465, 8:30 a.m.–6:00 p.m. ET

General FOSSweb technical questions

FOSSweb Tech Support
support@fossweb.com

Investigation 1: What Is Force?

INVESTIGATION 1 – What Is Force?

Part 1
Push and Pull 94

Part 2
Friction 109

Part 3
Forces in Action 118

Guiding question for phenomenon:
How are force and motion related?

Science and Engineering Practices
- Asking questions
- Developing and using models
- Planning and carrying out investigations
- Analyzing and interpreting data
- Using mathematics and computational thinking
- Constructing explanations
- Engaging in an argument from evidence
- Obtaining, evaluating, and communicating information

Disciplinary Core Ideas
PS2: How can one explain and predict interactions between objects and with systems of objects?
PS2.A: Forces and motion

Crosscutting Concepts
- Patterns
- Cause and effect
- Systems and system models
- Energy and matter
- Stability and change

PURPOSE

In *What Is Force?* students are introduced to the anchor phenomena of forces, the ways they interact, and their effects. This investigation starts out with an exploration into observable phenomena including motion and resistance to motion (friction).

Content
- A force is a push or a pull.
- The metric unit for force is the newton (N).
- Friction is a force that acts to oppose a force acting to put a mass in motion.
- Net force is the sum of the forces acting on a mass.

Practices
- Plan and carry out investigations to measure the force required to push and pull various objects on various surfaces.
- Analyze and interpret data from force experimentation to draw conclusions about force and friction.
- Use mathematics and computational thinking when analyzing data about friction and net force.
- Develop and use models to explain net force on an object.

FOSS *Full Option Science System*

INVESTIGATION 1 – What Is Force?

	Investigation Summary	Time	Focus Question for Phenomenon, Practices
PART 1	**Push and Pull** Students start their inquiry of force using spring scales to push and pull objects, noting that some objects require more push or pull to put them into motion. They complete a series of push and pull experiments, and quantify force in terms of the amount of stretch of a steel spring. Students are introduced to the idea that forces add, producing more force or canceling one another.	**Active Inv.** 3 Sessions* **Assessment** 1 Session	**What makes things move?** **Practices** Planning and carrying out investigations Analyzing and interpreting data Using mathematics and computational thinking Constructing explanations Obtaining, evaluating, and communicating information
PART 2	**Friction** Students use spring scales to measure the force needed to move loads on different surfaces. They review class results to consider patterns. Friction is developed as a force opposing motion, a force that changes depending on the two surfaces that are touching.	**Active Inv.** 1 Session	**How does friction affect the force needed to move an object?** **Practices** Asking questions Planning and carrying out investigations Analyzing and interpreting data Using mathematics and computational thinking Engaging in argument from evidence Obtaining, evaluating, and communicating information
PART 3	**Forces in Action** Students observe force exerted on one side of a rolling cart and on both sides of the cart. The idea of net force is developed to explain how force can cause motion in some instances but not in others. Students observe force being exerted on a cart that is positioned against the wall and try to explain why it is not moving. The idea that inanimate objects, like walls, can push is considered. Students use the idea of net force to analyze a number of force problems.	**Active Inv.** 1 Session **Reading** 1 Session **Assessment** 1–2 Sessions	**How do multiple forces affect motion?** **Practices** Developing and using models Using mathematics and computational thinking Constructing explanations Obtaining, evaluating, and communicating information

* A class session is 45–50 minutes.

At a Glance

Content Related to DCIs	Literacy/Technology	Assessment
• A force is a push or a pull. • The metric unit for force is the newton (N).	**Science Notebook Entry** *Pushes and Pulls A–C* **Science Resources Book** *"The Force Is with You"*	**Benchmark Assessment** *Entry-Level Survey* **Embedded Assessment** *Science notebook entry*
• Friction is a force that acts to oppose a force acting to put a mass in motion.	**Science Notebook Entry** *Friction Comparison* **Science Resources Book** *"The Discovery of Friction"*	**Embedded Assessment** *Performance assessment*
• Net force is the sum of the forces acting on a mass.	**Science Notebook Entry** *Forces on Carts A–B* *Response Sheet—Investigation 1* **Science Resources Book** *"Net Force"* **Video** *Forces*	**Embedded Assessment** *Response sheet* **Benchmark Assessment** *Investigation 1 I-Check* **NGSS Performance Expectation addressed in this investigation** MS-PS2-2

Electromagnetic Force Course—FOSS Next Generation

INVESTIGATION 1 — What Is Force?

SCIENTIFIC and Historical Background

The anchor phenomena investigated in this course are force interactions and effects. The driving question for the course is what is the relationship between magnetic and electric forces? In order to delve into an understanding of electromagnetic force, which produces the properties of electricity and magnetism, students begin by exploring observable motion phenomena, using their own muscle action to apply and measure force on objects with a **spring scale**. The guiding question for this investigation is how are force and motion related?

What Makes Things Move?

What is force? The most concrete way to approach force is to think of it as a push or a pull. A push is an **interaction**, and interaction is one of the keys to getting comfortable with force. Because force is an interaction, it can't exist by itself—it is an interplay between two (or more) things. It just isn't reasonable to think about a push without thinking about both the pusher and the pushee. Force is what happens between two objects while the push (or pull) is in progress.

Sir Isaac Newton (1643–1721) sorted out the relationships among force, matter, and motion. He laid it out in his three laws of motion. Let's consider Newton's second law: a **net force** applied to a mass accelerates that mass. Any number of forces of many different magnitudes can act on a mass from various directions simultaneously.

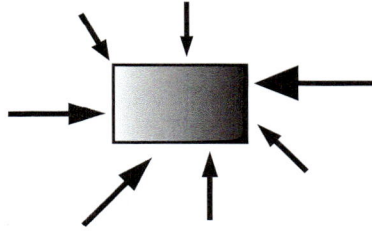

> **TEACHING NOTE**
> Refer to the grade-level Planning Guide chapter in Teacher Resources for a summary explanation of the phenomena students investigate in this module using a three-dimensional learning approach.

"Because force is an interaction, it can't exist by itself—it is an interplay between two (or more) things."

What happens when forces act on a mass? It depends on the magnitudes of the forces. Let's look at the simplest case: one force acting on a stationary mass.

The force acting to the right will cause the mass to accelerate to the right. It will accelerate as long as the force continues to be exerted on the mass.

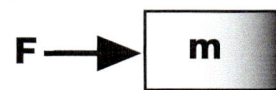

Often multiple forces act on a mass simultaneously. In the simplest case, two forces act in opposite directions on a mass.

F→ m ←−F

Scientific and Historical Background

Now what happens? To find out, add up all the forces acting on the mass to determine the grand total. The grand total is the net force. One extremely important point: force has direction. If a force from left to right is assigned a positive sign (+), then force from right to left is assigned a negative sign (–). If the two forces in the illustration above are equal in magnitude and opposite in direction, they will add to zero; that is, the net force will be zero.

The equation for calculating the net force acting on a mass is

$$F_{net} = F_1 + F_2 + F_3 + \ldots + F_n.$$

Force can be quantified in **newtons** (**N**). With this information, we can calculate the force acting on a mass, using the equation for adding force.

$$F_{net} = 5\ N + (-5\ N) = 0\ N$$

When the net force acting on a mass is zero, no change of motion will occur. If there is even a tiny net force acting in some direction, the mass will move. When force is used to make an object move, **energy** transfers to the object in the form of **kinetic energy**, energy of motion.

How Does Friction Affect the Force Needed to Move an Object?

In life we push and pull things around all the time. You might pull the refrigerator out to dust, reposition your computer on your desk, or nudge the dog's food bowl back into its customary position. None of these objects will move unless you apply a net force to make the motion happen. But why does it take so much more force to move the refrigerator than the food bowl? One reason is that the force needed to accelerate an object a certain amount depends on the mass of the object. Another reason is that there is a force acting in the opposite direction that is much greater for the refrigerator than for the food bowl.

The cryptic force at work opposing motion everywhere on Earth is **friction**. Friction is an interaction between surfaces. Friction is complex and can be reduced by things like wheels and lubricants. But one variable determining the magnitude of the friction force is mass—in general, the greater the mass, the greater the magnitude of the friction force.

When you pull on the refrigerator with a force of 10 N, it doesn't move. Recalling Newton's second law, we know that when a force is applied to an object in one direction, and it doesn't move, the net force is 0 N. That means there is a 10 N force acting in the opposite direction. It is the force applied by friction.

"When force is used to make an object move, energy transfers to the object in the form of kinetic energy, energy of motion."

Electromagnetic Force Course—FOSS Next Generation

INVESTIGATION 1 – What Is Force?

Apply more force—20 N ... 30 N ... 40 N. Eventually the refrigerator begins to move, and you pull it out. When the applied force exceeds the force of friction, the net force moves the refrigerator.

You may have noticed that it takes more force to get something started moving than it does to keep it in motion. That's because the *static* friction force between objects that are not moving relative to each other is generally more than the frictional force when the object is in motion, known as *kinetic* friction force. To keep the object moving at a constant speed, you need to exert a force exactly equal to the force of kinetic friction. Net force = 0 N.

When there is no net force, the moving object stops, right? No. When the net force is zero, the motion of the object stops *changing*. This is important. The velocity attained by the inertial burst of acceleration is maintained as long as there is no net force. This is in accord with Newton's first law: An object at rest stays at rest and an object in motion stays in motion with a constant velocity unless acted upon by a non zero net force.

"An object at rest stays at rest and an object in motion stays in motion with a constant velocity unless acted upon by a non zero net force."

How Do Multiple Forces Affect Motion?

Newton had penetrating vision. He was able to look into force-and-mass interactions and see that when a force is exerted on a mass, the mass exerts a reciprocal force to oppose the initiating force. The popular expression of Newton's third law is, for every action there is an equal and opposite reaction. Action and reaction are more commonly referred to as force.

A third-law look at the original single force exerted on a mass reveals that the mass is pushing back with a force that is equal and opposite to the applied force.

This makes sense when you accept the notion of force as an interaction. The object must be pushing back with a force equal to the applied force or the mass would be crushed, distorted, or otherwise changed. Notice that we are not now looking at the effect the applied force has on the motion of the mass—it could be moving or not—we are looking at the mass's response to having force applied to it.

Real motion. When one mass exerts a force on another mass, Newton's second and third laws are always working together. When you push a book cart around, you exert a force on the cart and the cart pushes back. If two people push on opposite sides of the cart, the cart pushes back on both people. The cart might or might not move (accelerate), depending on the net force exerted on the cart from outside.

Scientific and Historical Background

In class, students use spring scales to apply a measured force to objects. Here is a nominal book cart with spring scales installed on both sides. At rest, both scales indicate 0 N of lateral force.

Alexa arrives at the cart and applies a 5 N force to the left side of the cart. The kinetic frictional force of the wheels resists lateral movement, so there is −0.5 N force at each set of wheels.

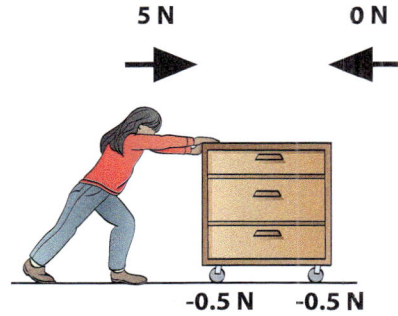

The 5 N push on the cart is greater than the −1 N frictional force from the wheels rolling on the ground, so there is a net force on the cart of 4 N. The cart will experience acceleration in the positive direction.

Now Roger comes along and exerts a 5 N force on the cart in the opposite direction. Now we can see the application of Newton's second and third laws when a 5 N force on one side of the cart is countered with a 5 N force in the opposite direction. There is no kinetic frictional force because the cart is not in motion.

Then Alexa increases the magnitude of the force she exerts on the cart. The net force from the pushers is 3 N in the positive direction, and when accounting for the frictional force of −1 N, the overall net force of

Electromagnetic Force Course—FOSS Next Generation

INVESTIGATION 1 – What Is Force?

the system is 2 N in the positive direction. The 2 N net force results in acceleration of Roger and the cart in the positive direction.

When Alexa rolls the cart over to the wall and continues to push on the cart, what happens? The cart doesn't move, so the net force must be zero. But who exerts the force that counters Alexa's force in the positive direction to bring the sum to zero? It's the wall. Alexa pushes on the cart with a 5 N force and the cart transfers that force to the wall, which in turn pushes back with a -5 N force, making a net force of 0 N.

What if there is no cart and Alexa just pushes on the wall? Alexa pushes on the wall with a 5 N force, and the wall pushes on Alexa with an equal but opposite 5 N force.

Forces in the universe. We live in a universe that functions with four fundamental forces. Only four. One of them—electromagnetism—is the focus in this course, to understand how force affects our daily lives. The other three forces are gravity and two nuclear forces. Gravity will be considered briefly in this investigation, and the nuclear forces will not be covered in this particular course.

Electricity and magnetism are two expressions of the same force, the electromagnetic force. In later investigations, we will examine this force more deeply, but one expression of electromagnetism is worth describing briefly here to better understand how walls can push.

Matter is made of fundamental building blocks called atoms. Atoms establish complex relationships with one another, forming chemical substances. Substances are held together at the atomic level by the electromagnetic force. The force is manifest in different kinds of chemical bonds. Bonds determine the average distances between atoms and the strength of the affinity atoms have for one another.

Walls are made of countless atoms maintained in durable structures by the electromagnetic force. If the wall is made of wood, the cellulose and

Scientific and Historical Background

lignin molecules are the most important of these structures. When Alexa pushes on the wall, the bonds between molecules can be stretched out of their at-rest condition. The interatomic forces (bonds) resist being moved from their at-rest positions. The more they are pushed out of position, the greater the force pulling them back. The electromagnetic force at work maintaining the integrity of the wall pushes against any force applied to it (Newton's third law). The force is equal and opposite to Alexa's force.

The wall is actually an intermediary, just as the cart is an intermediary when it is pushed up against the wall. The wall is attached to the school building, which is attached to Earth. Earth is pushing back (electromagnetic force) with a force equal in magnitude to Alexa's push on the wall. The wall doesn't move because the push in the negative direction (Earth) is equal and opposite to the push on the wall by Alexa (Newton's second law.) Net force = 0 N.

The force applied by Alexa is another expression of electromagnetism. Biochemical wonders taking place in the muscles, holding bones together, and coordinating every action are all manifestations of the electromagnetic force. Virtually all structures and actions in the macroscopic world that are not attributable to gravity are the domain of the electromagnetic force.

Vocabulary
Energy
Force
Friction
Interaction
Kinetic energy
Net force
Newton
Spring scale

INVESTIGATION 1 – *What Is Force?*

TEACHING AND LEARNING *about Force*

Developing Disciplinary Core Ideas (DCI)

"I know that a force makes something happen, or maybe it's powerful." Students have heard of force by middle school, but their ideas are probably missing a few key points. Students will start to explore force as an interaction between two or more parties, rather than a singular influence that just happens to something else. This is also the time for students to start exploring the concept of energy and to think about the difference between force and energy.

Students use spring scales to measure the force as they push and pull various objects. They will quantify the force and study it as an interaction. One idea that becomes obvious quickly during experimentation is that there cannot be an unbalanced force. Students will consider a force that cannot be seen, the force of friction, and then they will start to make connections between net force and movement.

Students will move from these experiences to the later investigations, which deal with unseen magnetic and electric forces. The physical manipulation of pushes and pulls with a spring scale in this investigation will help students build a conceptual model of force that they can apply to explain the abstract concept of electromagnetic force.

The experiences students have in this investigation contribute to the disciplinary core idea **PS2.A: Forces and motion**. In addition to introducing students to laws of physics that explain force, each investigation in the **Electromagnetic Force Course** provides students with opportunities to experience two other dimensions of the scientific enterprise—the dimension of science and engineering practices and the dimension of crosscutting concepts.

NGSS Foundation Box for DCI

PS2.A: Forces and motion

- For any pair of interacting objects, the force exerted by the first object on the second object is equal in strength to the force that the second object exerts on the first, but in the opposite direction (Newton's third law). (MS-PS2-1)

- The motion of an object is determined by the sum of the forces acting on it; if the total force on the object is not zero, its motion will change. The greater the mass of the object, the greater the force needed to achieve the same change in motion. For any given object, a larger force causes a larger change in motion. (MS-PS2-2)

- All positions of objects and the directions of forces and motions must be described in an arbitrarily chosen reference frame and arbitrarily chosen units of size. In order to share information with other people, these choices must also be shared. (MS-PS2-2)

Teaching and Learning about Force

Engaging in Science and Engineering Practices (SEP)

Engaging in the practices of science helps students understand how scientific knowledge develops; such direct involvement gives them an appreciation of the wide range of approaches that are used to investigate, model, and explain the world. Engaging in the practices of engineering likewise helps students understand the work of engineers, as well as the links between engineering and science. Participation in these practices also helps students form an understanding of the crosscutting concepts and disciplinary ideas of science and engineering; moreover, it makes students' knowledge more meaningful and embeds it more deeply into their worldview. (National Research Council, *A Framework for K–12 Science Education*, 2012, page 42)

The focus questions and notebook sheets provide scaffolds for students in this investigation that can be carefully removed in later investigations, as students become more experienced engaging in practices. In this first investigation, students engage in these practices.

- **Asking questions** of classmates to probe fellow students' data analysis and conclusions.
- **Developing and using models** to explain net force on an object.
- **Planning and carrying out investigations** when selecting surfaces to test friction and doing multiple force experiments.
- **Analyzing and interpreting data** about force that were collected and organized in tables to draw conclusions about force and friction.
- **Using mathematics and computational thinking** when comparing the frictional force on different surface types and when considering net force.
- **Constructing explanations** based on experimental data to describe how force affects motion.
- **Engaging in argument** when defending claims about which surfaces provide the most frictional force.
- **Obtaining, evaluating, and communicating information** by considering force scenarios and working in groups to explain ideas in writing.

> **NGSS Foundation Box for SEP**
>
> - **Ask questions** that arise from careful observation of phenomena, models, or unexpected results, to clarify and/or seek additional information.
> - **Ask questions** to identify and/or clarify evidence and/or the premise(s) of an argument.
> - **Develop and/or use a model** to predict and/or describe phenomena.
> - **Plan an investigation individually and collaboratively,** and in the design: identify independent and dependent variables and controls, what tools are needed to do the gathering, how measurements will be recorded, and how many data are needed to support a claim.
> - **Collect data to serve as the basis for evidence** to answer scientific questions or test design solutions under a range of conditions.
> - **Construct, analyze, and/or interpret graphical displays of data** and/or large data sets to identify linear and nonlinear relationships.
> - **Analyze and interpret data** to provide evidence for phenomena.
> - **Apply mathematical concepts and/or processes** (e.g., ratio, rate, percent, basic operations, simple algebra) to scientific and engineering questions and problems.
> - **Respectfully provide and receive critiques** about one's explanations, procedures, models, and questions by citing relevant evidence and posing and responding to questions that elicit pertinent elaboration and detail.
> - **Communicate scientific and/or technical information** (e.g., about a proposed object, tool, process, system) in writing and/or through oral presentations.

INVESTIGATION 1 – What Is Force?

> **NGSS Foundation Box for CC**
>
> - **Patterns:** Patterns can be used to identify cause-and-effect relationships.
> - **Cause and effect:** Cause-and-effect relationships may be used to predict phenomena in natural or designed systems.
> - **Systems and system models:** Systems may interact with other systems; they may have subsystems and be a part of larger complex systems.
> - **Energy and matter:** Energy may take different forms (e.g., energy in fields, thermal energy, energy of motion).
> - **Stability and change:** Systems in dynamic equilibrium are stable due to a balance of feedback mechanisms.

Exposing Crosscutting Concepts (CC)

The third dimension of instruction involves the crosscutting concepts, sometimes referred to as the unifying principles, themes, or big ideas, that are fundamental to the understanding of science and engineering.

These concepts should become common and familiar touchstones across the disciplines and grade levels. Explicit reference to the concepts, as well as their emergence in multiple disciplinary contexts, can help students develop a cumulative, coherent, and usable understanding of science and engineering. (NRC *Framework*, page 83)

In this investigation, the focus is on these crosscutting concepts.

- **Patterns.** Surface properties are related to the frictional force of that surface when interacting with objects.
- **Cause and effect.** Objects move because of forces applied to them.
- **Systems and system models.** Any masses interacting within a system affect the net force of the system.
- **Energy and matter.** Movement indicates kinetic energy.
- **Stability and change.** Objects at rest may still have forces acting on them, but the net force is zero.

Connections to the Nature of Science

- **Scientific knowledge is based on empirical evidence.** Scientific knowledge is based on logical and conceptual connections between evidence and explanations. Science disciplines share common rules of obtaining and evaluating empirical evidence.

Connections to Engineering, Technology, and Applications of Science

- **Interdependence of science, engineering, and technology.** Engineering advances have led to important discoveries in virtually every field of science, and scientific discoveries have led to the development of entire industries and engineered systems. Science and technology drive each other forward.

Teaching and Learning about Force

Conceptual Flow

In this course, students explore the anchor phenomena of forces, their interactions, and their effects. The driving question for the course is what is the relationship between magnetic and electric forces?

The **conceptual flow** starts in Part 1 with students exploring observable motion phenomena to answer the guiding question for the investigation, how are force and motion related? They use **spring scales** to measure the **force** required to move objects with a push or a pull. They learn that **force is an interaction between objects**, and that force can be measured in **newtons**. They learn that when they apply a force to make an object move, which is evidence of **kinetic energy**, they are transferring **energy** to the object.

In Part 2, students investigate friction by pushing and pulling objects over different surfaces. They learn that **friction is the force between surfaces that resists motion**, and draw conclusions about the type of surfaces that have the most friction.

In Part 3, students consider the effect of multiple forces on an object. They learn that **net force represents the sum of all the forces acting on the object**, including the force of friction, and that an **object will move if the net force in a direction is greater than zero**. Students make predictions about which objects will move based on calculations of multiple known forces.

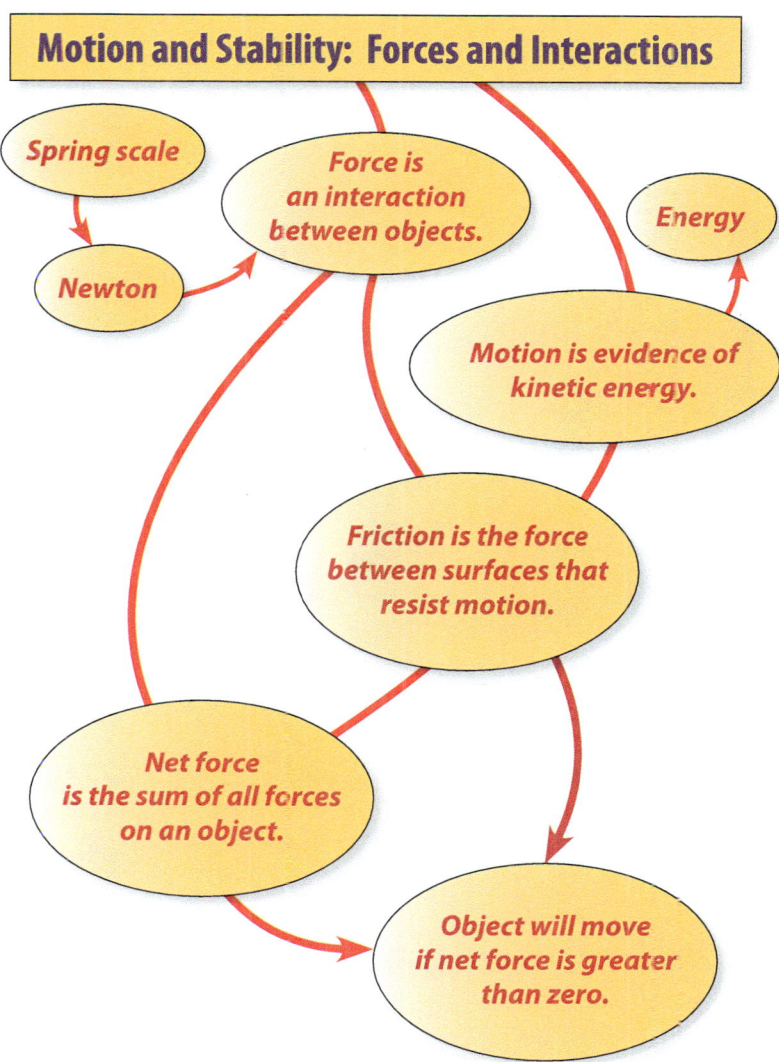

Electromagnetic Force Course—FOSS Next Generation

INVESTIGATION 1 – What Is Force?

FOSS Science Resources

> **NOTE**
> See the Materials chapter for more information on teacher-supplied items.

MATERIALS for
Part 1: *Push and Pull*

Provided equipment

For each student
- 1 *FOSS Science Resources: Electromagnetic Force*
  - "The Force Is with You"

For the class
- 1 *FOSS Science Safety* poster

For each group
- 2 Spring scales
- 2 Force markers
- 3 Loads, 240 g
- 1 Plastic mat
- 1 Rubber band, #33
- 1 Car
- 2 Paper clips

Teacher-supplied items

For each student
- 1 Science notebook (composition book)

For the class
- Chart paper

FOSSweb resources

For each student
- 1 *Entry-Level Survey*
- 1 Notebook sheets 1–3, *Pushes and Pulls A–C*

For the teacher
- *Embedded Assessment Notes*
- Teaching slides, 1.1

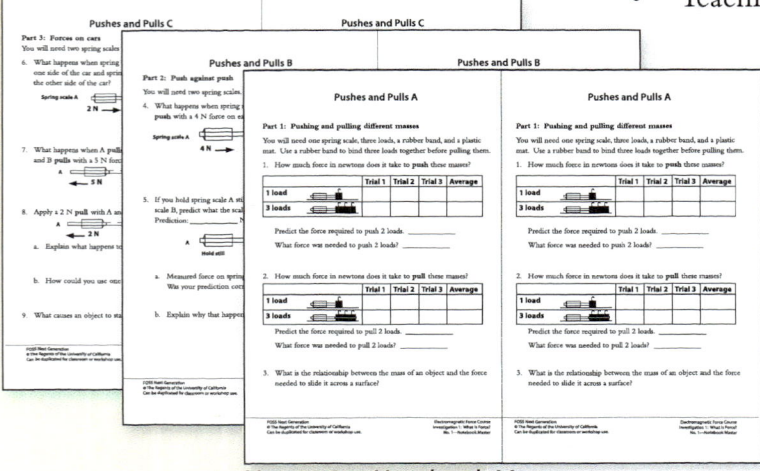

Nos. 1–3—Notebook Masters

Part 1: Push and Pull

GETTING READY for
Part 1: *Push and Pull*

Quick Start

Schedule	1 session assessment 3 sessions active investigation
Preview	• Preview the FOSSweb Resources by Investigation for this part (such as printable masters, teaching slides, and online activities) • Preview the homework reading: "The Force Is with You," Step 26
Print or Copy	**For each student** • *Entry-Level Survey,* or schedule it on FOSSmap • Notebook sheets 1–3 **For the teacher** • *Embedded Assessment Notes*
Prepare Material	• Hang the *FOSS Science Safety* poster • Prepare for initial use and assessment **A** • Plan for student notebooks **B** • Prepare spring scales **C**
Plan for Assessment	• Review Step 25, "What to Look For" in the notebook entry

▶ **NOTE**
Preview the teaching slides on FOSSweb for this part.

▶ **NOTE**
After you give the *Entry-Level Survey*, plan to spend the rest of the first session setting up science notebooks and starting the course.

Embedded Assessment Notes

Electromagnetic Force Course—FOSS Next Generation

INVESTIGATION 1 – What Is Force?

> **TEACHING NOTE**
>
> Notebook entries serve as assessment opportunities for learning. Research shows that if you spend time reviewing student work each day and use that information to guide next instructional steps, students achieve significantly more. Use the reflective-assessment practice to make this a quick and easy process. Choose a random sample across your classes and plan 15 minutes to review student work. The important thing is that you are looking at student work on a daily basis as much as possible.

Force marker

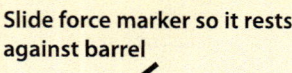

Slide force marker so it rests against barrel

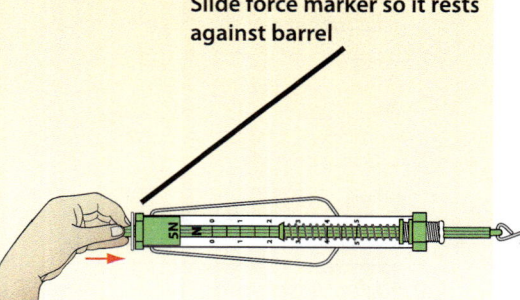

Preparation Details

A ▸ Prepare for initial use and assessment

If this is your first use of the course, review the Materials chapter for critical information about accessing online resources, organizing the classroom and materials stations, and planning for materials. Review the Assessment chapter to plan for embedded assessments and benchmark assessments.

If you have never logged in to FOSSweb before, visit the site to set up your account. For more information on how to set up an account and to access the digital resources, see the Technology chapter. Once you've logged in, check the course page for any course updates. Preview any resources for this part by going to Resources by Investigation.

B ▸ Plan for student notebooks

In preparation for each part of each investigation, you will make copies of the specified notebook masters. In this investigation, make sure students have prepared their notebooks by setting up a table of contents, creating an index for vocabulary words, and numbering the pages. For more information on notebook use in FOSS, see the Science Notebooks in Middle School chapter.

Students encounter new vocabulary in this part. Encourage students to define the new vocabulary in their own words, to use labeled drawings to help them make sense of the terms, and to add the terms to the indexes in their notebooks.

C ▸ Prepare spring scales

If this is the first time using the spring scales, prepare them by placing one plastic force marker on the rod end of each device. Position the marker so it rests against the barrel. When the push rod plunges into the barrel and then bounces back, the marker will cling lightly to the rod, indicating how far it was depressed. Calibrate the scales so that when they sit at rest, the wide green marker in the barrel rests at 0 N (0 g). Twist the white nut near the hook end of the scale as needed to zero it.

Try out the spring scale. The rod can easily be pushed a short distance into the barrel. It is quite a bit harder to push the rod all the way into the barrel. This is because the rod compresses a spring in the barrel. The more the spring is compressed, the harder it is to push the rod. The numbers on the barrel show you how hard you are pushing. Use the side marked "N" to quantify the force of your push in newtons.

Part 1: Push and Pull

GUIDING the Investigation
Part 1: *Push and Pull*

SESSION 1
Students will . . .
- Express prior knowledge with *Entry-Level Survey* (Step 1)

SESSION 2
Students will . . .
- Think about motion (Steps 2–4)
- Test motion with spring scales (Steps 5–7)
- Learn about force, interaction, and newtons (Steps 8, 9)
- Share results of experimentation and clean up (Steps 10, 11)

SESSION 3
Students will . . .
- Use spring scales to measure force required to move loads (Steps 12–15)
- Test interactions between spring scales (Steps 16, 17)

SESSION 4
Students will . . .
- Use spring scales to move a rolling object (Steps 18, 19)
- Think about energy, kinetic energy, and friction (Steps 20–22)
- Review vocabulary and revisit the focus question (Steps 23–25)
- Extend the investigation with homework and review notebook entries (Steps 26, 27)

FOCUS QUESTION
What makes things move?

> **TEACHING NOTE**
>
> The focus question in each part engages students with the phenomenon to investigate. The first investigation introduces the anchor phenomena for the course. In this case, the anchor phenomena are forces, their interactions, and their effects.

EL NOTE

EL notes present an opportunity for you to differentiate instruction for English-language learners and other students who may need additional language supports. You may decide to implement strategies depending on your students' needs.

Start a word wall for this investigation and add the words in bold.

SESSION 1 45–50 minutes

1. **Assess prior knowledge with *Entry-Level Survey***
   Check students' understanding before instruction, using the *Entry-Level Survey* benchmark assessment. The *Entry-Level Survey* is administered before instruction begins. It can be used to help you determine what students already know and what they need to learn, so that you can plan which lessons to spend more time on. Encourage students to answer the *Entry-Level Survey* questions as best they can. Even if they think they don't know the answers, they should try to think about something related that they do know and apply that knowledge.

   Collect the completed *Entry-Level Surveys*, look at them for diagnostic purposes, but don't make any marks on them. Save them until the end of this part, when students will refer to them as they work on their focus-question response.

Electromagnetic Force Course—FOSS Next Generation

INVESTIGATION 1 – What Is Force?

SESSION 2 45–50 minutes

2. Discuss motion
Tell students,

We are about to begin a study in physics. We will consider electricity and magnetism, and the fundamental laws of physics that explain them. But let's start by thinking about a more simple question: What makes things move? For instance,

➤ *What makes skateboards move down the street?*
➤ *What makes bicycles go uphill?*
➤ *What makes a book move from your book bag to your desk?*
➤ *What makes an apple fall from a tree?*

3. Focus question: What makes things move?
Display the focus question.

➤ *What makes things move?*

Have students record the focus question in their notebook. Point out to students that they just answered this question on the *Entry-Level Survey* so they do not need to record responses yet. They should leave space below the focus question so that they can return to the question.

4. Discuss causes of motion
Ask students to turn to a partner and share their ideas and questions about what makes things move. Ask students to share their partner's or their own ideas and questions with the class. Ask,

➤ *Did anyone consider whether some things move by themselves?*

Give students a few moments to share their thoughts.

5. Introduce *spring scale*
Suggest continuing the inquiry into the causes of motion by putting some objects into motion. Tell students,

*I suggest that we try to put some objects in motion by pushing. I have a tool for you to use for pushing. It is called a **spring scale**. Spring scales can be used to push or pull on things, and the spring inside helps us measure how strong the push is.*

Show students a spring scale and describe the working procedure.

a. Work in pairs with one spring scale.
b. Grip the barrel without touching the push rod.
c. Push on an object with the end of the push rod.

EL NOTE
Write the question on the board. You might project or provide images of these and other examples of things moving for students to discuss with a partner.

TEACHING NOTE
The focus question in each part engages students with the phenomenon to investigate.

TEACHING NOTE
Students often have interesting ideas about the cause of motion. They usually acknowledge that there are classes of motion that result from human action. A person can put an object into motion purposefully—throwing a ball, pushing the pedals on a bike, pulling a wagon, and so on.

Other kinds of motion are produced by machines with motors or engines—trucks, boats, planes, and so forth. These kinds of motion are attributed to an identifiable, observable agent, a credible source of energy or power.

More difficult to understand are the kinds of motion that happen "by themselves," that is, without any observable initiating action. Objects fall and roll downhill, apparently by themselves, with perhaps some loose link to gravity.

Part 1: Push and Pull

d. Use the marker disk on the push rod to record how far the rod pushed into the barrel, which indicates how hard you were pushing.

In order to make a precise and consistent measurement of force, move the spring scale slowly and gently.

6. **Discuss respectful behavior**
   Tell students in clear language that the spring scale is for investigating the relationship between pushes and motion. Inappropriate behaviors include
   - pushing on another student;
   - pulling the rod back, like an arrow in a crossbow, and releasing it;
   - excessively aggressive or rapid pushing, which can damage the device.

7. **Use the spring scales**
   Give an open-ended challenge, and let the exploration begin.

   Find out if you can use the spring scales to move any objects.

   Students usually start by pushing binders and books on the surface of their desks. If they extend the exploration on their own, let them guide their own inquiry. If they need suggestions, offer one or more of the following:

   ➤ *Can you push a shoe? A shoe with a book on it? Does it take a harder push to move a shoe with a book on it? Whose shoe is hardest to move? Why do you think that is?*

   ➤ *Can you move a chair? A desk? How can you move an object that won't move when you push your rod all the way in?*

   ➤ *Can you push a door open? Do you have to push harder near the doorknob or near the hinge to move the door?*

   ➤ *Does it take the same amount of push to move a book on different surfaces? Up or down a slope?*

   This last challenge is particularly informative, as the force of gravity comes into play.

8. **Introduce *force* and *interaction***
   Tell students,

   *When you push on an object, you are exerting a **force** on that object. When you pushed on a shoe, book, or door with your spring scale, you were using the spring scale to exert a force on the object.*

   *A force is an **interaction**. There is no such thing as a push without something to push on. Thus, a force can happen only when one object pushes on another object. A force is an interaction between two objects.*

SCIENCE AND ENGINEERING PRACTICES
Planning and carrying out investigations

TEACHING NOTE
If students are struggling to move something large, like a chair, encourage them to work together to push it.

ELA CONNECTION
This suggested strategy addresses the Common Core State Standards for ELA for literacy.

L 5: Demonstrate understanding of word relationships and nuances in word meaning.

EL NOTE
Write these words on the word wall or chart paper, along with a simple diagram using arrows to show force. You might also briefly discuss the origins and meanings of the word interaction *(inter from the Latin* entre, *meaning between or among; action from the Latin* actio *meaning the state or process of doing something), as well as examples of how it is used outside of science.*

Electromagnetic Force Course—FOSS Next Generation 99

INVESTIGATION 1 – What Is Force?

Ask,

➤ *Can you identify the objects that interacted when you exerted force with your spring scale?* [An example might be the rod/spring in the spring scale and a book being moved.]

➤ *Did you exert the same amount of force every time you used your spring scale?* [No.]

➤ *How do you know?* [The rod pushed into the barrel more or less.]

➤ *How did you know when you exerted a lot of force and when you exerted a little force?* [By how far the rod pushed into the barrel, and by where the marker ended up on the rod.]

9. **Introduce** *newtons*
Tell students,

*The marks under the **N** on the barrel are units of force. When the rod pushes in 1 unit, the force exerted is very small. When the rod pushes all the way into the barrel, the push is 5 units of force.*

*The unit of force in the metric system is the **newton**. The symbol for newton is an uppercase **N**. On the barrel of the spring scale, you will see two scales, one measuring grams and one measuring newtons. When you measure force, be sure you are looking at the side with newtons.*

10. **Share spring-scale results**
Start a class summary chart to record student observations and inferences. Make a column for the activities, for cause-and-effect relationships observed, and for possible explanations for these interactions. Summarize the key observations and explanations in the chart.

Activity	Cause and effect	Explanation

Begin by asking students to record their observations about force and motion in their notebooks. They should describe what they did with the spring scale, how much force they exerted, and what, if anything, moved.

Encourage students to think about cause and effect and to use the words *force* and *interaction* when describing their pushing investigations. Ask for volunteers to share their discoveries, and record or project them on the board. As a class, narrow in on the key interactions and record them on the class chart in the cause-and-effect column. Then, move to the next column and ask students to think about why these interactions occurred. Here is a completed chart.

EL NOTE

Use a document camera or large image to show the spring scale as you explain. Add the word *newton* and the symbol to the word wall.

CROSSCUTTING CONCEPTS

Cause and effect

TEACHING NOTE

Make one summary chart for each class. Keep the charts available for the rest of the investigation to add more information.

Part 1: Push and Pull

Activity	Cause and effect	Explanation
Spring-scale exploration	• Larger objects require more force (a stronger push) to move. • Two or more spring scales working together can apply enough force to move an object that can't be moved by one spring scale. • Different surfaces require different amounts of force to move an object.	• It takes more force to move bigger, heavier objects. • A push can involve more than one force. • The surface affects the amount of force needed to move an object.

11. Clean up
Collect the spring scales at the end of the session.

SESSION 3   45–50 minutes

12. Introduce pull technique
Tell students,

We are going to try some more investigations with spring scales, using a procedure to measure how much force it takes to push or pull a load. A load is the total mass you are trying to move. You will be asked questions about pulls in addition to pushes. You can use your spring scales as a puller as well. A pull is also a force.

Demonstrate how to use the hook to pull on an object and measure the pulling force, using the force marker as before.

TEACHING NOTE

Students will get inconsistent data if their pushes and pulls are jerky. Model and remind students to move the spring scale slowly and gently to collect a more precise measurement.

13. Preview the notebook sheet
Distribute a copy of notebook sheet 1, *Pushes and Pulls A* to each student. Project it and read through the questions quickly, clarifying the challenges and showing the new materials as they are called for.

- Point out the large black cubes that students will use as loads. More loads = more mass.
- Caution students to be extremely careful with the loads for safety reasons. They should band the loads together to pull a group as one mass.
- The long plastic mat makes a uniform surface on which students can push and pull loads.

Electromagnetic Force Course—FOSS Next Generation

INVESTIGATION 1 – What Is Force?

MATH CONNECTION

This supports Common Core State Standards for Math 7.NS 1.

TEACHING NOTE

Students will need the data from the plastic-mats experiment in Part 2 to compare to other surfaces.

TEACHING NOTE

If you would like students to explore the relationship further, you can ask them to create simple graphs of their results and to use the graphs as they describe the relationship between the variables.

MATH CONNECTION

This supports Common Core State Standards for Math 8.F 4.

SCIENCE AND ENGINEERING PRACTICES

Planning and carrying out investigations

Analyzing and interpreting data

Using mathematics and computational thinking

CROSSCUTTING CONCEPTS

Cause and effect

MATH CONNECTION

This supports Common Core State Standards for Math 7.NS 1.

14. Conduct the investigations

Advise students to perform the investigations carefully, moving the spring scales slowly and measuring force as precisely as possible. They should talk in their groups after each observation and write answers to each question.

Remind students to conduct their testing on the plastic mats. Give students about 5–8 minutes to complete the activities in *Pushes and Pulls A*.

15. Discuss findings for *Pushes and Pulls A*

Call on students to share their findings for questions 1 and 2. Allow several students to contribute their findings and explanations for each question. Ask students to share responses to question 3. Students should revise their own responses as needed as they listen to the class discussion.

➤ *What is the relationship between the mass of an object and the force needed to slide it across a surface?* [The greater the mass, the greater the force needed to move it; the pulling force needed to move a mass is the same as the pushing force to move the same mass.]

Add information about the relationship to the class summary chart, using students' wording. Here's a sample completed chart.

Activity	Cause and effect	Explanation
Pushes and Pulls A	• It takes _____ N to push 1 load and _____ N to push 3 loads. • It takes _____ N to push 1 load and _____ N to pull 1 load.	• The greater the mass, the more force is needed to move it. • The pulling force needed to move a mass is the same as the pushing force.

Ask students to record the class explanation at the bottom of the notebook sheet.

16. Move to *Pushes and Pulls B*

Tell students they will be working with just the spring scales, not with the masses. Project and distribute notebook sheet 2, *Pushes and Pulls B*. Give students about 5 minutes to complete the activities and answer the questions, then ask students to share findings.

➤ *What happens when spring scale A and spring scale B both push with a 4 N force on each other?* [The scales move closer to each other.]

Part 1: Push and Pull

➤ *What happens to spring scale A when you hold it still and push with a 4 N force with spring scale B?* [Spring scale A pushes back with a force of 4 N.]

Give each group a chance to present their thinking for question 5b. Then lead a class discussion until there is general agreement.

➤ *Why did that happen?* [Spring scale A couldn't move because it was held in place, but a force (spring scale B) was acting on it. Spring scale A pushed back on spring scale B with a force exactly equal to the force of spring scale B pushing on spring scale A.]

If any new cause-and-effect relationships came up in the class discussion, add them to the class summary chart. Tell students,

This is evidence of one of three laws of physics expressed by Isaac Newton a few hundred years ago. His third law is "For every action there is an equal and opposite reaction." In this context, action and reaction can mean force. "For every force there is an equal and opposite force" is a good summary of what you observed in Pushes and Pulls B.

17. **Collect materials**
    Have Getters return the loads, spring scales, and plastic mats to the materials station.

SESSION 4   45–50 minutes

18. **Preview** *Pushes and Pulls C*
    Tell students that they will conduct one more set of experiments using similar equipment, but with the addition of a car that can roll when force is applied to it. Distribute notebook sheet 3, *Pushes and Pulls C*, and point out how to use the cars with care. Show students how a paper clip can be used to hook one end of the car to the spring scale to measure pulls. Tell students to predict what they think will happen in each step before applying forces.

    Give students about 10 minutes to work with the cars and record their results. Remind students to think carefully about their response to question 9.

19. **Discuss findings for** *Pushes and Pulls C*
    Call on students to share the results of the final experiment.

    ➤ *What happens when spring scale A pushes with a 2 N force on one side of the car and spring scale B pushes with a 3 N force on the other side of the car?* [It doesn't really work. The car moves away from spring scale B, and spring scale A gets pushed in to 3 N as well.]

TEACHING NOTE

More information about speaking and listening strategies is in the Science-Centered Language Development for Middle School chapter.

SCIENCE AND ENGINEERING PRACTICES

Using mathematics and computational thinking

MATH CONNECTION

This supports Common Core State Standards for Math 7.NS 1.

EL NOTE

Encourage students to use reasoning to explain their predictions.
Based on what I know about _____, I predict _____ because _____.

Electromagnetic Force Course—FOSS Next Generation

INVESTIGATION 1 – What Is Force?

> ➤ *What happens when A pulls with a 5 N force on one side of the car and B pulls with a 5 N force on the opposite side of a car?* [Equal forces try to move the car in opposite directions. The car does not move.]

> ➤ *What happens when you apply a 2 N pull with A and a 2 N push with B on the car?* [The forces add because they are acting in the same direction. The car moved toward the puller because both forces are applied in that direction.]

> ➤ *How could you use one pusher to achieve the same result?* [You could push with 4 N or pull with 4 N.]

Question 9 relates to the focus question and requires deeper thinking and constructing explanations. Encourage students to add to their original responses as they hear new ideas from other groups.

> ➤ *What causes an object to start moving?* [A force exerted on the object.]

Add this information to the class summary chart, using students' wording. Here is a sample completed chart.

SCIENCE AND ENGINEERING PRACTICES
Constructing explanations

Activity	Cause and effect	Explanation
Pushes and Pulls C	• When two forces are pushing on an object, it will move in the direction of the push with the greatest force. • When equal forces are pushing on opposite sides, the object does not move. • If you pull on one side and push on the other, it's the same as pushing or pulling with the combined force.	• An object will start to move if a force is exerted on it. • Two equal forces pushing on an object cancel each other. • Two forces (a push and a pull) moving in the same direction add together.

Ask students to record the final statement at the bottom of the notebook sheet.

CROSSCUTTING CONCEPTS
Energy and matter

20. Introduce *energy* and *kinetic energy*
Tell students,

*When you use force to move an object, you are transferring **energy** to the object. In this case, we considered the energy needed to apply a force over a distance. **Kinetic energy** is energy of motion. In this course, we are going to look for other examples of kinetic energy, and we will also explore other forms of energy that do not appear as movement.*

21. Collect materials
When students have completed the activities and written their observations and interpretations, have Getters return the cars and spring scales to the materials station.

Part 1: Push and Pull

22. **Introduce** *friction*

    Remind students that force is a kind of interaction. When they applied force to the loads using the spring scale, the loads would not move at first, and then they did.

    ➤ *Why didn't the loads move when you applied a small force to one side?* [The loads weighed too much; there wasn't enough force to move the load.]

    Tell students,

    The loads didn't move until there was enough force from the spring scale to overcome the force of **friction**. *Friction is the force between surfaces that resists motion. When you pushed or pulled lightly, you didn't use enough force to exceed the force of friction. Therefore, the object didn't move.*

23. **Record vocabulary**

    Give students a few moments to review and clarify the vocabulary developed in this part. Suggest they make a diagram in their notebooks that shows the relationship between these words. This is also a good time for students to start or to update their vocabulary indexes if they haven't already done so.

24. **Revisit the focus question**

    Have students return to the page where they recorded the focus question.

    ➤ *What makes things move?*

    Return the *Entry-Level Surveys* to students and let them read their original response. Ask students to build on their *Entry-Level Survey* responses as they answer the focus question.

    When students are finished, collect the *Entry-Level Surveys* and hold them until Investigation 4, when students will revisit them again.

25. **Assess progress: notebook entry**

    After students have had a chance to respond, collect a sample of notebooks from each class to consider students' thinking about what makes things move. The sample you select should give you a snapshot of the range of student understanding at this point in time.

    What to Look For

    - *Students use academic vocabulary such as* force, action, lift, push, pull, *and* gravity *in their answers to explain what makes something move.*

EL NOTE
Add *friction* to the word wall. Rub your hands together as you explain.

> **TEACHING NOTE**
>
> Students will only have a developmental definition of energy at this time; it will be further developed throughout the course.

energy
force
friction
interaction
kinetic energy
newton
spring scale

Electromagnetic Force Course—FOSS Next Generation

INVESTIGATION 1 – What Is Force?

> **TEACHING NOTE**
>
> More information about using *Embedded Assessment Notes and* examples of next-step strategies are in the Assessment chapter.

- *Students write that it takes force to move things.*
- *Students understand that objects that appear to act on their own, such as by rolling down a hill, are still being acted upon by forces, even if the forces aren't seen.*

Plan to spend 15 minutes reviewing the selected student responses. Using *Embedded Assessment Notes* as a tool, review the responses, record any alternative concepts that are evident, and decide if any next-step strategies are required before moving forward.

Part 1: Push and Pull

READING *in Science Resources*

26. Extend the investigation with homework

The article "The Force Is with You" can be assigned as homework to reinforce ideas from the class discussion. To support reading comprehension, suggest students follow these strategies:

- Start by previewing the text, by examining the images, captions, subtitles, and the words in bold. Analyze the diagrams by asking yourself questions such as: What do I know about this image? What is new to me? What do the arrows represent? What do the different colors mean?

- Read the captions and compare your interpretations to what the text says. Read the subtitles and think about how the article is organized. Ask yourself what you will learn from reading this article.

- Use a note-making strategy to help you keep track of the central ideas, such as Cornell Notes. Keep in mind the focus question and write it above two columns: *What makes things move?* Write down key words, questions, and main ideas in the left column, and in the right column write down definitions, diagrams, and thoughts you have as you read the text. Pay attention to the cause-and-effect relationships described in the examples. You might want to include a labeled drawing of the spring scale showing how it works. When you finish, make a space at the bottom to write a summary.

- Use the information in your Cornell Notes to answer the Think Questions at the end of the article. Make sure to include evidence from the text to support your answers.

Have students answer the Think Questions using evidence from the text to support their answers.

➤ *What are the objects interacting in these actions? A bicycle moves.* [A human is pushing on the bicycle pedals to move the gears that move the wheels.]

➤ *You throw a ball straight up in the air.* [You use force to push the ball up and then gravity pulls the ball down.]

➤ *What is the force in newtons on each load?* [2.5 N.]

➤ *What is the difference between mass and weight?* [Mass is how much matter an object has, and weight is the downward force of gravity on a mass.]

➤ *Do you know of any other invisible forces like gravity?* [Electrical force and magnetic force are some other invisible forces.]

FOSS Science Resources

SCIENCE AND ENGINEERING PRACTICES

Obtaining, evaluating, and communicating information

Using mathematics and computational thinking

ELA CONNECTION

These suggested strategies address the Common Core State Standards for ELA for literacy.

RST 7: Integrate quantitative or technical information expressed in words in a text with a version of that information expressed visually.

RST 5: Analyze the structure an author uses to organize a text.

RST 2: Determine the central ideas or conclusions of a text; provide an accurate summary.

WHST 8: Gather relevant information from print.

RST 1: Cite evidence to support analysis of science texts.

Electromagnetic Force Course—FOSS Next Generation

INVESTIGATION 1 – What Is Force?

CROSSCUTTING CONCEPTS

Cause and effect

SCIENCE AND ENGINEERING PRACTICES

Constructing explanations

ELA CONNECTION

These suggested strategies address the Common Core State Standards for ELA for literacy.

WHST 5: Develop and strengthen writing.

SL 6: Adapt speech to a variety of contexts and tasks.

WRAP-UP/WARM-UP

27. Review notebook entries

Give students a few minutes to share review and share their notebook entries with a partner. Have them take turns explaining their diagrams to each other. Encourage them to give each other constructive feedback and to revise their entries if needed. This is also a good opportunity to have students discuss how the concept of cause and effect helps them understand motion.

If this is a warm-up, have students share their responses to the think questions from the reading.

Part 2: Friction

MATERIALS for
Part 2: *Friction*

Provided equipment

For each student
- 1   *FOSS Science Resources: Electromagnetic Force*
  - "The Discovery of Friction"

For each group
- 1   Spring scale
- 3   Loads
- 1   Rubber band, #33

Teacher-supplied items

For the class
- Friction surface materials such as newspaper, old blanket, or sandpaper

FOSSweb resources

For each student
- 1   Notebook sheet 4, *Friction Comparison*

For the teacher
- Teacher master A, *Friction Comparison Data*
- *Performance Assessment Checklist*
- Teaching slides, 1.2

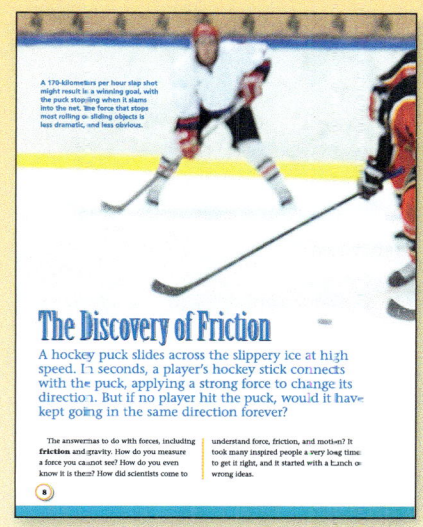

FOSS Science Resources

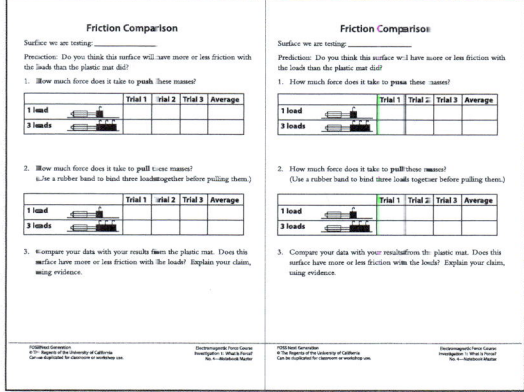

No. 4—Notebook Master

Teacher Master A

Electromagnetic Force Course—FOSS Next Generation

109

INVESTIGATION 1 – *What Is Force?*

GETTING READY for
Part 2: *Friction*

Quick Start

Schedule	1 session active investigation
Preview	• Preview the FOSSweb Resources by Investigation for this part (such as printable masters, teaching slides, and online activities) • Preview the homework reading: "The Discovery of Friction," Step 12
Print or Copy	**For each student** • Notebook sheet 4 **For the teacher** • *Performance Assessment Checklist*
Prepare Material	• Collect materials for friction surfaces **A**
Plan for Assessment	• Review Step 7, "What to Look For" in the performance assessment **B**

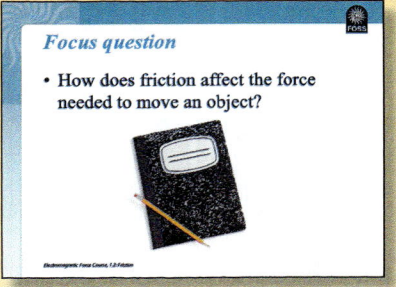

Teaching slides, 1.2

Part 2: Friction

Preparation Details

A. Collect materials for friction surfaces

Students will push and pull loads across different surfaces and compare the results to those they collected using the plastic mat. Each group should test one or two different surfaces. Classroom tables, floors, carpet, and other locations may provide sufficient variety. If not, consider providing several alternate surface materials, including fabric, paper, or sandpaper. Sprinkling a granular substance on the plastic mat is an interesting modification. Consider providing talc or flour.

B. Plan for performance assessment

Assessing the three dimensions envisioned in the NRC Framework and the NGSS performance expectations requires you to peek over students' shoulders while they are doing science or engineering. Observing the rich conversation among students and the actions they are taking to investigate phenomena or design solutions to problems can provide important information about student progress.

In Step 6, students collect measurements of the force needed to push and pull loads on a new surface and use these data to determine whether the new surface has more or less friction with the loads. This is an opportunity to observe students' use of science practices, content understanding, and crosscutting concepts. Preview What to Look For in Step 7.

Print or photocopy *Performance Assessment Checklist* for this investigation part. You will need one copy for each class. There are two forms of the checklist, one for groups and one for individuals. You can also download the checklist as an electronic spreadsheet from FOSSweb in *Teacher Resources*. You will need to enter student names or group names on the sheet before using it.

Carry the checklist with you as you observe and listen to students' discussions and observe their interactions. For more information about how to conduct performance assessments, see the Assessment chapter.

> **TEACHING NOTE**
> While more challenging to obtain, a low-friction surface such as a sheet of ice or an air-hockey table would provide interesting results.

Performance Assessment Checklists

INVESTIGATION 1 – What Is Force?

FOCUS QUESTION

How does friction affect the force needed to move an object?

GUIDING the Investigation
Part 2: Friction

SESSION 1

Students will . . .
- Review pushes and pulls (Step 1)
- Think about friction and possible surfaces to test (Steps 2–5)
- Collect and analyze friction data (Steps 6–9)
- Record vocabulary and revisit the focus question (Steps 10, 11)
- Extend the investigation with homework and review notebook entries (Steps 12, 13)

SESSION 1   45–50 minutes

1. **Review force**
   Ask students to open their notebooks and review the *Pushes and Pulls* notebook sheets. Use the class summary chart from Part 1 to review the big ideas. Depending on what you discovered from the embedded assessment in Part 1, you can modify this review to address student misconceptions as needed. Use these questions to guide the discussion.

   ➤ *What did you do to move the heavy loads?* [Pushed and pulled them with a spring scale.]

   ➤ *What is the scientific word for a push or a pull?* [Force.]

   ➤ *If the force exerted on one side of an object is greater than the force exerted on an object in the opposite direction, what will happen?* [The object will be pushed away from the greater force (assuming that the force is greater than the force of friction).]

   ➤ *If equal forces are exerted on an object in opposite directions, what will happen?* [The object will not move.]

   ➤ *Are there other times when the object will not move if a force is applied?* [When there isn't enough force to overcome friction.]

   ➤ *What is friction?* [A force acting between two surfaces that resists motion.]

ELA CONNECTION

This suggested strategy addresses the Common Core State Standards for ELA for literacy.

L 5: Demonstrate understanding of word relationships and nuances in word meaning.

EL NOTE

You might want to discuss that the word **friction** *is also commonly used to describe conflict or animosity caused by a clash of wills, temperaments, or opinions.*

2. **Focus question: How does friction affect the force needed to move an object?**
   Remind students that friction is a force. Display the focus question.

   ➤ *How does friction affect the force needed to move an object?*

112   Full Option Science System

Part 2: Friction

Have students record the focus question in their notebook and record their initial answers to the question. Students should leave room in their notebooks to return to the focus question at the end of this part.

3. Discuss friction
Ask,

➤ *When you completed* Pushes and Pulls A, *what two surfaces were interacting to cause friction?* [The loads and the plastic mat.]

➤ *If we used a different surface than the plastic mat, how would that affect the force of friction?*

Give students a few moments to discuss this in their groups, then have them share ideas with the class. Ideas may include that a rough surface might have more friction than a smooth one, or putting a lubricating substance between the two surfaces could reduce the frictional force.

Tell students that in today's experiment, all groups will use the same loads, but each group will select a different surface to push and pull the loads across.

4. Generate list of surfaces
Give groups 2 minutes to come up with a list of modifications or alternatives in the classroom that they might test. Students can suggest personal items like sweatshirts as long as they are large and flat enough for the test surface.

SCIENCE AND ENGINEERING PRACTICES
Planning and carrying out investigations

Generate a list on the board as each group suggests one possible test surface. If any surface seems unrealistic (too small, too dangerous, or otherwise off limits), discuss the reasoning and omit the surface from the list. Add to the list until groups' suggestions have been exhausted, then add any additional items that you are providing.

> **TEACHING NOTE**
>
> *Go to FOSSweb for* Teacher Resources *and look for the* Science and Engineering Practices *chapter for details on how to engage students with the practice of planning and carrying out investigations.*

Give groups 1 minute to select their top two choices for testing. Let one group at a time select their test surface, and mark the group number next to the surface listed on the board.

5. Review procedures
Have students set up in their notebooks a table to record data, or distribute a copy of notebook sheet 4, *Friction Comparison*, to each student. Show students where to write the name of their surface and to record their prediction.

Students will repeat the push-and-pull experiment with one and three loads on their new test surface. They will compare the results with their previous results from *Pushes and Pulls A* to determine

Electromagnetic Force Course—FOSS Next Generation

INVESTIGATION 1 – What Is Force?

> **MATH CONNECTION**
> This supports Common Core State Standards for Math 7.NS 1.

SCIENCE AND ENGINEERING PRACTICES

Planning and carrying out investigations

Analyzing and interpreting data

Using mathematics and computational thinking

CROSSCUTTING CONCEPTS

Cause and effect

DISCIPLINARY CORE IDEAS

PS2.A: Forces and motion

SCIENCE AND ENGINEERING PRACTICES

Asking questions

Analyzing and interpreting data

Engaging in argument from evidence

CROSSCUTTING CONCEPTS

Patterns

---

whether the interaction of the loads with the selected surface had more or less friction than the interaction of the loads with the unaltered plastic mat.

6. **Collect data and determine measurements**
   Let students begin collecting data. They will need to be precise with their technique and observations to make comparisons. Only then will they be able to make a claim as to whether their experimental surface imposed more or less friction. If time permits, students can test their second choice of surface.

7. **Assess progress: performance assessment**
   In this investigation, students test surfaces to collect data and compare friction on different surfaces. Listen to the group discussions and observe how students work together to assess students' three-dimensional learning. Note student progress on the *Performance Assessment Checklist*.

   What to Look For

   - *Students use precision in pushing and pulling the loads, and adjust their techniques if data are not clear. (Planning and carrying out investigations.)*

   - *Students analyze and interpret data to provide evidence that if more force is required on a surface, there is more friction between the surface and loads; or if less force is required on this surface, there is less friction between the surface and loads. (Analyzing and interpreting data; using mathematics and computational thinking; PS2.A: Forces and motion; cause and effect.)*

8. **Analyze class results**
   As groups finish collecting their data, they should come to the front and record them on teacher master A, *Friction Comparison Data*.

   Ask this important question.

   ▶ *How did you determine if a new surface imposed more or less friction than the plastic mat?* [If the new surface required more force, there must be a greater opposing force due to friction. If the new surface required less force, there must be less frictional force.]

   Ask everyone to review the class results and discuss in their group any patterns or inconsistencies they may see, such as a group using sandpaper who reports less friction. Encourage groups to ask questions about any anomalous data, and then ask the group who provided those data to explain the evidence that led them to their conclusion.

114
Full Option Science System

Part 2: Friction

9. **Discuss surface characteristics**
   Ask,

   ➤ *What patterns do you notice about the surfaces that created less friction?* [They are smoother than the plastic or covered in tiny particles (if flour, talc, or similar substances were used).]

   ➤ *What patterns do you notice about the surfaces that created more friction?* [They are more rough or fuzzy than the plastic.]

10. **Record vocabulary**
    Students should revisit their diagrams and explanations of *friction* and add ideas to them at this time.

11. **Revisit the focus question**
    Have students return to the page where they recorded the focus question.

    ➤ *How does friction affect the force needed to move an object?*

    Give students time to respond to the focus question. Tell them that they should use examples in their response and include data from the experiment.

TEACHING NOTE

The reason that a powder decreases friction is that it decreases the area of surface contact between the load and the resting surface.

EL NOTE

For students who need support, give them a few minutes to discuss the question before writing. You can also provide a writing frame such as
Friction is ___.
We observed that ___.
Based on these observations, we determined that ___.
Now I'm wondering ___.

Electromagnetic Force Course—FOSS Next Generation

INVESTIGATION 1 – What Is Force?

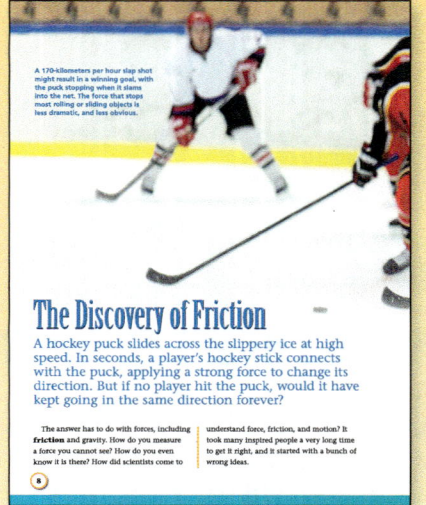

FOSS Science Resources

SCIENCE AND ENGINEERING PRACTICES
Obtaining, evaluating, and communicating information

ELA CONNECTION

These suggested strategies address the Common Core State Standards for ELA for literacy.

RST 7: Integrate quantitative or technical information expressed in words in a text with a version of that information expressed visually.

RST 5: Analyze the structure an author uses to organize a text.

RST 2: Determine the central ideas or conclusions of a text; provide an accurate summary.

WHST 8: Gather relevant information from print.

RST 1: Cite evidence to support analysis of science texts.

READING *in Science Resources*

12. Extend the investigation with homework

The article "The Discovery of Friction" can be assigned as homework to reinforce ideas from the class discussion. To support reading comprehension, suggest students follow these strategies:

- Start by previewing the text, by examining the images, captions, subtitles, and the words in bold. Analyze the diagrams by asking yourself questions such as: What do I know about the scientists in these images? What do these diagrams explain?

- Read the captions and compare your interpretations to what the text says. Read the subtitles and think about how the article is organized. Ask yourself what you will learn from reading this article.

- Use a note-making strategy to help you keep track of the central ideas, such as Cornell Notes described in Part 1. Keep in mind the focus question and write it on the top line: How does friction affect the force needed to move an object? Write down key words, questions, and main ideas in the left column, and in the right column write down definitions, diagrams, and thoughts you have as you read the text. Record Newton's laws of motion and include an illustration for each one. Pay attention to how these ideas became law and how the process illustrates the "nature of science." When you finish, make a space at the bottom to write a summary. See the example from Part 1.

- Use the information in your Cornell Notes to answer the Think Questions at the end of the article. Make sure to include evidence from the text to support your answers.

➤ *How does the texture of a surface affect friction?* [A smooth surface has less friction and a rough surface has more friction.]

➤ *What might happen if you tried to walk across the room and there was no friction?* [You wouldn't be able to take a normal step, because you wouldn't be able to push forward off the floor. You could pull yourself on other furniture, but those would slide, too! And once you started moving, you would just keep sliding until you could apply a force in the opposite direction.]

➤ *What do you think Newton meant when he said, "If I have seen further (than most people) it is by standing on the shoulders of giants?"* [He meant that he reviewed the work and ideas of others, such as Aristotle and Galileo, to give him new ideas and help him develop new experiments.]

Part 2: Friction

WRAP-UP/WARM-UP

13. Review notebook entries

Give students a few minutes to share responses to the focus question with someone from a different group. Encourage them to give each other constructive feedback and to revise and/or add ideas to their responses under a line of learning. If this is a warm-up, have students share their responses to the Think Questions from the reading.

ELA CONNECTION

This suggested strategy addresses the Common Core State Standards for ELA for literacy.

WHST 5: Develop and strengthen writing.

INVESTIGATION 1 – What Is Force?

FOSS Science Resources

MATERIALS for
Part 3: Forces in Action

Provided equipment
For each student
- 1 *FOSS Science Resources: Electromagnetic Force*
  - "Net Force"

For the class
- Spring scales

Teacher-supplied items
For each group
- 1 Mini-whiteboard or piece of paper
- 1 Whiteboard marking pen (optional)
- 1 Whiteboard eraser (optional)

For the class
- 1 Rolling cart, rolling chair, or small desk
- Chart paper

FOSSweb resources
For each student
- 1 Notebook sheets 5–6, *Forces on Carts A–B*
- 1 Notebook sheet 7, *Response Sheet—Investigation 1*
- 1 *Investigation 1 I-Check*

For the class
- Video, *Forces*

For the teacher
- *Embedded Assessment Notes*
- 1 *Assessment Record*
- Teaching slides, 1.3

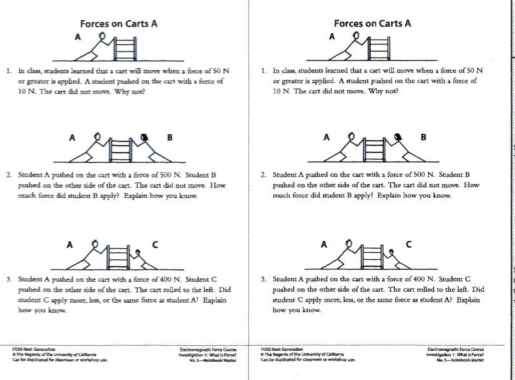

Nos. 5–7—Notebook Masters

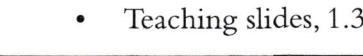

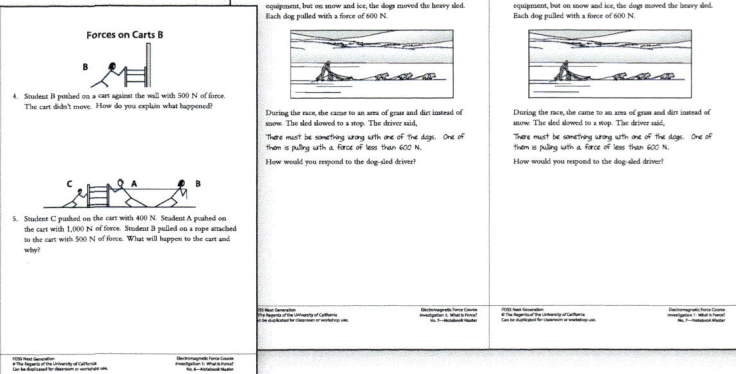

Full Option Science System

Part 3: Forces in Action

GETTING READY for
Part 3: Forces in Action

Quick Start

Schedule	1 session active investigation 1 session reading and review 1–2 sessions assessment and next steps
Preview	• Preview the FOSSweb Resources by Investigation for this part (such as printable masters, teaching slides, and online activities) • Preview the video: *Forces*, Step 7 • Plan for homework: response sheet, Step 9 • Preview the in-class reading: "Net Force," Step 11
Print or Copy	**For each student** • Notebook sheets 5–7 • *Investigation 1 I-Check*, or schedule it on FOSSweb **For the teacher** • *Embedded Assessment Notes* • *Assessment Record*
Prepare Material	• Reorganize classroom space **A**
Plan for Assessment	• Review Step 10, "What to Look For" in the response sheet • Plan for benchmark assessment, Step 17, I-Check 1 **B**

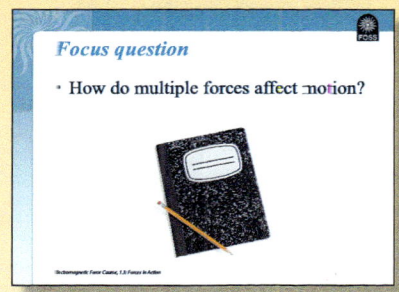

Teaching slides, 1.3

Electromagnetic Force Course—FOSS Next Generation

INVESTIGATION 1 – What Is Force?

Preparation Details

A ▶ Reorganize classroom space

This part of the investigation is a series of class activities. You and your students push and pull an object, like a rolling book cart, a rolling table, or a small desk, around the room. The demonstrations use space, so you may need to reorganize the furniture.

B ▶ Plan benchmark assessment: I-Check

Plan to administer and discuss the results of the I-Check for Investigation 1. The I-Check serves as a checkpoint for student learning. Refer to the Assessment chapter for details.

If students will be taking the I-Check online, schedule the session on FOSSmap. If not, print or make a copy of the I-Check for each student.

At least 1 day before taking the I-Check, give students time to review their notebook entries to prepare for the benchmark assessment. When taking the I-Check, students should not use their notebooks, but the notebooks are a good tool to use when students later reflect on their answers.

To track achievement (a summative use of the I-Checks), use the coding guides found on FOSSweb to code the items, or review the FOSSmap reports that automatically code most items.

I-Checks can also be used for formative assessment. Research has shown that students learn more when they take part in evaluating their own responses. When students check their own understanding, you are creating a class culture of assessment as a tool in the service of learning. Here's how to do this.

a. Have students complete an I-Check unassisted.

b. Code I-Check items, but do not make any marks on students' written responses. Record scores on the *Assessment Record,* or a grade book. Note important points about the items to review with students. If the assessment is given online, all scores will be automatically recorded except for open-response items.

c. Return I-Checks to students. Use next-step strategies as described in the Assessment chapter to facilitate reflection and clarify student thinking.

> **TEACHING NOTE**
>
> If you have not used FOSSmap (the FOSS online assessment system) before, see the Assessment chapter for more information about how to register and set up your classes.

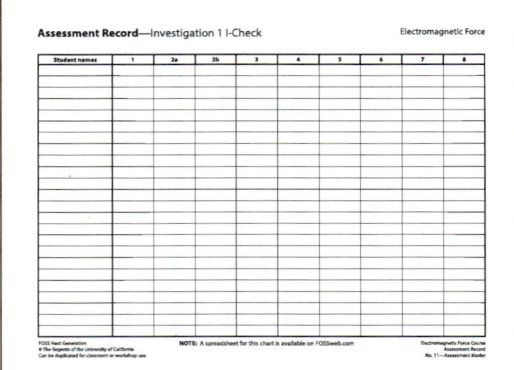

Assessment Record

Part 3: Forces in Action

GUIDING *the Investigation*
Part 3: *Forces in Action*

SESSION 1
Students will . . .
- Test forces on a cart (Steps 1–3)
- Record the focus question (Step 4)
- Learn about net force (Steps 5, 6)
- Watch *Forces* video (Step 7)
- Explain thinking on notebook sheets (Steps 8–10)

SESSION 2
Students will . . .
- Read about net force (Steps 11, 12)
- Record vocabulary and revisit the focus question (Steps 13, 14)
- Review notebook entries (Step 15)
- Answer the guiding question (Step 16)

SESSIONS 3–4
Students will . . .
- Demonstrate understanding on I-Check 1 (Step 17)
- Review I-Check items through next-step strategies (Step 18)

FOCUS QUESTION
How do multiple forces affect motion?

SESSION 1 45–50 minutes

1. **Introduce the activity**
   Bring your rolling cart into the best location for all students to observe the activities. Point to the cart and ask,

   ➤ *This cart is just sitting here. It is not moving. How can the cart be made to move?* [Push or pull it.]

2. **Apply force to move a cart**
   Ask,

   ➤ *How much force do you think it will take to move this cart? How could we find out?*

   Listen to student ideas. Students may suggest using a spring scale.

   Call on a student to get a spring scale to move the cart. If the single spring scale cannot supply enough force to move the cart, call on additional students to take up spring scales to apply force to the cart until it moves.

   Ask students to figure out how much force it takes to make the cart move.

Electromagnetic Force Course—FOSS Next Generation

INVESTIGATION 1 – What Is Force?

3. **Discuss cart motion**
   Ask,

   ➤ *How much force was needed to put the cart into motion?*

   Students usually add up the several individual forces to arrive at a total number of newtons needed to move the cart. (A typical number might be 20–50 N.)

   Reinforce this important idea. When multiple forces are applied to a mass, the forces add together. Ask about a force that is somewhat less than the force needed to move the cart.

   ➤ *When you exerted a force of <X> newtons on the cart, why didn't it move?*

   Entertain student explanations for why the cart didn't move, even when a significant force was applied. Here are likely suggestions.

   - The cart is too heavy or too hard to move.
   - The force isn't large enough to overcome the force of friction in the system.
   - The wheels need more grease to roll easier.

4. **Focus question: How do multiple forces affect motion?**
   Ask students to think about what would happen if four students came up and pushed on the cart, one on each side. What would happen then? Display the focus question.

   ➤ *How do multiple forces affect motion?*

   Have students record the focus question in their notebooks and record their preliminary ideas.

5. **Introduce** *net force*
   Draw a diagram of a cart on the board. Draw an arrow pushing on the cart. Label it "F_1."

   Ask,

   ➤ *If we assume that the cart is on a frictionless surface, a surface with no friction, what will happen when F_1 is exerted on the cart?* [The cart will start moving to the right.]

Part 3: Forces in Action

Add a second force, F_2, to the diagram.

Ask,

➤ If F_1 and F_2 are equal in strength, what will happen to the cart? [Nothing.]

➤ If F_1 is larger in strength than F_2, what will happen to the cart? [The cart will move to the right. The cart will move toward the smaller force (in the direction of the larger force).]

Definition part 1. Tell students,

*If two opposing forces act on an object, the difference between the strength of the two forces is the **net force** acting in the direction of the greater force. The net force can be thought of as the total of all the forces acting on an object.*

If F_1 and F_2 are equal, the net force is zero, and the cart will not move.

If F_1 is 100 N and F_2 is 90 N, there is a net force of 10 N to the right.

➤ How will the cart move? [The cart will move to the right.]

Definition part 2. Tell students that another way to look at the idea of net force is to think of force applied in the direction left to right (F_1) as force in the positive direction. Force applied from right to left (F_2) is force applied in the negative direction. Draw this diagram on the board.

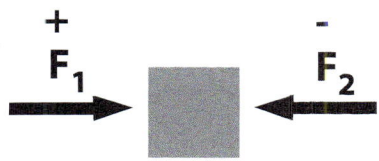

Tell students,

The sum of the forces acting on an object is the net force. If the net force is positive, the object moves to the right. If the net force is negative, the object moves to the left. If the net force is zero, no change of motion results.

TEACHING NOTE

Note that students are thinking in terms of net forces at this time. They will soon be introduced to the concept of balanced forces as a way to describe a "net force of zero."

TEACHING NOTE

You might point out that the use of + and – is arbitrary. It would work out the same if you labeled the forces with + on the right and – on the left.

SCIENCE AND ENGINEERING PRACTICES

Developing and using models

Using mathematics and computational thinking

Electromagnetic Force Course—FOSS Next Generation

INVESTIGATION 1 – What Is Force?

6. **Modeling net force**

   Return to your cart. Push gently on one side of the cart (not hard enough to put it into motion).

   Tell students,

   ➤ *I'm pushing on the cart in the positive direction with a force of about 20 N, but it isn't moving. Tell your partner why.* [A 20 N friction force is pushing on the cart in the negative direction. The net force is zero.]

   ➤ *How do you know the net force is zero?* [If the net force were not zero, the cart would move.]

   Call a student up to push on the opposite side of the cart. Resist the push so that the cart doesn't move. Tell the class,

   ➤ *(Taylor) was pushing with a force of 500 N in the negative direction. Why didn't the cart move?* [You were pushing with a 500 N force in the positive direction; the net force was zero.]

   Reduce your force a bit so that the cart moves toward you. Ask,

   ➤ *(Taylor) was still pushing with –500 N. Why did the cart move?* [You were pushing with a force of less than +500 N. There was a net force acting in the negative direction.]

SCIENCE AND ENGINEERING PRACTICES

Using mathematics and computational thinking

Part 3: Forces in Action

Push the cart over against the wall. Have a student push on the cart. Ask,

➤ (Alex) is pushing with a lot of force on the cart. Is it moving? [No.]

➤ How do you explain the fact that the cart doesn't move?

Students often revert to a kind of primitive common sense to explain why the student can't make the cart move: The wall is too heavy or too strong; you can't push through a wall—it's connected to the rest of the building; a person is too weak to break through the wall. Entertain lots of ideas from students. Encourage them to put as many interpretations out for consideration as possible.

Lead the class discussion to this conclusion: The wall is exerting an equal force in the direction opposing the force exerted by (Alex). The net force is 0 N, so the cart's motion does not change.

7. **View video:** *Forces*

Tell students that another way to think about net force of zero is to consider the force as balanced or equal. Ask students to open their notebooks to a new page and create two columns, one for balanced forces and one for unbalanced forces. As they watch the video, students should record examples of each.

Play the *Force* video chapter in Resources by Investigation. You may need to pause for students to record their responses.

- Chapter 2: "What is Force & When are Forces Balanced?" (duration 2.5 minutes)

At the end of the video, give students a moment to share recorded examples in their groups.

CROSSCUTTING CONCEPTS

Systems and system models

> **TEACHING NOTE**
>
> The notion that walls push on the cart with a force equal to that exerted by the student is often discounted when students first consider it. Students know that people, other animals, and possibly machines can push. Passive resistance exerted by a tree, wall, or Earth's surface is not easily conceived as a pushing force. Indeed, the actual force coming from an inanimate object is a result of the combined electric force from electrons in atoms of which the object is composed.

> **TEACHING NOTE**
>
> Go to FOSSweb for *Teacher Resources* and look for the Science and Engineering Practices chapter for details on how to engage students with the practice of obtaining, evaluating, and communicating information.

Electromagnetic Force Course—FOSS Next Generation

INVESTIGATION 1 — What Is Force?

MATH CONNECTION
This supports Common Core State Standards for Math 7.NS 1.

SCIENCE AND ENGINEERING PRACTICES
Using mathematics and computational thinking

8. **Introduce the notebook sheets**
   Distribute a copy of notebook sheets 5–6, *Forces on Carts* to each student. The sheets describe five situations in which students are putting force on a cart.

   Work through question 1 as a class, to make sure everyone understands the premise for the question and an approach to answering it.

   Give students time to work on each subsequent question in small groups. After each question, lead a brief class discussion, using mini-whiteboards or sheets of paper. Groups can record their responses to the question and hold them up, and then the class can discuss answers with your guidance until there is an agreed-upon explanation for the question. Then move on to the next item. See the Notebook Answers section of *Teacher Resources* for sample student responses.

9. **Extend the investigation with homework**
   Students can complete notebook sheet 7, *Response Sheet— Investigation 1*, as homework.

10. **Assess progress: response sheet**
    Collect the sheets and use a sample to consider students' thinking. This assessment will help you determine students' preparedness for the benchmark assessment at the end of this investigation.

    What to Look For

    - *Students consider the interaction of two forces: the 1800 N from the three dogs and the force of friction from the new surface (which must be at least 1800 N if it stopped the sled).*

    - *Students suggest that if the dogs are still pulling with the same force, the sled stopped moving because the force of friction between the sled and the grass/dirt surface is greater than between the sled and the snow/ice surface.*

    Plan to spend 15 minutes reviewing the selected student responses. Using *Embedded Assessment Notes* as a tool, review the responses, record any alternative concepts that are evident, and decide if any next-step strategies are required before moving forward.

    After your review, return the sheets to students to be taped or glued into their science notebooks.

SESSION 2 *45–50 minutes*

Part 3: Forces in Action

READING in Science Resources

11. Read "Net Force"

Tell students that the article "Net Force" will give them more examples and ways to think about the concept of net force. Give them a moment to jot down an example they are familiar with and share their ideas with a partner.

Distribute copies of FOSS Science Resources to every student. If you haven't already done so, introduce FOSS Science Resources. Give students a few minutes to look at and discuss the cover of the book, and to examine and discuss the table of contents. Point out that the book has readings in the front and data in the back. Students should also locate the glossary and the index.

12. Use a reading comprehension strategy

Have students preview the article by looking at and discussing the photographs and diagrams with a partner, reading the captions and subtitles, and noting the words in bold.

Tell students to read the article independently.

As you read the article, use self-stick notes to mark an important point, or a word or phrase you don't understand. And if you have a question about part of the reading, or an interesting idea related to the reading, record it in your notebook.

When students are finished reading, give them a few minutes to share their notes and help each other determine or clarify the meaning of unknown words or phrases. Then, use the guide on the following pages to lead an in-class discussion of the article.

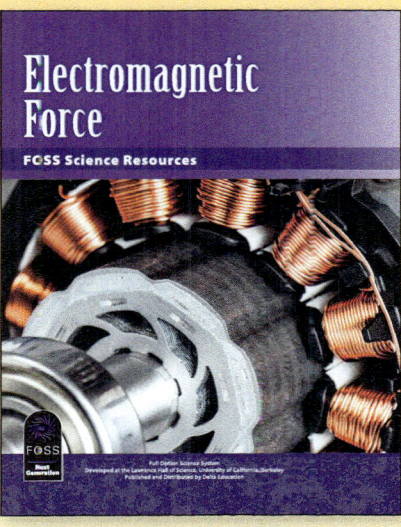

FOSS Science Resources

SCIENCE AND ENGINEERING PRACTICES

Obtaining, evaluating, and communicating information

ELA CONNECTION

These suggested strategies address the Common Core State Standards for ELA for literacy.

RST 10: Read and comprehend science texts independently and proficiently.

WHST 8: Gather relevant information from multiple print and digital sources.

L 4: Determine or clarify meaning of unknown words or phrases.

FOSS Science Resources

Electromagnetic Force Course—FOSS Next Generation

INVESTIGATION 1 — What Is Force?

Connect to real life: Give students a moment to think about any experiences they've had playing tug of war and how it felt to pull and be pulled by the force of the other team.

Net Force

Tug of war is a fierce game. Each team holds the rope tightly, waiting for the signal. The whistle blows, and the competition begins. Which team will win? It all depends on the force each team applies.

You know that a force is a push or a pull. You also know that an object will stay at rest unless a force that is strong enough acts on the object. In tug of war, opposing teams apply opposing forces through a rope. If each player in the picture could pull with exactly the same force, the game would be a tie. Neither team would move the other team.

As long as each team is pulling with an equal amount of force, the forces are balanced and the rope does not move. What will happen if someone joins the team on the left?

Part 3: Forces in Action

A seesaw is not much fun unless someone sits on the other end. Then, depending on the net force, this girl will go up or down. It takes two to seesaw!

Let's assume each player pulls with 200 newtons (N), so the total force one team is exerting would be

(+200 N) + (+200 N) + (+200 N) = +600 N.

Since the other team is pulling in the opposite direction, each one has a negative force. Their total force is

(−200 N) + (−200 N) + (−200 N) = −600 N.

The **net force** on the rope is

(+600 N) + (−600 N) = 0 N.

If one player pulls with 201 N, the total force of the team would become 601 N. Their team would win unless the opposing team members could meet or exceed the extra force.

Every day, you encounter situations that involve net force. Net force determines whether an object moves. Think about the forces involved in these examples.

- Different-sized people sit on a seesaw and push off the ground.
- You stand on a moving bus and try to not to fall over when the driver hits the brakes.
- You lean back in a chair without tipping over.
- You sit in your chair without floating off into space.

Use an example: Pause here to let students do the task described in Think Question 1. You might assign one of the examples to each group and have them work together to make a model that explains the forces involved in their example. Encourage them to use cause-and-effect relationships in their explanations.

SCIENCE AND ENGINEERING PRACTICES

Developing and using models

Using mathematics and computational thinking

CROSSCUTTING CONCEPTS

Cause and effect

ELA CONNECTION

This suggested strategy addresses the Common Core State Standards for ELA for literacy.

SL 5: Integrate visual displays into presentations.

INVESTIGATION 1 — What Is Force?

Draw a force diagram: Pause here to let students consider and do the task described in Think Question 2. Students can work individually, in pairs, or as a group to develop and present their models.

Encourage them to explain their models in terms of stability and change.

SCIENCE AND ENGINEERING PRACTICES

Developing and using models

Using mathematics and computational thinking

CROSSCUTTING CONCEPTS

Stability and change

ELA CONNECTION

This suggested strategy addresses the Common Core State Standards for ELA for literacy.

SL 5: Integrate visual displays into presentations.

Finding Net Force

Some objects simply lay on a table. Some people might think that no forces are acting upon the objects. But you know that is not true. Any net force other than zero will make an object move. As in the tug-of-war analysis, a little math helps us figure out the net force on an object.

What are the forces on the laptop? Because the laptop is not moving, we know the forces acting on it are balanced. Two equal forces act on the laptop in opposite directions. Gravity pulls the laptop down, and the table pushes the laptop up. All the forces acting on the laptop together represent the net force.

We know the net force on the laptop is zero, because it is not moving. If gravity is pulling the laptop down with a force of 20 N, what is the force of the table pushing up? If you said 20 N, you are correct. Equal forces are acting on the laptop in opposite directions.

Now consider the pen on the table. The pen has a smaller mass than the laptop. The force of gravity depends on the mass of the object, so the force of gravity pulling down on the pen is just 0.4 N. What is the force of the table pushing up? We know that it must be 0.4 N.

Explain what forces are represented by the up and down arrows.

Balanced forces keep the laptop and the other objects in place on the tabletop instead of falling down or flying up.

Part 3: Forces in Action

Some forces are easy to see, like a kick to a soccer ball. Other forces are invisible, like gravity, friction, and wind. Can you see the effects of these unseen forces acting in this room?

Invisible Forces

How does the table "know" to push up on the laptop with a force of 20 N and on the pen with a force of 0.4 N? The difference in force depends on invisible properties of matter.

A gentle breeze comes from the window. Papers on the desk move to the side, fall, and come to rest on the floor. What happened? The force of the breeze (0.2 N) was greater than the force of friction on the paper (0.1 N). Even a tiny net force will cause motion. During all these motions, the net forces on the papers were not zero, so the paper fell to the floor. When the paper comes to rest on the floor, the net forces are again zero.

As you continue to study force, you will encounter other forces that are invisible. But their effects can be directly observed. What causes a sock to stick to your shirt when you take it out of the dryer? What causes a **magnet** to hold your report card to the refrigerator? What causes your bedroom light to turn on? The short answer is force.

Think Questions

1. Choose one example from the bulleted list on page 16. Draw a model of how forces are acting upon the object (blue arrows) and how they affect the object's motion (red arrows). Use larger and smaller arrows to represent the strength of the forces.

2. Consider the laptop on a table. Let's say you apply a little horizontal push (force) to the laptop and it does not move sideways. What force is resisting the laptop's motion? Draw a diagram to explain your answer.

3. Think about tug of war. Team X has three members who pull with the following forces: +180 N, +200 N, and +190 N. Team Y has three members who pull with the following forces: −200 N, −180 N, and −191 N. Which team would win?

Consider stability and change: Focus students' attention on this idea (balanced and unbalanced forces) and have them think about how the crosscutting concept of stability and change helps them to explain invisible forces.

Discuss Think Questions:

▶ *Choose one example in the bulleted list on page 16.* [Answers will vary.]

▶ *What force is resisting the laptop's motion?* [The force of friction.]

▶ *Which team would win?* [Team Y would win. It has 1 N more net force, which is enough to make the other team move.]

SCIENCE AND ENGINEERING PRACTICES

Constructing explanations

CROSSCUTTING CONCEPTS

Stability and change

ELA CONNECTION

This suggested strategy addresses the Common Core State Standards for ELA for literacy.

RST 1: Cite evidence to support analysis of science texts.

Electromagnetic Force Course—FOSS Next Generation

INVESTIGATION 1 – What Is Force?

net force

SCIENCE AND ENGINEERING PRACTICES

Developing and using models

13. **Record vocabulary**

    If necessary, give students a few moments to review and clarify the vocabulary developed in this part. Ask students to update their vocabulary indexes if they haven't already done so.

14. **Revisit the focus question**

    Have students return to the page where they recorded the focus question.

    ➤ *How do multiple forces affect motion?*

    Students should draw a line under their original response and enter any new or additional ideas. Encourage students to draw models in their notebook to explain the forces involved in the cart example or to use another example.

Part 3: Forces in Action

WRAP-UP

15. Review notebook entries

Ask students to go through their notebook entries and select one key point that summarizes an important finding from this investigation. They should record this point in their notebooks.

Have students share their key point with their group, selecting one key point to share with the class. Create a class chart of key points by recording each group's idea on a piece of chart paper, whiteboard, or document projected from the computer. You might need to help groups rephrase their key points for clarity.

Students should record the key points in their notebooks and reference the page numbers in their notebooks where additional information supports each key point. By using science and engineering practices and exploring core ideas through the lens of crosscutting concepts, students should come forward with these big ideas in the review discussions. These concepts set the stage for learning more about magnetic and electric forces.

- Force is an interaction between objects, and can take the form of a push or a pull. (Asking questions; planning and carrying out investigations; analyzing and interpreting data; constructing explanations; PS2.A: Forces and motion; cause and effect; energy and matter.)
- Friction is a force that acts between surfaces to resist motion. (Asking questions; planning and carrying out investigations; analyzing and interpreting data; using mathematics and computational thinking; engaging in argument from evidence; obtaining, evaluating, and communicating information; PS2.A: Forces and motion; patterns; cause and effect.)
- The sum of the forces acting on an object is the net force. (Developing and using models; using mathematics and computational thinking; constructing explanations; obtaining, evaluating, and communicating information; PS2.A: Forces and motion; cause and effect; systems and system models; stability and change.)

16. Answer the guiding question

Ask students to discuss the investigation guiding question.

➤ *How are force and motion related?*

You might use an image from the *FOSS Science Resources* book (such as the one on pages 8 and 9, upper) to connect their thinking to the real world. Students can also ask additional questions about the phenomena of friction and net force.

SCIENCE AND ENGINEERING PRACTICES

Asking questions
Developing and using models
Planning and carrying out investigations
Analyzing and interpreting data
Using mathematics and computational thinking
Constructing explanations
Engaging in argument from evidence
Obtaining, evaluating, and communicating information

DISCIPLINARY CORE IDEAS

PS2.A: Forces and motion

CROSSCUTTING CONCEPTS

Patterns
Cause and effect
Systems and system models
Energy and matter
Stability and change

SESSION 3 45–50 minutes

INVESTIGATION 1 – What Is Force?

17. Assess progress: I-Check

Administer *Investigation 1 I-Check*, asking students to respond to the items on paper or online on FOSSmap. Students should independently answer the questions. When taking the I-Check, students should not use their notebooks, but the notebooks are a good tool to use when students later reflect on their answers.

SESSION 4 *45–50 minutes*

18. Discuss I-Check results

Code the I-Check items, but do not make any marks on student responses. Note that FOSSmap automatically codes most of the items and provides you with student and class reports. Coding guides can be found on FOSSweb. You can record student results on the *Assessment Record* or download spreadsheets from FOSSmap for recording. Note important points about the items to review with students.

Return the I-Checks to students. Use self-assessment strategies as described in the Assessment chapter for each item to facilitate reflection and clarify student thinking.

TEACHING NOTE

During or after these next steps with the I-Check, you might ask students to make choices for possible derivative products based on their notebooks for inclusion in a summative portfolio. See the Assessment chapter for more information about creating and evaluating portfolios.

Extending the Investigation

EXTENDING *the Investigation*

- **Develop force problems**
  Students can invent force problems based on real-life situations similar to the notebook sheets *Forces on Carts A* and *B*. Students should select a different scene and characters. The problems should have answers such as "The object will move to the left (or right)" or "The object will not move," or perhaps something more complex. Students can bring the problems to class and trade with other students. Have students solve the problems and discuss their answers with the original problem author.

- **Test force in online simulation**
  Students can experiment with net force, motion, and friction using an online simulation, "Force and Motion: Basics." Visit FOSSweb to access the link.

> **TEACHING NOTE**
>
> Encourage students to use the Science and Engineering Careers Database on FOSSweb.

INVESTIGATION 1 – What Is Force?

Investigation 2: The Force of Magnetism

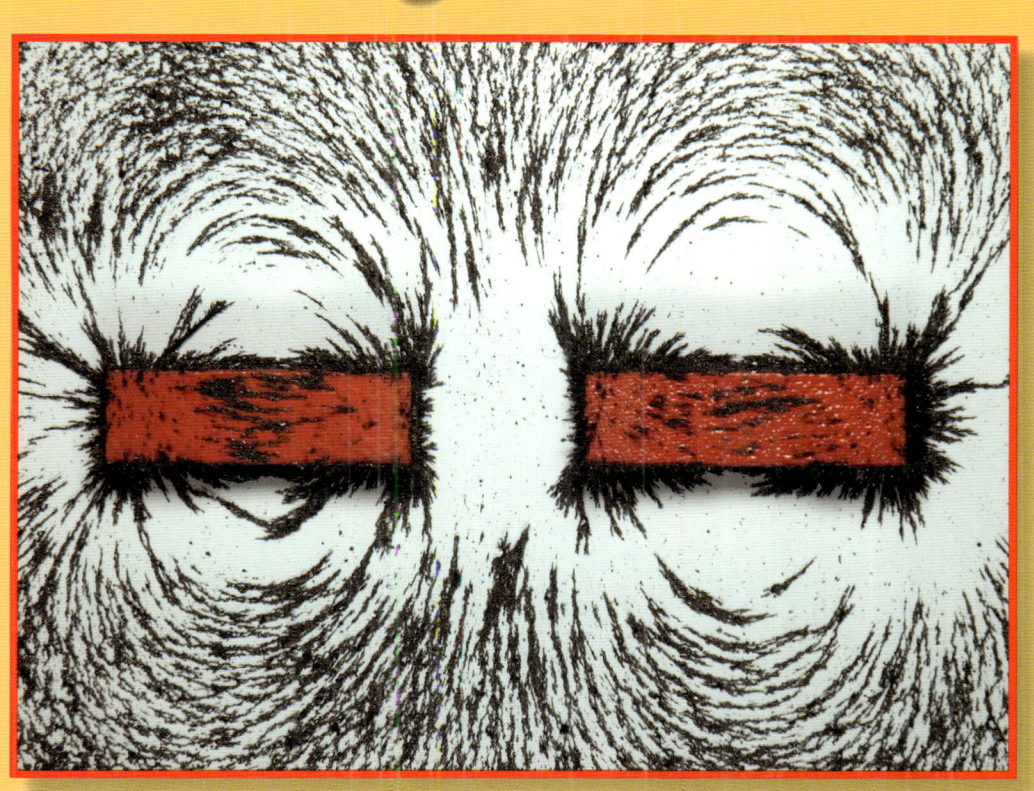

INVESTIGATION 2 – The Force of Magnetism

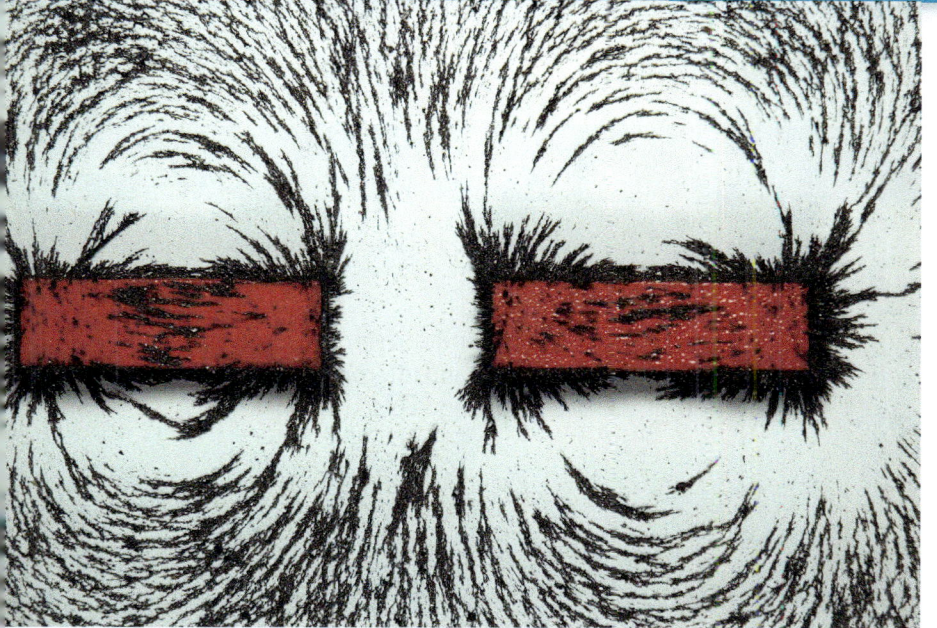

PURPOSE

In *The Force of Magnetism*, students explore the phenomenon of magnetism. They test properties of magnets to study their force. They develop a model of magnetic fields and use it to explain magnets' force over distance.

Content

- Magnets stick to (attract) objects that contain iron.
- All magnets have two poles, a north pole on one side and a south pole on the other side. Like poles of magnets repel each other; opposite poles attract.
- Magnets are surrounded by an invisible magnetic force field, which acts through space and through all nonmagnetic materials.
- Magnetic materials may become temporary magnets when they interact with magnetic fields.
- The magnitude of the magnetic force between two interacting magnetic fields decreases as the distance between them increases.

Practices

- Analyze and interpret data about magnetic force in a series of experiments looking at force over distance and force when more magnets are introduced.
- Develop and use models to construct explanations about magnetic fields and explain their properties and interactions.

Part 1
Properties of Magnets 150

Part 2
Magnetic Fields 160

Part 3
Force over Distance 178

Guiding question for phenomenon:
How can we describe magnetic force?

Science and Engineering Practices

- Asking questions
- Developing and using models
- Planning and carrying out investigations
- Analyzing and interpreting data
- Using mathematics and computational thinking
- Constructing explanations
- Engaging in argument from evidence
- Obtaining, evaluating, and communicating information

Disciplinary Core Ideas

PS2: How can one explain and predict interactions between objects and with systems of objects?
PS2.A Forces and motion
PS2.B Types of interactions
PS3: How is energy transferred and conserved?
PS3.A Definitions of energy
PS3.C Relationship between energy and forces

Crosscutting Concepts

- Patterns
- Cause and effect
- Systems and system models
- Energy and matter

FOSS Full Option Science System

INVESTIGATION 2 – The Force of Magnetism

	Investigation Summary	Time	Focus Question for Phenomenon, Practices
PART 1	**Properties of Magnets** Students observe that the two sides (poles) of magnets are different, attracting or repelling one another, depending on orientation. While they conduct an investigation to determine if like or opposite poles attract, students learn the north/south convention for naming poles.	**Active Inv.** 1 Session*	**What happens when magnets interact?** **Practices** Planning and carrying out investigations Analyzing and interpreting data Constructing explanations
PART 2	**Magnetic Fields** Students work with magnets and other objects to discover that magnetism acts through certain materials including air, nonmagnetic metals, and nonmetals. They also discover that bringing a magnet close to a piece of iron induces magnetism in the iron. Students learn that these effects are manifestations of the invisible magnetic field that surrounds every magnet.	**Active Inv.** 2 Sessions **Reading** 1 Session	**How can we detect a magnetic field?** **Practices** Asking questions Developing and using models Planning and carrying out investigations Analyzing and interpreting data Constructing explanations Engaging in argument from evidence Obtaining, evaluating, and communicating information
PART 3	**Force over Distance** Students use a spring scale to measure the force of attraction between magnets. They increase the distance between the magnets and remeasure the force. Students learn that the force of attraction between magnets decreases as the distance between them increases. Next, they add additional magnets to a system to learn how magnetic fields overlap. Students then use an online activity to help visualize magnetic fields and to test further predictions.	**Active Inv.** 2 Sessions **Review** 1 Session **Assessment** 1–2 Sessions	**What factors affect the force of attraction between magnets?** **Practices** Developing and using models Planning and carrying out investigations Analyzing and interpreting data Using mathematics and computational thinking Constructing explanations Obtaining, evaluating, and communicating information

*A class session is 45–50 minutes.

At a Glance

Content Related to DCIs	Literacy/Technology	Assessment
• All magnets have two poles, a north pole on one side and a south pole on the other side. Like poles of magnets repel each other; opposite poles attract. • Magnets stick to (attract) objects that contain iron.	**Science Notebook Entry** Answer the focus question	**Embedded Assessment** Science notebook entry
• Magnets are surrounded by an invisible magnetic force field, which acts through space and through all nonmagnetic materials. • Magnetic materials may become temporary magnets when they interact with magnetic fields.	**Science Notebook Entry** Response Sheet—Investigation 2 **Science Resources Book** "Magnetic Force" **Video** Magnetism	**Embedded Assessment** Response sheet
• The magnitude of the magnetic force between two interacting magnetic fields decreases as the distance between them increases.	**Science Notebook Entry** Adding Magnets **Online Activity** "Adding Magnetic Fields"	**Embedded Assessment** Performance assessment **Benchmark Assessment** Investigation 2 I-Check **NGSS Performance Expectations addressed in this investigation** MS-PS2-2 MS-PS2-3 MS-PS2-5 MS-PS3-2

Electromagnetic Force Course—FOSS Next Generation

INVESTIGATION 2 – The Force of Magnetism

SCIENTIFIC and Historical Background

We tend to take magnetic phenomena for granted because **magnets** are all around us. Refrigerator doors are notorious gathering places for multitudes of little magnetic doodads, and magnets are at work behind the scenes, keeping refrigerator and cabinet doors securely closed. **Compasses**, loudspeakers, and electric motors all use magnets. The magnet on the refrigerator door and the ones used in this investigation are **permanent magnets**. Magnets that can be turned on and off have a different magnetic pedigree, and they are the subject of Investigation 3. The guiding question for this investigation is how can we describe magnetic force?

For many years permanent magnets were made of iron. Magnet technology has made tremendous strides in the past several decades, and modern magnets are stronger and less susceptible to losing their **magnetism** than their iron predecessors. New alloys like alnico (aluminum, nickel, and cobalt) make very powerful, long-lasting magnets, and magnets made from a powdered iron oxide called ferrite are not only strong but versatile, because magnetic ferrite dust can be put in a ceramic or rubber matrix and molded into an endless variety of sizes and shapes. The doughnut-shaped magnets used in this investigation are ceramic ferrite magnets. The ferrite-infused ceramic liquid is poured in a mold, subjected to a **magnetic field** to align the tiny ferrite particles in the orientation desired, and fired to lock the ferrite particles in place.

The strongest consumer permanent magnets are called neodymium magnets. They are manufactured from an alloy composed of the rare earth element neodymium, iron, and boron ($Nd_2Fe_{14}B$). Neodymium magnets are often used by welders to hold steel pieces in place while they work. These magnets are so strong that they can be dangerous if handled carelessly. A pinch of skin caught between two neodymium magnets can be seriously damaged.

What Happens When Magnets Interact?

Magnets interact with objects in two ways; they either stick to the object or they do not. Magnets stick only to other magnets and a select few metals. The most common metals that stick to magnets contain iron, nickel, and cobalt, either pure or as alloys. Nickel and cobalt are quite rare in our everyday environment, so if a magnet sticks to an object that is not itself a magnet, chances are good that the object is made of iron or an iron alloy, such as steel.

> "The most common metals that stick to magnets contain iron, nickel, and cobalt, either pure or as alloys."

Scientific and Historical Background

Magnets have two opposing natures—they **attract** and **repel**. Whether they attract or repel depends on how two magnets are oriented to one another. Every permanent magnet has an end or a side that attracts a second magnet, and another end or side that repels the same location on the second magnet.

Two unmarked magnets attract, and when one magnet is turned around, they repel. It is straightforward to then conclude that the two ends of a magnet are different. The two ends of a magnet can arbitrarily be labeled "X" and "Y."

The next question is, when a second magnet is brought close to the Y end of this first magnet, and it attracts, which end of the second magnet is attracted, the X end or the Y end?

Through exploration, students can determine if similar ends (two Xs or two Ys) attract, or two different ends (one X and one Y) attract.

Solving this problem requires a third magnet. Here's how.

First, lay a magnet on the table. Call it magnet 3. Magnet 3 is the reference magnet.

Then bring magnet 1 up to one end of magnet 3. Label the end of magnet 1 that repels "X." Bring magnet 2 up to the same end of magnet 3 and label the end of that magnet that repels "X," too.

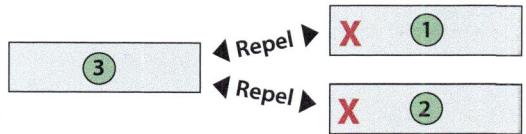

This procedure identifies the ends of two magnets that are the same. The two ends labeled X can then be brought together. Students will find that two similar ends repel. In an analogous fashion, students confirm that opposite ends attract.

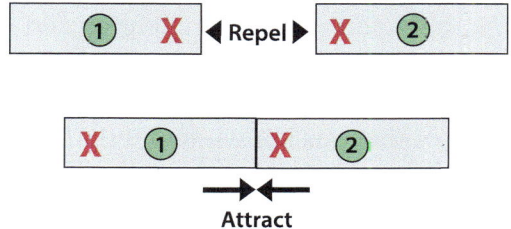

Electromagnetic Force Course—FOSS Next Generation

INVESTIGATION 2 – The Force of Magnetism

For historical reasons, and because Earth itself is a magnet, the "ends" of magnets are called **poles**, north pole and south pole. The pole on a permanent magnet that points north when allowed to pivot freely is the north pole of the magnet. When the north poles on two magnets are brought together, they repel.

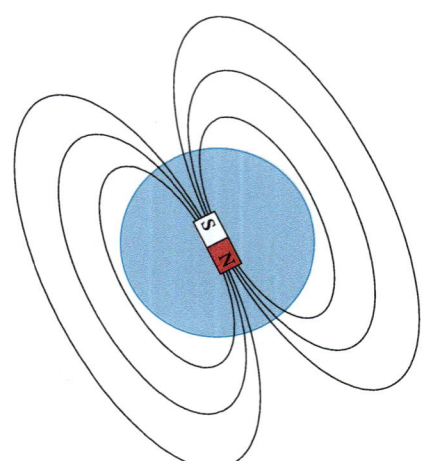

There is a contradiction in the conventional language associated with the poles of a magnet and the conceptual understanding of the behavior of magnets. The north pole of a magnet is attracted to Earth's northern magnetic pole. It would seem that similar poles attract.

The end of a magnet (compass needle) that points toward Earth's northern magnetic pole is, in fact, a north pole. Therefore, the magnetic pole up there near the North Pole in the Arctic is actually a south magnetic pole. This can be very confusing for students. The issue is dodged in some instances by referring to the north pole of the compass as the "north-seeking pole," but this is incorrect. Be very careful in the development of this concept.

How Can We Detect a Magnetic Field?

A magnet is surrounded by an invisible magnetic field that extends from the north pole of a permanent magnet and converges at the south pole. A field is a mathematical description of the magnetic force at each point in space surrounding the magnet. The field is often represented by a set of lines that runs through the magnet and loop from north pole to south pole in ever larger loops.

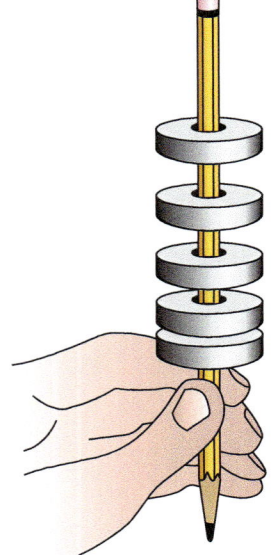

Magnetic fields act through air and the vacuum of outer space. They also act through water, plastic, wood, paper, cloth, and most metals. The magnetic field does not, however, act through iron. The field is transformed by the process of inducing magnetism in the iron.

You might want to try this magnetic stunt: Put four or five of the doughnut-shaped magnets on a pencil, oriented so that adjacent magnets repel each other. Hold the pencil straight up and down. Note the differential spacing of the magnets. This elegant, simple demonstration (which students will do during the investigation) shows the interaction between two of the four known forces in the universe—the electromagnetic force and the **gravitational force**. These forces, along with the strong and weak nuclear forces that hold atoms together and produce radioactivity, are the only physical forces that exist in the universe.

Scientific and Historical Background

What Factors Affect the Force of Attraction between Magnets?

Technically, magnets don't stick to metals at all—they stick to other magnets. Iron, nickel, and cobalt, because of their chemical (atomic) properties, temporarily become magnets when they enter a magnetic field. This **induced magnetism** exists only as long as the metal is influenced by a magnetic field. As soon as the metal moves some distance from the field, the metal ceases to be a magnet. So when a magnet comes close to a piece of iron, cobalt, or nickel, the metal becomes a magnet, and the two magnets stick together. (Students may notice that an object that was stuck to a magnet for a while maintains a small amount of permanent magnetism even after they remove the magnet.)

The magnetic field surrounding a permanent magnet is created by the orientation of microscopic associations of atoms called magnetic domains in the mass of metal. Domains have polarity; that is, they have a positive end and a negative end. When the domains in a piece of iron are all oriented in the same direction, the piece of iron is a magnet, and the magnet is surrounded by a magnetic field. When the domains are randomly oriented, the polar effect is neutralized, and the piece of iron is not a magnet and thus has no magnetic field. Nonmagnetic materials, such as plastic or aluminum, are unaffected when a magnetic field comes near.

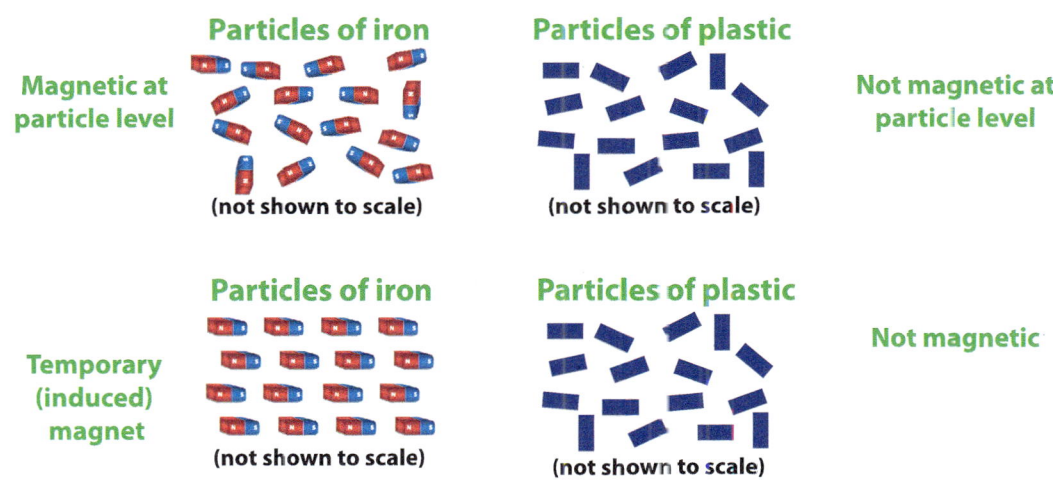

When the magnetic field of a permanent magnet comes near a piece of nonmagnetized iron, such as a steel nail, the magnetic field affects

Electromagnetic Force Course—FOSS Next Generation

INVESTIGATION 2 – The Force of Magnetism

the domains in the nail. The domains in the nail reorient to align with the lines of the magnetic field. The field induces magnetism in the nail, and the nail becomes a **temporary magnet**. When the magnet is taken away from the nail, two things might happen. The domains may reorient randomly, rendering the nail nonmagnetized, or a sufficient number of domains might stay oriented to maintain a weak permanent magnetism.

The orientation of the induced magnetism plays by the rules of magnetic interaction: as the north pole of the magnet approaches the nail, the domains in the nail reorient with their south poles toward the magnet. The magnet and nail then attract, with the north pole of the magnet sticking to the south pole of the nail in which magnetism has been induced.

If a paper clip is close to the point of the nail, induced magnetism will make the paper clip stick to the nail for the same reason. If the magnet is withdrawn from the nail, the paper clip may stay attached to the nail . . . until the magnet is flipped over and brought close to the nail once again. As the magnet approaches the nail, the paper clip will drop off. Flipping the magnet reverses the induced poles in the iron nail but not in the paper clip, so the clip is repelled by the nail.

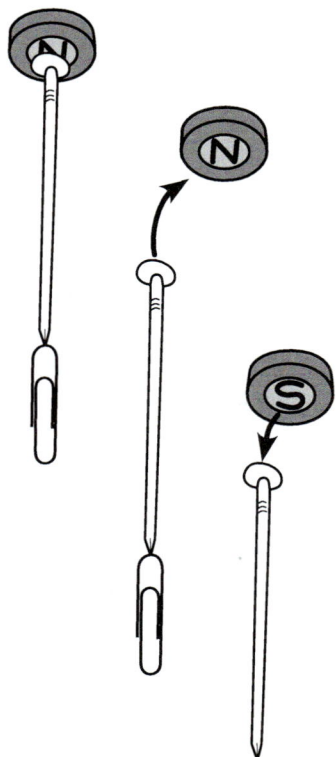

Scientific and Historical Background

When you hold two magnets, you can actually feel the magnets either pulling toward each other or pushing each other away, depending on how they are oriented. The agent responsible for the push or pull is the magnetic force. This force can cause motion, and where there is motion, there is energy. The **potential energy** of a magnetic object placed in a magnetic field, such as a paper clip placed near a permanent magnet, transfers to kinetic energy when the magnetic force is stronger than the force of friction, and the paper clip slides toward the magnet.

The strength of the force of attraction (or repulsion) between two magnets is the product of several variables. Most important are the native strengths of the magnetic fields produced by the magnets and the distance between them. The general rule is the stronger the magnets, and the closer they are together, the stronger the force acting between them.

The greater the distance between two magnets, the weaker the force of attraction. As the distance between magnets approaches infinity, the force of attraction approaches, but never reaches, zero. Wow!

Vocabulary
Attract
Compass
Gravitational force
Induced magnetism
Magnet
Magnetic field
Magnetism
Permanent magnet
Pole
Potential energy
Repel
Temporary magnet

INVESTIGATION 2 – The Force of Magnetism

TEACHING AND LEARNING about *Magnetism*

Developing Disciplinary Core Ideas (DCI)

"Magnets stick things together, or they could push apart from each other." The attraction and repulsion of magnets is familiar by middle school. In this investigation, students will work to develop a mental model for *how* magnets attract and repel, which is something they have probably not considered before.

Experiments with magnetic objects and over distances will help students draw conclusions about magnetic force. They will develop models to help them understand the magnetic field that surrounds the magnet and exerts force on objects at a distance, which is related to their potential energy. They will learn how magnets can induce magnetism in magnetic objects. And students will start to explore magnetic force as additive when magnets are assembled in one area and their magnetic fields overlap. The concepts of induced magnetism and additive magnetic fields are foundational to students' understanding of how electromagnets work, which is addressed in the next investigation.

The experiences students have in this investigation contribute to the disciplinary core ideas **PS2.A: Forces and motion**; **PS2.B: Types of interactions**; **PS3.A: Definitions of energy**; and **PS3.C: Relationship between energy and forces**.

NGSS Foundation Box for DCI

PS2.A: Forces and motion

- The motion of an object is determined by the sum of the forces acting on it; if the total force on the object is not zero, its motion will change. The greater the mass of the object, the greater the force needed to achieve the same change in motion. For any given object, a larger force causes a larger change in motion. (MS-PS2-2)

PS2.B: Types of interactions

- Electric and magnetic (electromagnetic) forces can be attractive or repulsive, and their sizes depend on the magnitudes of the charges, currents, or magnetic strengths involved and on the distances between the interacting objects. (MS-PS2-3)
- Forces that act at a distance (electric and magnetic) can be explained by fields that extend through space and can be mapped by their effect on a test object (a ball, a charged object, or a magnet, respectively). (MS-PS2-5)

PS3.A: Definitions of energy

- A system of objects may also contain stored (potential) energy, depending on their relative positions. (MS-PS3-2)

PS3.C: Relationship between energy and forces

- When two objects interact, each one exerts a force on the other that can cause energy to be transferred to or from the object. (MS-PS3-2)

Teaching and Learning about Magnetism

Engaging in Science and Engineering Practices (SEP)

In this investigation, students engage in these practices.

- **Asking questions** about magnets, magnetic fields, and magnetic force that can be answered in class.
- **Developing and using models** to describe magnetic fields and explain their properties and interactions.
- **Planning and carrying out investigations** when designing and testing mystery boxes that contain hidden magnets.
- **Analyzing and interpreting data** about magnetic force in a series of experiments looking at force over distance and force when more magnets are introduced.
- **Using mathematics and computational thinking** when analyzing results of magnetic force experiments to compare test conditions.
- **Constructing explanations** when reviewing the results of magnetic force experiments in terms of invisible magnetic fields.
- **Engaging in argument from evidence** when making claims about magnets hidden in a box.
- **Obtaining, evaluating, and communicating information** about magnetic fields after developing models and reading an article.

NGSS Foundation Box for SEP

- **Ask questions** that can be investigated within the scope of the classroom, outdoor environment, and museums and other public facilities with available resources and, when appropriate, frame a hypothesis based on observations and scientific principles.
- **Develop and/or use a model** to predict and/or describe phenomena.
- **Conduct an investigation** and/or evaluate and/or revise the experimental design to produce data to serve as the basis for evidence that meets the goals of the investigation.
- **Analyze and interpret data** to provide evidence for phenomena.
- **Apply mathematical concepts and/or processes** (e.g., ratio, rate, percent, basic operations, simple algebra) to scientific and engineering questions and problems.
- **Construct an explanation** using models or representations.
- **Construct, use, and/or present an oral and written argument** supported by empirical evidence and scientific reasoning to support or refute an explanation or a model for a phenomenon or a solution to a problem.
- **Communicate scientific and/or technical information** (e.g., about a proposed object, tool, process, system) in writing and/or through oral presentations.

INVESTIGATION 2 – The Force of Magnetism

NGSS Foundation Box for CC

- **Patterns:** Macroscopic patterns are related to the nature of microscopic and atomic-level structure. Patterns can be used to identify cause-and-effect relationships.
- **Cause and effect:** Cause-and-effect relationships may be used to predict phenomena in natural or designed systems.
- **Systems and system models:** Models can be used to represent systems and their interactions—such as inputs, processes, and outputs—and energy, matter, and information flows within systems.
- **Energy and matter:** Energy may take different forms (e.g., energy in fields, thermal energy, energy of motion).

Exposing Crosscutting Concepts (CC)

In this investigation, the focus is on these crosscutting concepts.

- **Patterns.** Magnetic poles attract and repel in specific patterns, based on the orientation of their magnetic field.
- **Cause and effect.** Magnetic force induces temporary magnetism in magnetic materials.
- **Systems and system models.** Magnetic fields extend infinitely far beyond the magnet, applying force to objects at a distance.
- **Energy and matter.** When a magnetic object is in a magnetic field, the magnet has potential energy.

Connections to the Nature of Science

- **Scientific knowledge assumes an order and consistency in natural systems.** Science assumes that objects and events in natural systems occur in consistent patterns that are understandable through measurement and observation. Science carefully considers and evaluates anomalies in data and evidence.

Connections to Engineering, Technology, and Applications of Science

- **Interdependence of science, engineering, and technology.** Engineering advances have led to important discoveries in virtually every field of science, and scientific discoveries have led to the development of entire industries and engineered systems. Science and technology drive each other forward.

Teaching and Learning about Magnetism

Conceptual Flow

In this investigation, students explore the phenomenon of magnetism. The guiding question is how can we describe magnetic force?

The **conceptual flow** starts in Part 1 when students test **magnets** to learn about their properties. They use multiple magnets with a **compass** and conclude that **opposite magnetic poles attract** and **like magnetic poles repel**. The force of magnetism is an invisible force, similar in some ways to **gravitational force**, which is always attractive.

In Part 2, students consider how a **magnetic field** spreading from a magnet explains properties of **magnetism**. They start by considering how a **permanent magnet can induce magnetism in a steel object** and create a temporary magnet. They make a preliminary model to describe the phenomena they observe. Using various tools and a reading, students collect more information about magnetic fields and add to their model.

In Part 3, students describe the force exerted by a magnet in terms of its **potential energy**. They conduct an experiment to measure how the **force of magnetism decreases as distance from the magnet increases**, and another experiment to consider how the **force of magnetism increases as magnetic fields from multiple magnets overlap**.

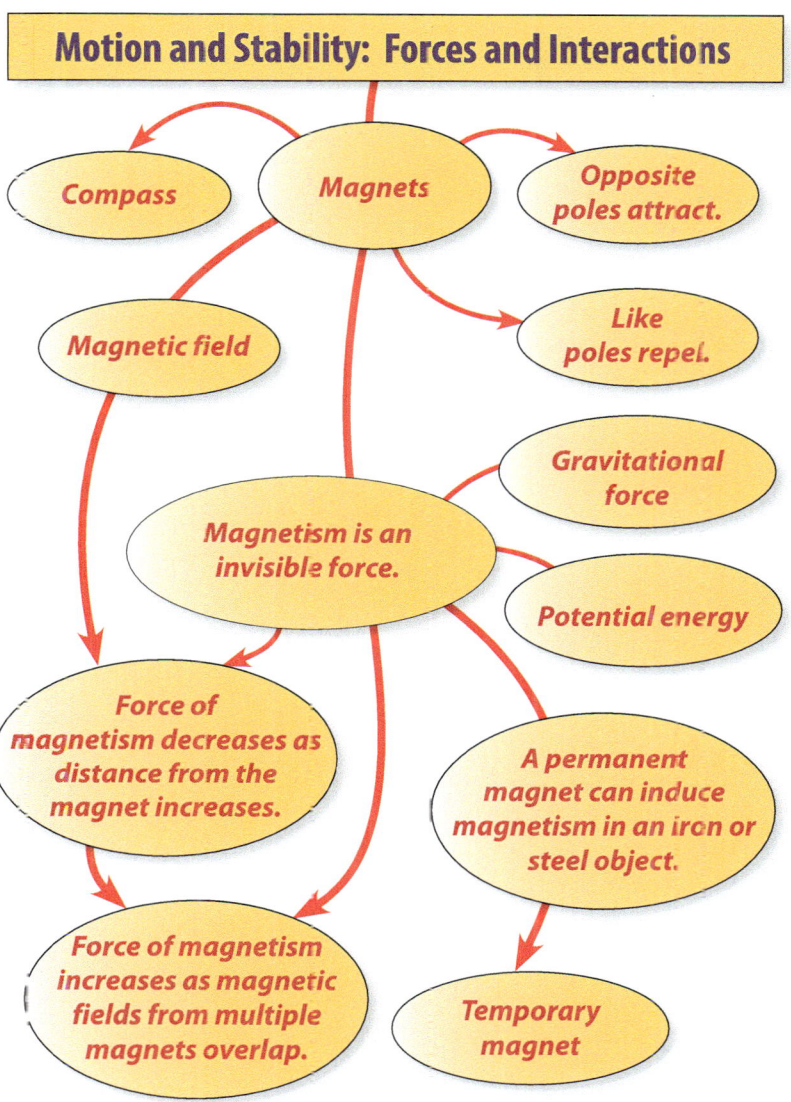

Electromagnetic Force Course—FOSS Next Generation

INVESTIGATION 2 – The Force of Magnetism

MATERIALS for
Part 1: *Properties of Magnets*

Provided equipment

For each group
- 4 Magnets, doughnut-shaped
- 4 Strings, 20 cm
- 1 Compass
- Masking tape

For the class
- 1 Magnet, doughnut-shaped
- 1 String, 20 cm

Teacher-supplied items

For the class
- 1 Scissors

FOSSweb resources

For the teacher
- *Embedded Assessment Notes*
- Teaching slides, 2.1

Part 1: Properties of Magnets

GETTING READY for
Part 1: Properties of Magnets

Quick Start

Schedule	1 session active investigation
Preview	• Preview the FOSSweb Resources by Investigation for this part (such as printable masters, teaching slides, and online activities) • Plan for homework: magnets at home, Step 19
Print or Copy	**For the teacher** • *Embedded Assessment Notes*
Prepare Material	• Cut enough 20 cm strings for each class, plus some extras • Tie one doughnut magnet to a string for demonstration • Check compasses **A**
Plan for Assessment	• Review Step 18, "What to Look For" in the notebook entry

▶ **NOTE**
Schedule computers for Part 3, one for each group or pair of students.

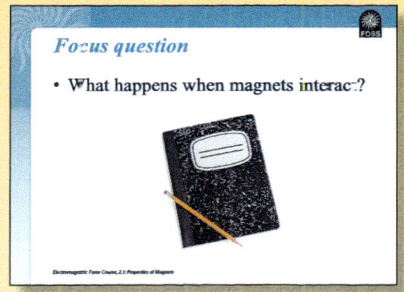

▶ **NOTE**
Preview the teaching slides on FOSSweb for this part.

Electromagnetic Force Course—FOSS Next Generation

INVESTIGATION 2 – The Force of Magnetism

Preparation Details

A. Check compasses

Make sure you know which direction is north in your classroom. You can check this using online mapping services to be sure, before you check the compasses.

Lay all the compasses on a flat surface away from the magnets and other iron objects. Verify the red arrow on all the compasses is pointing north. Compasses that are pointing elsewhere might have become demagnetized or even reverse magnetized.

A demagnetized compass can be remagnetized by letting it sit near a strong magnet for a long time. However, it's not guaranteed that it will have proper north-south orientation with respect to Earth. For a potential quick fix, run a magnet across the top of the compass from south to north and recheck it. If that doesn't work, do it again but run the magnet across the compass from north to south. Then check it. If you have many such compasses, you may need to issue a disclaimer to students about the accuracy of the compasses.

Part 1: Properties of Magnets

GUIDING *the Investigation*
Part 1: *Properties of Magnets*

FOCUS QUESTION
What happens when magnets interact?

SESSION 1

Students will . . .
- Review vocabulary (Step 1)
- Explore magnets to determine their properties (Steps 2–6)
- Think more deeply about attraction and repulsion (Steps 7–9)
- Use Earth's magnetism to determine poles of classroom magnets (Steps 10–14)
- Record vocabulary and revisit the focus question (Steps 15–18)
- Extend the investigation with homework and review notebook entries (Steps 19, 20)

SESSION 1 45–50 minutes

1. **Review force and energy**
   Ask students to review what they have learned about force so far, and how it relates to what they know about energy. Encourage students to look in their notebooks and review their notes if they aren't sure of the answers. Ask,

   ➤ *What is a force?* [A push or a pull.]

   ➤ *What is kinetic energy?* [Energy of motion.]

2. **Observe *magnets***
   Tell students that today they are going to explore a new force. They should consider the force and what it does as they work.

   Distribute a single magnet to each student. Hold up one doughnut magnet, and ask students to observe the object. Say,

   *Each of you has a **magnet**. Take a few minutes to observe its properties and to find out what it can do.*

3. **Introduce *permanent magnet***
   Students will figure out quickly that the magnet sticks to some other objects. Point out that because it is always magnetic, it is called a **permanent magnet**.

   Ask students to describe other permanent magnets that they know about (horseshoe magnets; bar-shaped magnets; big, small, or strong magnets; magnetic toys and alphabet letters), and where those magnets were found (often on refrigerator doors).

EL NOTE
If necessary, you could project or provide images of different types of magnets for students to discuss.

Electromagnetic Force Course—FOSS Next Generation

INVESTIGATION 2 – The Force of Magnetism

> **EL NOTE**
> Add "iron" to the word wall. You might add also add an image of the mineral and its chemical symbol.

> **TEACHING NOTE**
> If students ask if there are any other metals that stick to magnets, inform them that nickel and cobalt also stick, but they are nowhere near as common as iron.
>
> Also note that stainless steel contains other metals and is not magnetic.

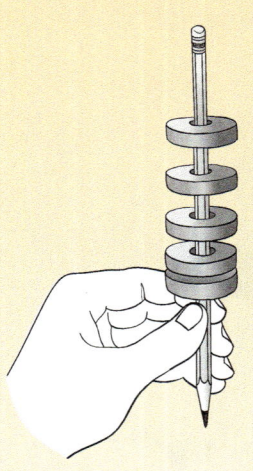

SCIENCE AND ENGINEERING PRACTICES
Planning and carrying out investigations

4. Discuss magnet properties

Call on several students to share their observations and what stuck to their magnets. Then ask the class,

➤ *Is there something that is the same about all the objects that stick to your magnets?* [They are all metal; they are all iron or steel.]

Students are likely to state that magnets stick to metal, but they may not realize that magnets only stick to certain metals. Ask for a show of hands from those who found that magnets stick to only some metals.

Tell students,

There is only one common metal that sticks to magnets: iron. Sometimes iron is mixed with other substances to make steel. Magnets stick to steel because it is mostly iron. If a magnet sticks to an object, that object is probably made of iron or steel.

5. Focus question: What happens when magnets interact?

Tell students,

You have some information about what kinds of materials stick to magnets. What happens when we bring two magnets together; in other words, how do they interact?

Introduce the focus question and write or project it on the board.

➤ *What happens when magnets interact?*

Have students record the focus question in their notebooks. They should record an initial response and leave space to revisit the question later.

6. Explore magnet interactions

Students should work in their groups to find out what happens when two or more magnets interact. Allow 4–5 minutes of free exploration of interesting ways magnets can interact.

If no group makes the following discoveries, suggest them.

- Place four or five magnets on a pencil to see what happens.
- Move one magnet on a desk, using another magnet under the desk.
- Duplicate other interesting discoveries made by other groups.

Part 1: Properties of Magnets

7. **Confirm *attract* and *repel***
   When you think students have had time enough to explore the interactions of magnets, call for attention. Ask different students to describe what they found out about the interaction between two or more magnets. Encourage students to express their observations in terms of cause and effect.

   Students will probably describe the two opposing characteristics of magnetic interaction: sometimes two magnets stick when brought together; sometimes they push each other away. Confirm vocabulary to describe the two interactions.

   *When two magnets come together so that they pull on each other and stick, we say they **attract**. When two magnets come together so they push apart, we say they **repel**.*

   *You know another invisible attractive force, which is the force of gravity. But **gravitational force** is always an attractive force between objects, like between Earth and objects on Earth. It never repels.*

8. **Discuss attraction and repulsion**
   Ask,

   ➤ *Why do you think two magnets repel sometimes and attract at other times?*

   Let students talk for a minute before calling on several groups to share their thinking. They should have an idea that every magnet has two different sides.

   ➤ *How do you know the two sides are different?* [When you bring them together in your hand, they attract—stick together. Then when you turn one around, they repel—push away. So the sides must be different.]

9. **Introduce poles**
   Tell students,

   *The two different sides of a magnet are called **poles**. One is called the south pole, and the other is called the north pole. Every magnet, including yours, has a south pole and a north pole. Your doughnut magnets have the poles on the flat surfaces.*

   Pose the challenge by asking,

   ➤ *Do magnets attract when the north pole of one magnet comes close to the north pole on a second magnet? Or do magnets attract when the north pole on one magnet comes close to the south pole on a second magnet?*

   Give students a few moments to think about how to acquire data to answer this question.

SCIENCE AND ENGINEERING PRACTICES
Constructing explanations

CROSSCUTTING CONCEPTS
Cause and effect

ELA CONNECTION

This suggested strategy addresses the Common Core State Standards for ELA for literacy.

L 5: Demonstrate understanding of word relationships and nuances in word meaning.

SCIENCE AND ENGINEERING PRACTICES
Planning and carrying out investigations

INVESTIGATION 2 – The Force of Magnetism

10. Identify Earth as a magnet

Write the following statement on the board.

Our planet, Earth, is a magnet.

Ask,

➤ *What evidence do you think supports this claim?*

➤ *What evidence would we need to gather to support this claim?*

Give students a few minutes to discuss this in their groups. Have a Recorder from each group write down the group's thoughts. Call on Reporters to share their group's ideas. If necessary, add,

Earth has a magnetic north pole and a magnetic south pole. Let's find out first which way is north.

Hold up a compass. Tell students,

*This is a **compass**. It has a small magnet that can freely pivot, or turn. This magnet is the pointer inside the compass. The red end points toward Earth's North Pole because near that area is one of Earth's magnetic poles.*

The compass may not behave correctly if it is near any other magnetic materials. Hold it away from metal objects and other magnets to get an accurate reading.

Give each group a compass, and have them use it to determine north. Come to a class consensus about which way is north and identify any compasses that are "misbehaving," either with the red pointer pointing south or pointing in some random direction.

11. Label magnet poles

Hold up a magnet on a string and tell students,

When a permanent magnet hangs from a string so that it can turn freely, the north pole on the magnet will align toward Earth's North Pole. I can use a magnet to find the direction north. By hanging this magnet from a string, the north pole of the magnet will point in the direction north.

Hang a magnet on a short string from the edge of a table, making sure that it is not too close to any steel structure, such as a steel table leg. When it comes to rest, confirm that one side is aiming toward north as determined by the class compasses. Then remove the hanging magnet. Tell students,

> **TEACHING NOTE**
>
> If the red pointer points south, the compass has become reversed for some reason. See tips in Preparation Details for repairing compasses.

> **TEACHING NOTE**
>
> Metal desks can interfere with the compass readings. Encourage students to pick up compasses, and if needed, stand a foot away from their desk with the compass and magnet in the air to get a reading.

Part 1: Properties of Magnets

Your magnets have a north pole and a south pole. The north pole of your magnet will point toward the north, just as the north pole of my magnet did. Your job is to work in your groups to find the north pole and south pole of your magnet. Your group can have four pieces of string to hang the magnets and four pieces of tape to label the north side of each magnet when you find it. Remember that the poles are on the flat faces of these magnets.

Have Getters get one 20 cm length of string and a small piece of masking tape for each person in their group. Give students 3–5 minutes to label their magnets with the tape to indicate north.

12. Determine interaction

Continue the investigation of magnetic interaction. Tell students,

We've confirmed that magnets have two different poles. Can you figure out which poles attract and which poles repel?

Give students a few moments to test this with their magnets, then repeat the question.

➤ *Which poles attract and which poles repel?* [Two north poles repel, two south poles repel, but one south pole and one north pole attract.]

13. Confirm poles

Each group can use a compass to confirm the poles on the labeled magnets. If student magnets are correctly labeled, the south pole on their magnets should attract the colored north end of the compass needle. The pole labeled with the tape to represent "north" should repel the colored end of the compass needle.

14. Clean up

Have students remove the tape and strings so the next class can repeat the exploration. The strings can be reused from class to class. Have Getters return the materials to the materials station. Be sure to inventory the magnets—students like to hold onto them.

15. Review *kinetic energy*

Ask students if they saw any evidence of kinetic energy in class today. Any example of movement is an acceptable response, including magnets moving toward or away from each other (including the compass tip).

Students may also correctly identify that the movement of their own bodies was kinetic energy.

SCIENCE AND ENGINEERING PRACTICES

Planning and carrying out investigations

Analyzing and interpreting data

CROSSCUTTING CONCEPTS

Patterns

Cause and effect

TEACHING NOTE

Students might notice the implications of this fact: If the north end of the compass needle is attracted to south pole magnets, that means that the Earth's North Pole must actually be a magnetic south pole!

CROSSCUTTING CONCEPTS

Energy and matter

Electromagnetic Force Course—FOSS Next Generation

INVESTIGATION 2 – The Force of Magnetism

attract
compass
gravitational force
magnet
permanent magnet
pole
repel

EL NOTE

For students who need support, give them a few minutes to discuss their observations and inferences with a partner. You can also provide writing frames such as
Today we explored with ___.
We were trying to find out ___.
I observed that ___.
I already knew ___.
Now, I also know that ___.
I'm wondering about ___.

16. Record vocabulary
Give students a few moments to review and clarify the vocabulary developed in this part. Tell students that some of these words should be included in their response to the focus question. Ask students to update their vocabulary indexes if they haven't already done so.

17. Revisit the focus question
Students should return to the focus question.

➤ *What happens when magnets interact?*

Give students a few minutes to reflect on the data and write an answer to the question. Encourage them to use accurate vocabulary in their answers, and to use evidence from the activity to support their answers.

18. Assess progress: notebook entry
After students complete their responses to the focus question, collect a sample of notebooks from each class. The sample should give you a snapshot of the range of student understanding at this point in time.

What to Look For

- *Students explain that magnets can attract or repel; opposite poles attract, like poles repel.*

Plan to spend 15 minutes reviewing the selected student responses. Using *Embedded Assessment Notes* as a tool, review the responses, record any alternative concepts that are evident, and decide if any next-step strategies are required before moving forward.

19. Extend the investigation with homework
Encourage students to find out how magnets are used around the home and to use their imaginations to invent something new that uses magnets. They can draw a picture of their invention, write a short paragraph explaining what it does, and describe the real-world magnet(s) that inspired their idea.

Part 1: Properties of Magnets

WRAP-UP/WARM-UP

20. Review notebook entries

Give students a few minutes to review and share their notebook entries with a partner. Ask students to listen for the vocabulary words and to encourage their partner to add them where appropriate. Students can work together to add a diagram that shows how the concepts from this part are related.

INVESTIGATION 2 – The Force of Magnetism

FOSS Science Resources

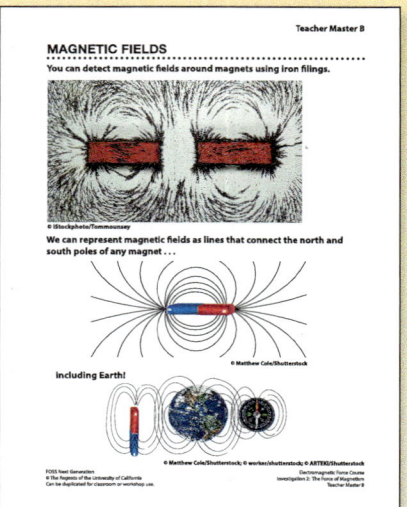

Teacher Master B

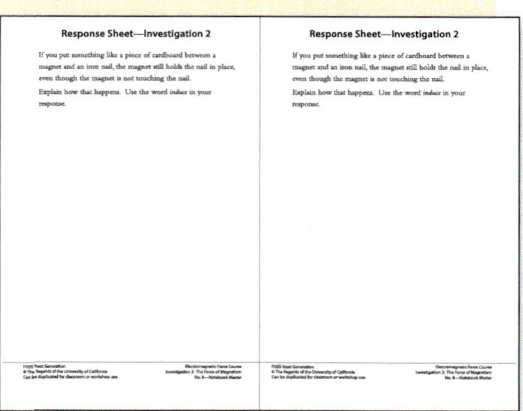

No. 8—Notebook Master

MATERIALS for
Part 2: Magnetic Fields

Provided equipment

For each student
- 1 *FOSS Science Resources: Electromagnetic Force*
  - "Magnetic Force"

For each group
- 4 Magnets, doughnut-shaped
- 2 Magnets, bar-shaped
- 4 Paper clips
- 1 Compass
- 1 Cardboard box
- • Iron filings
- 1 Paper plate, small
- 1 Zip bag, 1 L
- • Masking tape

For the class
- 1 Magnet, doughnut-shaped
- 1 Paper clip
- 1 String, 20–30 cm

Teacher-supplied items

For the class
- • Teaspoon, 1/4

FOSSweb resources

For each student
- 1 Notebook sheet 8, *Response Sheet—Investigation 2*

For the class
- • Video, *Magnetism*

For the teacher
- • Teacher master B, *Magnetic Fields*
- • *Embedded Assessment Notes*
- • Teaching slides, 2.2

Full Option Science System

Part 2: Magnetic Fields

GETTING READY for
Part 2: *Magnetic Fields*

Quick Start

Schedule	2 sessions active investigation 1 session reading
Preview	• Preview the FOSSweb Resources by Investigation for this part (such as printable masters, teaching slides, and online activities) • Preview the video: *Magnetism*, Step 17 • Preview the in-class reading: "Magnetic Force," Step 20 • Plan for homework: magnet questions, Step 24
Print or Copy	**For each student** • Notebook sheet 8 **For the teacher** • *Embedded Assessment Notes*
Prepare Material	• Set up iron filings **A** • Build magnet boxes **B** • Prepare for demonstration **C**
Plan for Assessment	• Review Step 19, "What to Look For" in the response sheet

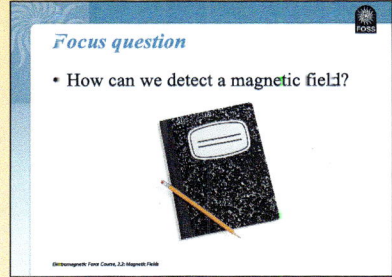

Teaching slides, 2.2

Electromagnetic Force Course—FOSS Next Generation

INVESTIGATION 2 – The Force of Magnetism

Preparation Details

A ▶ Set up iron filings
Put about a quarter teaspoon of iron filings on a small paper plate. Seal the paper plate in a 1 L zip bag. Make eight bags of filings.

You can place the plate of filings on top of a magnet, then gently shake the plate to see filings fall in line with the magnetic field. Or you can move a magnet below the plate, to see how the filings line up. It's best to keep the plates horizontal. If filings accidentally fall off the plate into the bag, turn the bag with the plate upside down and then very quickly flip the plate over, so that the filings land on top of the horizontal plate.

B ▶ Build magnet boxes
The cardboard magnet boxes are flat when they originally arrive in the kit. If you are the first to use the kit, assemble the boxes. Fold in the rectangle edges and insert the small tabs. The flap with the round edges will form the lid of the box. Place a piece of masking tape on the edge of the lid that will be reused throughout the day. The tape will seal the box during the activity and indicate which end of the box students should pry open. Label the outside of the box lids with numbers 1–8.

Practice using a magnet box. Tape two magnets inside one of the boxes, close the lid, and practice detecting the magnet locations with the detecting tools: paper clip, magnet, compass, and iron filings. You might want to keep this magnet box assembled to use for a demonstration in Step 9.

C ▶ Prepare for demonstration
Tie a paper clip to one end of a 20–30 cm length of string. Practice demonstrating induced magnetism with the floating paper clip, described in Step 5.

Part 2: Magnetic Fields

GUIDING *the Investigation*
Part 2: *Magnetic Fields*

FOCUS QUESTION

How can we detect a magnetic field?

SESSION 1

Students will . . .
- Investigate magnetism through materials (Steps 1–4)
- Develop a model of a magnetic field (Steps 5–7)
- Record the focus question (Step 8)
- Use mystery boxes to detect magnets by their magnetic fields (Steps 9–13)

SESSION 2

Students will . . .
- Discuss mystery box findings and learn more about magnetic fields (Steps 14, 15)
- Improve their magnetic field models (Steps 16–19)

SESSION 3

Students will . . .
- Read about magnetic force (Steps 20, 21)
- Record vocabulary and answer the focus question (Steps 22, 23)
- Extend the investigation with homework and review notebook entries (Steps 24, 25)

SESSION 1 45–50 minutes

1. **Investigate magnetism through materials**

   Suggest that students work again with their magnets and test objects to find out more about how magnets interact with materials. Introduce a challenge to students.

   ➤ *Can **magnetism** attract and repel through materials?*

2. **Begin the exploration**

   Ask Getters to get a doughnut-shaped magnet and a paper clip for each student. Inform students that paper clips are made of steel. Let students begin the investigation. Students may want to test magnetism through their books, desk, chair, shirt, and so on.

   Visit students as they work, and ask questions like these.

   ➤ *Can magnets attract steel (paper clips) through all kinds of materials?*

   ➤ *Can a magnet attract a paper clip through a piece of cardboard, through a desk, or through cloth?*

   ➤ *Can a magnet attract a paper clip through the air?*

Electromagnetic Force Course—FOSS Next Generation

INVESTIGATION 2 – The Force of Magnetism

3. **Introduce magnetic chain**

   If nobody has discovered this yet, ask students to make a magnetic chain of paper clips. Working in their group, they can use one magnet to pick up one paper clip, use that paper clip to pick up another paper clip, and so on. How long a paper-clip chain can they make using one magnet?

   Tell students,

   *When you make a paper-clip chain, you are **inducing magnetism** in the steel paper clips. To **induce** means to make something happen. You have turned a paper clip into a **temporary magnet**.*

   Students may want to use the temporary magnets (paper clips) to pick up other objects. Give them a few moments to explore the limitations in strength of these paper-clip magnets.

   As students are working, visit groups and offer support by asking,

   ➤ *Does the paper clip need to be touching the magnet to be a temporary magnet?*

   ➤ *How long will the temporary magnetism last?*

4. **Discuss results**

   Give groups a few minutes to discuss findings about whether magnetism can work through different materials. Ask a Reporter from each group to share an observation with the class. Students should discover that magnets can attract a piece of steel right through paper, cloth, a thin piece of cardboard, a book cover, and plastic, maybe even through a desk, as well as through air. Students may also report that if the material is too thick, the magnet will not attract the steel.

5. **Develop a model**

   Show students your paper clip on a string. Tape the free end of the string to the surface of a desk. Carefully lift a chair with steel legs onto the desk and stick a magnet on the leg. Stick the paper clip on the magnet. Slowly move the chair away until the paper clip is suspended in air.

   Ask students to talk in their groups to answer this question.

   ➤ *What keeps the paper clip suspended in air?*

   Students should work individually to make a preliminary model in their notebooks to explain the phenomenon. Encourage them to include a diagram with labels. They should label the page "Chair Demonstration" for later reference.

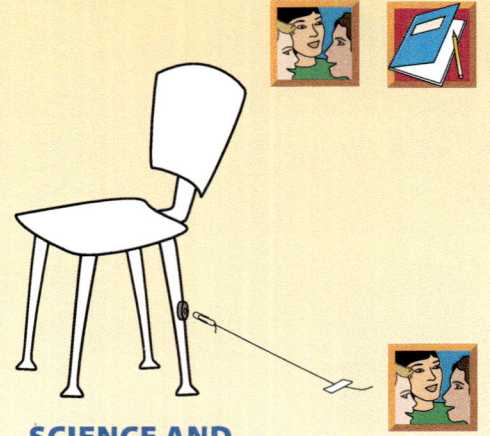

SCIENCE AND ENGINEERING PRACTICES

Developing and using models

Analyzing and interpreting data

Constructing explanations

TEACHING NOTE

Go to FOSSweb for Teacher Resources and look for the Science and Engineering Practices chapter for details on how to engage students with the practice of developing and using models.

Part 2: Magnetic Fields

Have students share their models with the rest of their group and revise their diagrams as needed. You may also choose to ask students to come up with a group model drawn on large paper.

6. **Introduce** *magnetic field*

   As a class, discuss the behavior of the paper clip. The group models can be used as artifacts for the discussion of students' ideas for the behavior of the paper clip. Students will probably say the magnet attracts the paper clip through the air. At that point, introduce a new term.

   Magnets can attract iron from a distance and through materials, because magnets are surrounded by an invisible **magnetic field** *that extends out from their poles. This force field is a region where the magnetic forces can be observed or detected. The magnet exerts a force that acts right through wood, paper, plastic, and air.*

7. **Explain the demonstration**

   Ask,

   ➤ *How would you represent the magnetic field in your models?*

   Give students a moment to discuss and add to their models. If necessary, add these ideas.

   The paper clip on a string is suspended in the air close to a magnet. The magnetic field around the magnet interacts with the steel paper clip, turning the clip into a temporary magnet. The paper clip seems to hang in the air.

   The force produced by gravity is pulling the paper clip down to Earth. The magnetic force acts to oppose the force of gravity. The net force keeps the clip in the air.

8. **Focus question: How can we detect a magnetic field?**

   Tell students that today's activity will focus on the magnetic field. Introduce the focus question and write or project it on the board.

   ➤ *How can we detect a magnetic field?*

   Have students record the focus question on the next page in their science notebooks.

9. **Set up magnet detection challenge**

   Show students one of the magnet boxes. Tell them there are two small bar magnets taped someplace inside. Ask,

   ➤ *Can you figure out where magnets are taped in a box without looking inside?*

Electromagnetic Force Course—FOSS Next Generation

INVESTIGATION 2 – The Force of Magnetism

10. **Introduce detecting materials**

    Ask students to suggest materials that might be used as magnet detectors. Then show them the materials you have assembled: compasses, bags of iron filings, paper clips, and doughnut-shaped magnets.

    Caution students to hold the bagged plate of iron filings horizontal to keep the iron filings on the plate. Show students how to replace the filings as needed by inverting the plate and then quickly flipping it over.

11. **Describe preparation of the magnet boxes**

    Give construction instructions.

    a. Each group will create a hidden arrangement of magnets, using
        - the box with their group's number on it,
        - two bar magnets, and
        - masking tape.
    b. Two team members will open the box and tape two magnets inside without letting the other team members see where the magnets are.
    c. The other team members will use one or more detecting devices to find the magnets and figure out how they are oriented.
    d. Remove tape carefully so the boxes are not damaged when it is time to open them and rearrange the magnets for the next test.
    e. No drawing on the boxes! Recording will be done on paper.

12. **Begin detecting**

    Have Getters get the box with their group's number and the other materials. Give groups 10–15 minutes to work. They should take turns setting up the box with hidden magnets and then using the different detecting materials to locate the magnets.

    Instruct students to record diagrams in their notebooks to show what they think the mystery boxes look like inside. Encourage students to use each available tool (iron filings, paper clip, compass, doughnut-shaped magnet) to detect and to modify their map as they gather new evidence, and to record notes about these tools in their notebook.

13. **Return detecting devices**

    When each pair of students has had a chance to detect at least once, have Getters return the detecting devices, boxes, and magnets to the materials station.

> **TEACHING NOTE**
>
> Students should use the two bar magnets in the box, and the doughnut-shaped magnet as a detector.

SCIENCE AND ENGINEERING PRACTICES

Planning and carrying out investigations

Analyzing and interpreting data

Engaging in argument from evidence

CROSSCUTTING CONCEPTS

Patterns

Cause and effect

SESSION 2   45–50 minutes

Part 2: Magnetic Fields

14. Discuss magnet detectors

Ask students to take a few minutes with their groups to discuss which object or material was the best magnet detector and why. Encourage students to think of the detectors in terms of their strengths and limitations. Ask,

> *What were some strengths and limitations of each detector?* [Paper clips showed location of magnets, but not pole; filings showed the area and shape of magnets and some circles around the magnets; magnets could show location and pole of other magnets; compass could show location and pole of magnets (but could be hard to interpret if magnets were near to each other).]

> *Do you think the compass has iron in it? Why do you think so?* [The needle must be made of iron, because it is affected by magnetic fields.]

> *Why do you think the filings made those interesting patterns?* [They are made of iron so they are influenced by the magnetic field.]

15. Confirm magnetic fields

Ask students in more detail about their experience using the metal filings to detect magnets. Encourage them to describe the patterns that they saw that allowed them to detect magnets. They might describe lines, curves, or circles. Tell students,

Iron filings are very small pieces of iron, so they move very easily in response to magnetic forces. As a result, the patterns they form help us identify magnetic fields. A magnetic field is invisible, but we can make inferences about its characteristics by looking at the pattern of the iron filings.

Project teacher master B, *Magnetic Fields*. Point out the photograph at the top, which uses bar magnets like the ones they put in the boxes. Confirm that with a bar magnet, north is at one end of the bar and south is at the other.

Direct attention to the diagram just below the photo, which shows how physicists represent magnetic fields in drawings. Point out how the lines connect between the north and south poles in ever-larger circles. The lines that appear to stick out from the ends of the poles would also connect if the diagram were much larger.

Give students a moment to consider the three diagrams at the bottom of the page, and to consider Earth's magnetic field. Point out that the diagrams are not to scale. Ask,

> *What do the lines surrounding each magnetic object represent?* [The magnetic field of that object.]

SCIENCE AND ENGINEERING PRACTICES
Developing and using models

CROSSCUTTING CONCEPTS
Patterns
Systems and system models

Electromagnetic Force Course—FOSS Next Generation

INVESTIGATION 2 – The Force of Magnetism

SCIENCE AND ENGINEERING PRACTICES
Developing and using models
Constructing explanations

➤ *What similarities and patterns do you notice?* [Curved lines connect the north and south poles of each object.]

16. Return to the model
Ask students to return to the "Chair Demonstration" notebook entry where they drew a model. If students' paper-clip/chair models did not include lines representing fields, encourage them to revise their drawings at this time. Students can refer to teacher master B as they revise their models.

17. View video: *Magnetism*
Ask students to think about their model as they watch a brief video summarizing what they've learned so far about magnets and magnetic fields.

Play the Magnetism video chapter in "Resources by Investigation."

- Chapter 2: "Basic Characteristics of Magnets and Magnetism" (duration 4.5 minutes)

At the end of the video, give students a moment to add any details to their model as needed.

18. Record ideas
Distribute a copy of notebook sheet 8, *Response Sheet—Investigation 2*, to each student. Have students work on the sheet individually.

19. Assess progress: response sheet
Collect a sample of the response sheets to consider students' ability to explain magnetic fields.

What to Look For

- *Students explain that magnetic fields are invisible regions (lines) extending out from and around magnets.*
- *Students explain that a magnetic field induces magnetism in iron to turn it into a temporary magnet, which is attracted to the magnet.*
- *Students write that a magnetic field can act through most materials.*

Plan to spend 15 minutes reviewing the selected student responses. Using *Embedded Assessment Notes* as a tool, review the responses, record any alternative concepts that are evident, and decide if any next-step strategies are required before moving forward.

After your review, return the response sheets to students to be taped or glued into their science notebooks.

Part 2: Magnetic Fields

SESSION 3 45–50 minutes

READING *in Science Resources*

20. Read "Magnetic Force"
Tell students that the article "Magnetic Force" will help them think about properties of magnets and magnetic fields. Distribute a copy of *FOSS Science Resources* to each student.

21. Use a reading comprehension strategy
Have students preview the text by discussing the images and diagrams with a partner. Discuss the structure of the text and suggest they set up their notebooks to take notes for each of the subtitles. Have them make each subtitle into a question they think will be answered in the text. For example, the first subtitle questions might be, "What are fields of force?" or "How do we know fields of force exist?"

Tell students to read the text independently, jotting down any unknown words or phrases, or questions they have along with their subheading notes.

When students finish reading, give them a moment to discuss any questions or difficulties they had with reading in their small groups. (For those who finish early, have them start writing their responses to the Think Questions.) Use the following guide to conduct a whole-class discussion.

FOSS Science Resources

ELA CONNECTION

These suggested strategies address the Common Core State Standards for ELA for literacy.

RST 4: Determine the meaning of symbols, key terms, and other domain-specific words and phrases.

RST 5: Analyze the structure an author uses to organize a text.

WHST 8: Gather relevant information from multiple print and digital sources.

RST 10: Read and comprehend science texts independently and proficiently.

SCIENCE AND ENGINEERING PRACTICES

Obtaining, evaluating, and communicating information

INVESTIGATION 2 – The Force of Magnetism

Connect to real life: Give students a moment to discuss any personal connections they've had using compasses. They might draw a model of a compass in their notebooks to explain how it works.

SCIENCE AND ENGINEERING PRACTICES
Developing and using models

Magnetic Force

The sky is overcast with thick clouds. A storm is coming in. You and your friends have been trying to find your way back to the ranger station for an hour.

Whose idea was it to go off the trail? That clump of rocks looks awfully familiar. You're pretty sure you are going in circles. If only you had brought a **compass** to show which way is north!

Fields of Force

When you are using a compass, the tiny magnet in the compass needle aligns with Earth's **magnetism** and helps you find your way. But closed in its plastic case, the needle never touches another magnet. How do magnets exert a force without touching?

Earth is a giant magnet with poles and a magnetic field that reaches far into space. A compass needle points north when it interacts with this planet-sized magnet.

Part 2: Magnetic Fields

It is similar to how a falling apple and Earth exert a force of gravity on each other. Both the apple and Earth have a gravitational force that extends from them because of their masses. It forms an invisible **gravitational field**. Like gravity, magnetism is another invisible force of nature. Magnetism extends out from a magnet into the surrounding space to form what is called a **magnetic field**.

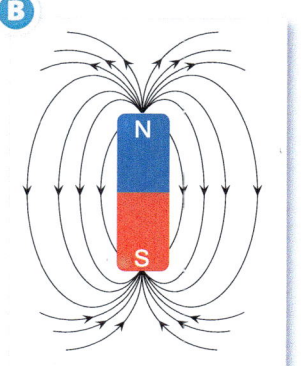

A field of magnetism extends out from every magnet. The magnetic force is strongest near the magnet's north and south poles.

Force of Attraction or Repulsion

You feel magnetic force when you try to separate two magnets that are stuck together. You also feel magnetic force when you push two magnets together and they push away from each other. Magnetic force makes magnets act the ways they do.

The magnets used in class are **permanent magnets**. They exhibit magnetic properties pretty much all the time. Every magnet has two different sides or ends called **poles**, the north pole and the south pole. A simple bar magnet has its two poles on opposite ends. A horseshoe magnet has a pole on each end of the horseshoe. The doughnut magnets you worked with have poles on the two flat sides.

What happens when you hold two magnets close to each other? They exert a force on each other, but will they **attract** or **repel**? It all depends on how the poles are oriented. Below are four pairs of bar magnets being held together. Which ones will push apart when they are released?

Magnets Held Together

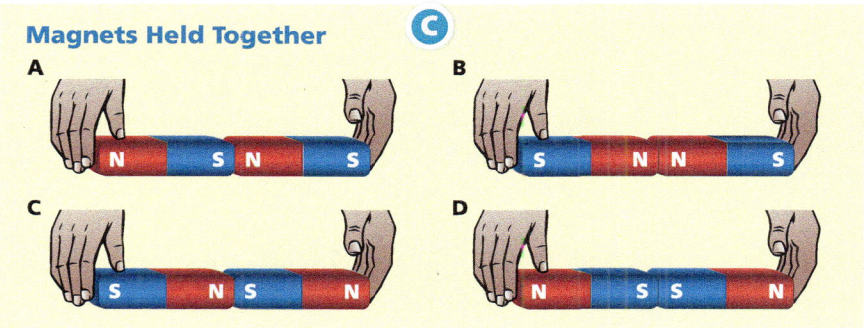

These pairs of magnets are held together in different configurations. What will happen when they are released?

Discuss reading strategy: Ask a volunteer to share his/her question and response for this section with the group. If they haven't noted the main idea in their notebooks yet, model how to summarize the important point here: *Gravity and magnetism are two of the invisible forces of the universe.*

Analyze diagrams: Pause for students to discuss what they notice and can infer from the lower set of diagrams.

➤ *What are they trying to explain?* [How magnets are held together in different configurations.]

➤ *What do the different colors and letters represent?* [Red with (N) indicates north pole; blue with (S) indicates south pole.]

ELA CONNECTION

These suggested strategies address the Common Core State Standards for ELA for literacy.

RST 2: Determine the central ideas or conclusions of a text; provide an accurate summary.

RST 7: Integrate quantitative or technical information expressed in words in a text with a version of that information expressed visually.

SCIENCE AND ENGINEERING PRACTICES

Developing and using models
Constructing explanations

INVESTIGATION 2 – The Force of Magnetism

Compare diagrams in the text: Have students compare their predictions with the diagrams here. Refer to Think Question 1 and have students come up with a general rule to record in their notebooks.

Develop vocabulary: Focus on the words in bold (temporary magnet and induced magnetism) and have students take turns explaining what these terms mean to a partner. These terms along with a definition and/or example should be in their notes.

Take note: Take a few minutes to have volunteers share examples from the classroom investigations and others they may have experienced.

ELA CONNECTION

These suggested strategies address the Common Core State Standards for ELA for literacy.

RST 9: Compare and contrast the information gained from experiments, simulations, video, or multimedia sources with that gained from reading a text on the same topic.

SL 6: Adapt speech to a variety of contexts and tasks.

L 6: Acquire and use academic and domain-specific words and phrases.

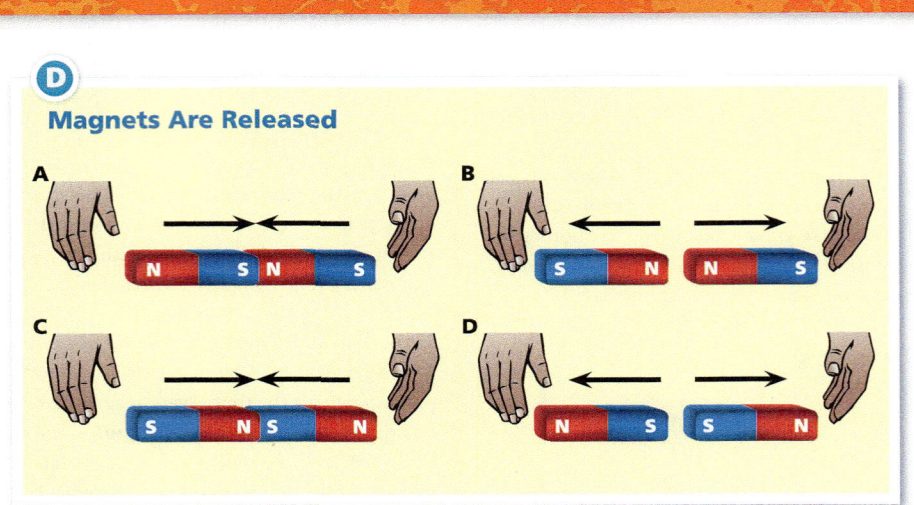

Magnets Are Released

Observe how the magnets move when they are not held together. Opposite poles pull together, or attract, and like poles push apart, or repel.

The diagram above shows what happens when the magnets are released. Two general rules apply here. Can you figure out what the rules are?

The two pairs of magnets on the left attract each other. The two pairs of magnets on the right repel each other. Two north poles always repel each other. Two south poles always repel each other. We can state a general rule: like poles repel.

A north pole and a south pole always attract each other. It does not matter which magnet has the north pole and which has the south pole. We can state another general rule: opposite poles attract.

How Magnets Stick to Iron

If opposite poles attract, why does a magnet stick to a piece of iron, like an iron nail, that is not a permanent magnet? Remember that magnetism extends out from a magnet in an invisible area called a magnetic field. When a magnet comes close to a piece of iron, such as an iron nail, the magnetic field interacts with the iron in the nail. The nail becomes a **temporary magnet**. The end of the nail becomes one pole of a magnet. The magnet then sticks to the temporary magnet.

So magnets do not really stick to iron. Magnets stick to other magnets, even if they are temporary. The temporary magnetism in the iron is called **induced magnetism**. Induced magnetism happens only when a magnet is nearby.

Take Note

What are some examples of induced magnetism you observed in class?

Investigation 2: The Force of Magnetism

Full Option Science System

Part 2: Magnetic Fields

Particle Properties

To understand why some materials have induced magnetism and others do not, we have to explore the properties of magnets at the **particle** level. That means at the level of atoms and molecules. We can start to think about particles by considering what happens when a bar magnet breaks. Do you have a magnet with just one pole?

No, both pieces still have a north pole and a south pole. The same is true for all other magnets. No matter how many pieces you cut a magnet into, each piece still has a north pole and a south pole.

Each magnet piece has poles lined up the same way. If you did this a million million times, until you had the tiniest particle of the magnet that was still a magnet, you would see that each particle has poles lined up the same way.

This property defines a permanent magnet. Each particle has properties of magnetism. As

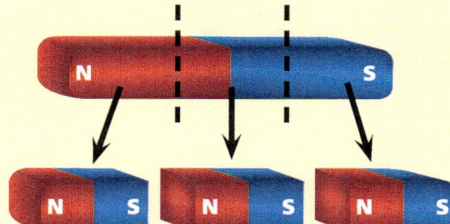

Magnets Cut Into Pieces

Cut a long bar magnet into three pieces. Each piece has a north pole and a south pole.

Particles of a permanent magnet (not shown to scale)

Even at the particle level, a magnet is still a magnet. Each atom of a magnet has a magnetic field and poles lined up in the same orientation.

Discuss reading strategy: Call on a few volunteers to share the question they formed from this subtitle and the answers they found from the text. If needed, guide students through the process of finding the main idea of this section. Have them discuss how the model is used to explain the concept of induced magnetism.

SCIENCE AND ENGINEERING PRACTICES
Developing and using models

ELA CONNECTION

This suggested strategy addresses the Common Core State Standards for ELA for literacy.

RST 2: Determine the central ideas or conclusions of a text; provide an accurate summary.

Electromagnetic Force Course—FOSS Next Generation

INVESTIGATION 2 – The Force of Magnetism

Analyze diagrams: Have students compare and contrast the diagrams in these models.

➤ *What is the same and different about the two kinds of particles outside a strong magnetic field and in a strong magnetic field?* [Outside a magnetic field, the particles of each substance are oriented in any direction (randomly). Inside a magnetic field, the plastic particles stay random but the iron particles line up.]

➤ *How does this model relate to phenomena they have observed?* [When iron objects are placed in a magnetic field (like a paper clip next to a magnet), they can become magnetized and act as a temporary magnet. Plastic materials are unaffected.]

SCIENCE AND ENGINEERING PRACTICES
Developing and using models

ELA CONNECTION

This suggested strategy addresses the Common Core State Standards for ELA for literacy.

RST 7: Integrate quantitative or technical information expressed in words in a text with a version of that information expressed visually.

---

the particles line up, each tiny magnetic field adds itself to form one big magnetic field.

Nonmagnetic Materials

All nonmagnets can be split into two general categories, magnetic materials and nonmagnetic materials. Magnetic materials, such as the elements iron, nickel, and cobalt, have magnetic properties at the particle level.

But the particles are not all aligned the same way. Those particles can line up when they are in a magnetic field. The materials become a temporary (induced) magnet.

Nonmagnetic materials, like plastic, do not have magnetic properties at the particle level. Those particles are not affected when they are in a magnetic field.

Materials outside a Strong Magnetic Field

The iron and plastic particles are oriented in different directions.

Materials inside a Strong Magnetic Field

The iron particles orient to the magnetic field and form a temporary magnet. The plastic particles do not change.

Investigation 2: The Force of Magnetism 23

Part 2: Magnetic Fields

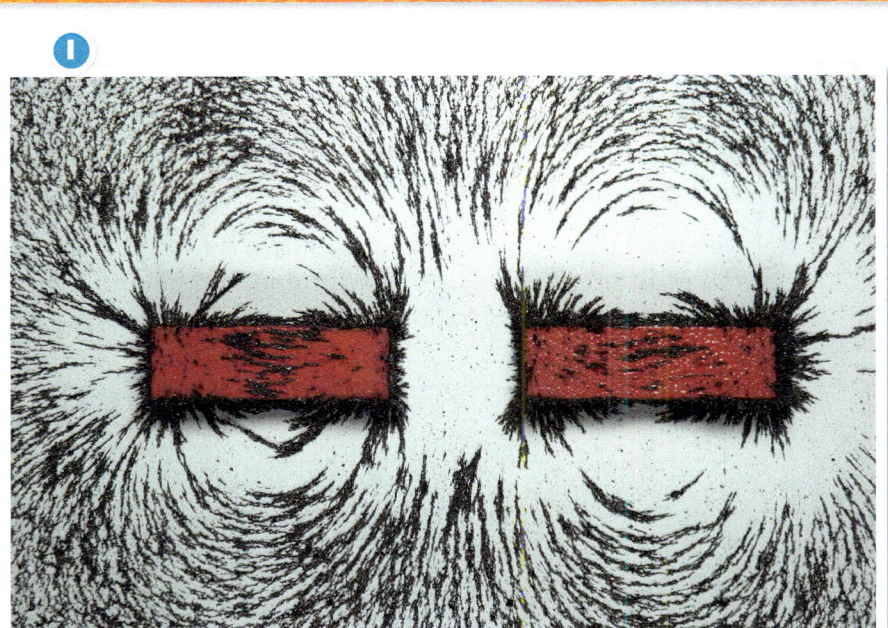

Iron filings spread around a magnet will form a pattern that shows the shape of the magnet's magnetic field.

If you bring a strong magnetic field close to a magnetic material, the particles in the material will line up with the magnetic field. They create weak temporary magnets. Particles in the nonmagnetic materials will not line up. So even the strongest magnet cannot attract or repel a material like plastic or wood.

Think Questions

1. What rules determine whether magnets will attract or repel each other?
2. How can a magnet attract or repel another magnet even if they are not touching?
3. If you bring the south pole of a magnet close to the head of an iron nail, what changes will happen to the iron particles?

Analyze image: Give students a moment to discuss the photograph and to share any other observations they have made that indicate the presence of a magnetic field.

▶ *How does this image relate to the models you've seen using lines to represent the magnetic field?* [The iron filings line up like the lines in models.]

Think Questions:
Have students discuss the last two Think Questions in their small groups, and then call on Reporters for each group to share their groups' responses.

▶ *What rules determine whether magnets will attract or repel each other?* [Opposite poles attract each other, and like poles repel each other.]

▶ *How can a magnet attract or repel another magnet even if they are not touching?* [A magnetic field extends out from a magnet. The magnetic force extends through the field.]

▶ *If you bring the south pole of a magnet close to the head of an iron nail, what changes will happen to the iron particles?* [The iron particles are like tiny magnets. The particles will line up when they are within a strong enough magnetic field. The iron particles will have their north poles attracted to the south pole of the nearby magnet. The iron nail becomes a temporary magnet.]

Electromagnetic Force Course—FOSS Next Generation

INVESTIGATION 2 – The Force of Magnetism

induced magnetism
magnetic field
magnetism
temporary magnet

ELA CONNECTION

This suggested strategy addresses the Common Core State Standards for ELA for literacy.

L 5: Demonstrate understanding of word relationships and nuances in word meaning.

EL NOTE

For students who need support, give them a few minutes to discuss the question before writing. You can also provide writing frames such as
A magnetic field is ___.
We observed ___.
The diagram shows ___.

SCIENCE AND ENGINEERING PRACTICES

Asking questions

22. Record vocabulary

Give students a few moments to review and clarify the vocabulary developed in this investigation. Have students add diagrams and explanations of these terms in their notebooks, and to update their indexes if they haven't done so already. Students can also add to their existing definition of *force*.

If students need more support, have them make a concept definition map for *magnetism*. They should include all the terms in bold from the reading. See example.

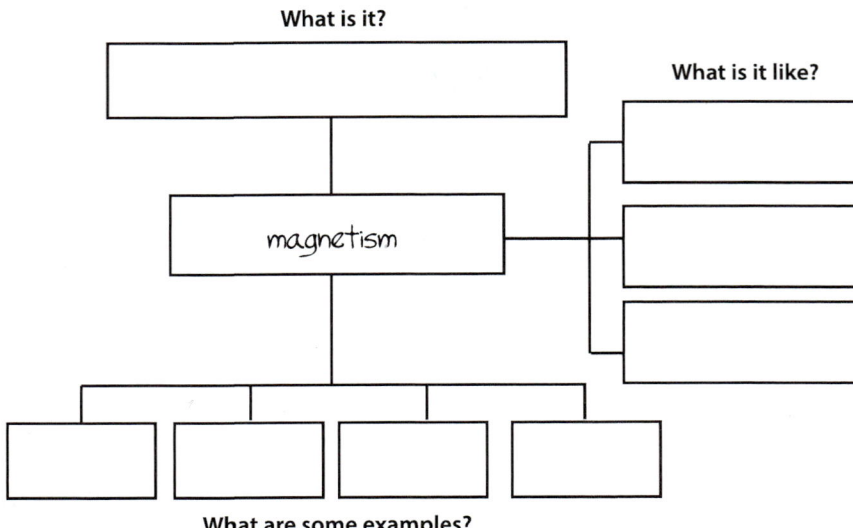

23. Answer the focus question

Have students review the focus question.

➤ *How can we detect a magnetic field?*

Give students a few minutes to write an answer to the focus question. Encourage them to think about multiple examples from the investigation and to use diagrams where appropriate.

24. Extend the investigation with homework

What questions do students have about magnets, magnetic fields, and magnetic force? Have students write a list of ten or more questions that could be answered in the rest of the investigation or later researched online.

Part 2: Magnetic Fields

WRAP-UP/WARM-UP

25. Review notebook entries
Ask students to return to the notebook entry where they drew their model of the "Chair Demonstration." Give students a few minutes to share responses with someone from a different group. Encourage them to give each other constructive feedback and to revise and/or add ideas to their responses under a line of learning.

SCIENCE AND ENGINEERING PRACTICES
Obtaining, evaluating, and communicating information

INVESTIGATION 2 – The Force of Magnetism

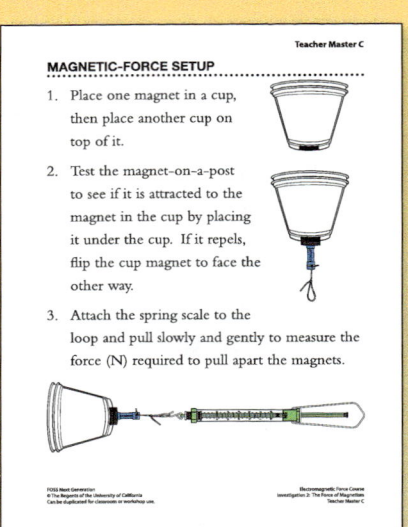
Teacher Master C

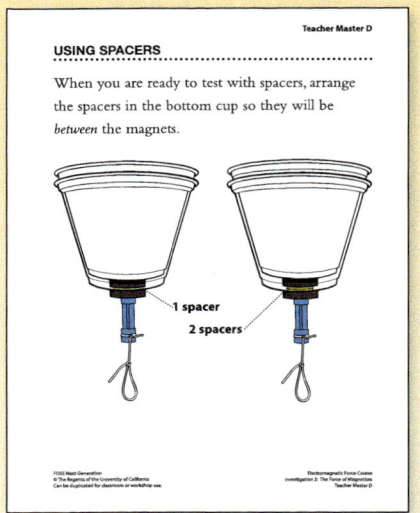
Teacher Master D

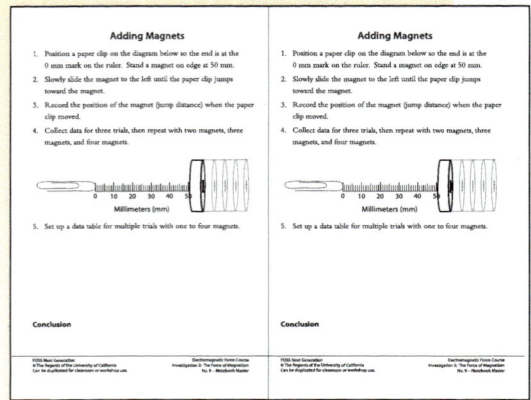
No. 9—Notebook Master

MATERIALS for
Part 3: *Force over Distance*

Provided equipment
For each group
- 1 Spring scale
- 2 Plastic cups
- 4 Magnets, doughnut-shaped
- 1 Magnet-on-a-post
- 1 String, 20 cm
- 3 Spacers
- 1 Paper clip

Teacher-supplied items
For each group
- 1–2 Computers or tablets with Internet access
- 1 Calculator (optional)

For the class
- 1 Scissors
- Chart paper

FOSSweb resources
For each student
- 1 Notebook sheet 9, *Adding Magnets*
- 1 *Investigation 2 I-Check*

For the class
- Online activity, "Adding Magnetic Fields"

For the teacher
- Teacher master C, *Magnetic-Force Setup*
- Teacher master D, *Using Spacers*
- *Performance Assessment Checklist*
- *Assessment Record*
- Teaching slides, 2.3

Full Option Science System

Part 3: Force over Distance

GETTING READY for
Part 3: Force over Distance

Quick Start

Schedule	• Computers with Internet access, one for each group or pair of students 2 sessions active investigation 1 session review 1–2 sessions assessment and next steps
Preview	• Preview the FOSSweb Resources by Investigation for this part (such as printable masters, teaching slides, and online activities) • Test the online activity: "Adding Magnetic Fields," Step 21 • Plan for homework: magnet testing, Step 28
Print or Copy	**For each student** • Notebook sheet 9 • *Investigation 2 I-Check*, or schedule it on FOSSweb **For the teacher** • *Performance Assessment Checklist*
Prepare Material	• Prepare magnets-on-a-post **A**
Plan for Assessment	• Review Step 14, "What to Look For" in the performance assessment • Plan for benchmark assessment, Step 29

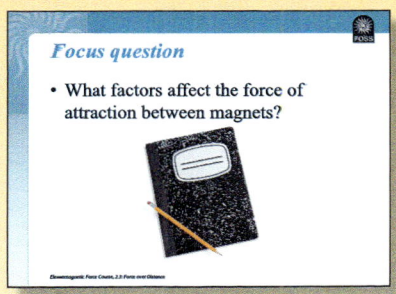

Teaching slides, 2.3

Preparation Details

A Prepare magnets-on-a-post

The magnets-on-a-post need a string attached to them so the spring scale can hook onto them. Cut a section of string about 20 cm long, and tie one end around the ridge on the end of the post. Tie a loop in the other end. Review teacher master C and practice the setup that students will use in the first session.

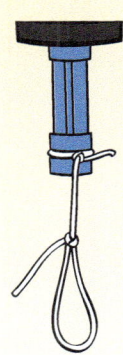

Electromagnetic Force Course—FOSS Next Generation

INVESTIGATION 2 – The Force of Magnetism

FOCUS QUESTION

What factors affect the force of attraction between magnets?

GUIDING the Investigation
Part 3: *Force over Distance*

SESSION 1
Students will . . .
- Learn about potential energy and record the focus question (Steps 1, 2)
- Test force between magnets at various distances (Steps 3–9)
- Discuss findings as a class (Step 10)

SESSION 2
Students will . . .
- Think about how adding magnets may affect force (Step 11)
- Test magnetic force when magnets are added to a system (Steps 12–15)

SESSION 3
Students will . . .
- Consider concepts of energy and force (Step 16)
- Have a sense-making discussion about distance and force fields (Steps 17–19)
- Test predictions using an online activity (Steps 20–23)
- Record vocabulary and revisit the focus question (Steps 24, 25)
- Review notebook entries and answer the guiding question (Steps 26, 27)
- Extend the investigation with homework (Step 28)

SESSIONS 4–5
Students will . . .
- Demonstrate understanding by responding to the *Investigation 2 I-Check* (Step 29)
- Review I-Check items through next-step strategies (Step 30)

SESSION 1   45–50 minutes

1. **Introduce** *potential energy*
   Review how magnets interact at a distance.

   ➤ *What happens when a magnet comes close to another magnet?* [The magnets either attract or repel, depending on orientation.]

   ➤ *What is a magnetic field?* [The region around the magnet where the magnetic force can be detected.]

   ➤ *What is a force?* [A push or a pull.]

   Tell students,

   You can't see the magnetic field, but you can feel it with another magnet or piece of iron. When two magnets come close to one another, you can feel them push or pull each other. The push or pull you feel is a force, the force of magnetism.

EL NOTE

Demonstrate with two magnets as you explain, and/or make a diagram on chart paper or the word wall.

Part 3: Force over Distance

When two magnets repel each other, the force of magnetic repulsion pushes the magnets apart. When two magnets attract each other, the force of magnetic attraction pulls the magnets together. That motion indicates kinetic energy.

When a magnetic object is in a magnetic field, the force exerted on the magnetic object has the potential to make it move. The amount of that potential is magnetic **potential energy**.

CROSSCUTTING CONCEPTS
Energy and matter

2. **Focus question: What factors affect the force of attraction between magnets?**
   Write or project the focus question on the board.

   ➤ *What factors affect the force of attraction between magnets?*

   Have students open their science notebooks to a new page and write the focus question at the top.

3. ### Introduce equipment
   Tell students that you have some equipment that will help them answer the focus question. They will use the equipment to put space between two magnets and to see how that affects the force of attraction between them. Project teacher master C, *Magnetic-Force Setup*, and hold up the equipment as you demonstrate how to set up the cup-and-magnets system, how to attach a spring scale, and how to apply force (pull) slowly.

4. ### Discuss how to measure the force
   Tell students,

   Now I'd like you to work in your groups to carefully determine the amount of force (N) needed to break the force of attraction between magnets.

   ➤ *How many newtons does it take to break the force between two magnets?*

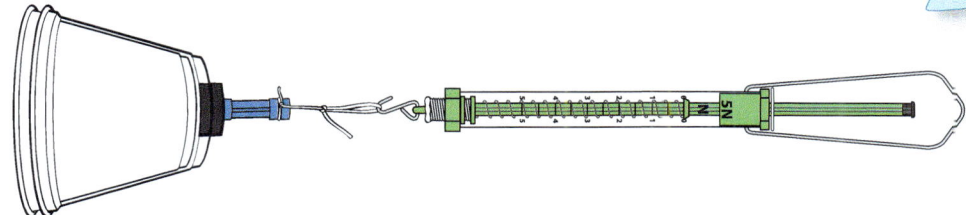

TEACHING NOTE

If students have difficulty setting up this system in a horizontal plane, they can do it vertically. However, this adds an additional force, gravity, in the downward direction, and you may want to bring that force into the resulting discussion.

Tell students that when they pull to break the force, they must pull extremely slowly—no yanking on the system. Otherwise they will not be able to make an accurate measurement of force.

Groups should test the initial setup, without any spacers in place. Have students test the equipment three or four times to measure the force (N) required to pull the magnets apart.

Electromagnetic Force Course—FOSS Next Generation

181

INVESTIGATION 2 – The Force of Magnetism

5. **Share results**

   Ask Reporters to report their group's results. Expect some variation in the measurements. Ask,

   ➤ *How can you explain the different results?* [Magnets differ in strength, spring scales may not all be exactly the same, techniques vary, etc.]

6. **Introduce spacers**

   Confirm that every group determined the number of newtons needed to break the force of attraction between their two magnets, and review the possible reasons for variation among groups. Ask,

   ➤ *What do you think will happen to the force of attraction between your two magnets if you put some distance between the magnets? Do you think the force will get stronger, weaker, or stay the same?*

   Ask students to write a prediction in their notebooks. You could provide these sentence frames for students to complete.

   - When I increase the distance between the magnets, the force will _____.
   - I think this will happen because _____.

7. **Distribute spacers**

   Show students the plastic spacers that will be used to separate the magnets by a small distance. Give each group three spacers. Project teacher master D, *Using Spacers*, and show the class how to place a spacer in the cup under the cup magnet so it will be trapped between magnets when students assemble the system.

8. **Develop a data table**

   Have students create a data table in their notebooks that will allow them to record the force needed over multiple trials with 0, 1, 2, and 3 spacers. If they need help, you might draw something like this on the board. The data below is sample data. Your students' data may or may not be similar.

Spacers	Trial 1 force (N)	Trial 2 force (N)	Trial 3 force (N)	Average force (N)
0	0.8	0.8	0.9	0.83
1	0.6	0.7	0.7	0.67
2	0.6	0.6	0.7	0.63
3	0.5	0.5	0.5	0.5

> **TEACHING NOTE**
>
> The force is extremely small as spacers are added—less than 0.5 N. Students must pull slowly and watch the spring scale closely to collect data. For an added challenge, you can ask students to test 0, 1, and 3 spacers, then make predictions about 2 spacers based on the patterns, before testing to confirm their ideas.

Part 3: Force over Distance

Tell students that as they work, they should look for patterns in the data and record an initial answer to the focus question.

9. **Clean up**
When the groups have completed their data collection and recording, have them disassemble the equipment. Have Getters return everything to the materials station.

Remind groups to record an initial response to the focus question based on their discussion about patterns they see in the data.

10. **Discuss the force and distance relationship**
Ask the Recorder from one group to share the group's data and discuss what it shows about the force of magnetism. Have other groups share their data and discuss similarities and differences. Ask students to share their initial answers to the focus question.

➤ *What happens to the force of attraction between two magnets as the distance between them changes?* [The force of attraction decreases as the magnets get farther apart.]

➤ *What is the relationship between the distance separating two magnets and the force of attraction between them?* [The greater the distance, the weaker the force; or the closer magnets are, the stronger the force between them.]

Point out the relationship between distance and force field. The magnetic field extends out from the magnet. If they increase the distance from the magnet, the force is smaller. The magnet still exerts a force, but the effect of the field's force is not measurable.

SESSION 2   45–50 minutes

11. **Review findings**
Ask students to review their notebook entries as you discuss how magnets interact at a distance.

➤ *What happens when a magnet comes close to another magnet?* [The magnets either attract or repel, depending on orientation.]

➤ *What is the relationship between the distance separating two magnets and the force of attraction between them?* [The greater the distance, the weaker the force; or the closer magnets are, the stronger the force between them.]

Ask three new questions, which students will explore next.

➤ *What happens to the force of attraction when you add more magnets?*

➤ *If you put two magnets together, does the force double?*

➤ *If you put two magnets together, what happens to the magnetic field?*

SCIENCE AND ENGINEERING PRACTICES
Planning and carrying out investigations

CROSSCUTTING CONCEPTS
Patterns

TEACHING NOTE
If students are stuck, suggest a sentence frame: "The (more/less) the distance between magnets, the (more/less) the force between them."

Electromagnetic Force Course—FOSS Next Generation

INVESTIGATION 2 – The Force of Magnetism

MATH CONNECTION

This supports Common Core State Standards for Math 7.NS 1.

SCIENCE AND ENGINEERING PRACTICES

Planning and carrying out investigations

Using mathematics and computational thinking

12. Conduct new experiments

Tell students that they are going to test the force of attraction by using multiple magnets and a paper clip. Distribute notebook sheet 9, *Adding Magnets*, and review the setup. Show students how they can position their paper clip and magnets as indicated by the dotted lines. This will help them remember the procedure.

Students will place a paper clip at the 0 end of the printed ruler, making sure it is lined up exactly. Starting at the other end of the ruler, they will slowly slide a magnet standing on edge toward the paper clip.

Ask,

➤ *What will happen when the magnet comes close to the paper clip?* [The clip will move toward the magnet.]

➤ *Why will the paper clip move?* [The clip is affected by the magnetic field. The magnetic force of the magnet will pull the clip toward the magnet.]

Point out that position is an important component of this experiment. Ask,

➤ *What is the kind of energy that is based on an object's position?* [Potential energy.]

Tell students that they will discuss potential energy again after the experiment.

Explain that students should collect data using one magnet, two magnets, three magnets, and four magnets. They need at least two trials for each magnetic arrangement. Students should create their own data table on notebook sheet 9 or in their notebooks. A sample data table is shown here. Your students' data may or may not be similar. Let students begin testing.

Magnets	Trial 1 jump distance (mm)	Trial 2 jump distance (mm)	Trial 3 jump distance (mm)	Average jump distance (mm)
1	17	17.5	19.5	18
2	30.5	29.5	24.5	28.2
3	32.5	31	33.5	32.3
4	34	35.5	36	35.2

Part 3: Force over Distance

13. Develop new model
As each group completes their data collection, have them turn to a new notebook page and label it "Multiple Magnets." Students should work as a group to draw a model of what happens to magnetic fields when multiple magnets are added together. Groups should refer to their "Chair Demonstration" models as they discuss what to include and how to represent concepts.

14. Assess progress: performance assessment
In this investigation, students use experimental data to develop a model for how magnetic fields interact. Listen to the group discussions and observe how students work together to assess students' three-dimensional learning. Note student progress on the *Performance Assessment Checklist*.

What to Look For

- Students use precision in measuring and recording jump distance and calculating averages. (Planning and carrying out investigations; using mathematics and computational thinking.)
- Students discuss patterns in the data and draw conclusions about how magnetic fields must be additive, then incorporate this information into their models. (Developing and using models; analyzing and interpreting data; PS2.B: Types of interactions; patterns; systems and system models.)

15. Clean up
When the groups have completed their data collection and recording, have them disassemble the equipment. Have Getters return everything to the materials station. Remember to inventory the magnets.

SCIENCE AND ENGINEERING PRACTICES

Developing and using models

Planning and carrying out investigations

Analyzing and interpreting data

Using mathematics and computational thinking

DISCIPLINARY CORE IDEAS

PS2.B: Types of interactions

CROSSCUTTING CONCEPTS

Patterns

Systems and system models

SESSION 3 45–50 minutes

16. Discuss net force and energy
Ask students to review their notebook entries as they discuss the system used in session 2 in terms of net force and energy.

➤ *What force was acting to prevent the paper clip from moving?* [Friction.]

➤ *Why did the clip eventually move?* [When the magnetic force was greater than the force of friction, the net force caused the clip to move toward the magnet.]

➤ *Is there any evidence of kinetic energy?* [When the clip moved, it had kinetic energy.]

➤ *Is there any evidence of potential energy?* [The fact that the paper clip eventually moved indicates that it had potential energy based on its position.]

CROSSCUTTING CONCEPTS

Energy and matter

INVESTIGATION 2 – The Force of Magnetism

TEACHING NOTE

Refer to the Sense-Making Discussions for Three-Dimensional Learning chapter in Teacher Resources on FOSSweb for more information about how to facilitate this with students.

SCIENCE AND ENGINEERING PRACTICES

Analyzing and interpreting data

Using mathematics and computational thinking

MATH CONNECTION

This supports Common Core State Standards for Math 6.RP 3 and 7.RP 2.

SCIENCE AND ENGINEERING PRACTICES

Constructing explanations

CROSSCUTTING CONCEPTS

Patterns

17. **Have a sense-making discusion**

   After students review what they observed in terms of net force and energy, gather the class for a sense-making discussion, in a circle if possible. Have students take their notebooks to the circle. Review class norms for discussion, and encourage students to build on each others' ideas and to ask clarifying questions of each other. Ask the Recorder from one group to share the group's data on chart paper so the entire class can see. Discuss what it shows about how magnetic fields add together to affect the force of magnetism. Have other groups share their data and discuss patterns they notice. Ask students to summarize their findings.

   ➤ *What happened to the jump distance that the paper clip moved when you added more magnets?* [It increased significantly between one magnet and two magnets, less so when we added a third or fourth magnet.]

   ➤ *What happened to the force of attraction when you added more magnets?* [The force was stronger with each additional magnet, but the second magnet added more force than the third or fourth.]

   ➤ *What evidence do you have that the force increased?* [The jump distance increased.]

   ➤ *Why do you think the force increased so much with the second magnet, and only a little with the third or fourth magnet?* [Accept all ideas.]

18. **Continue the discussion with distance**

   Continue the sense-making discussion, asking students to turn to a partner to ponder that last question. Give them a few minutes to come up with an explanation about why the third and fourth magnets didn't seem to increase the net force exerted on the paper clip as much as the second magnet did. Ask volunteers to share their ideas.

   Students might bring up the idea of magnetic fields, but they might need your help to get there. Ask,

   ➤ *What happens if an object is very far from a magnet?* [It is not affected much by the magnet.]

   ➤ *The third and fourth magnet you added were farther from the paper clip than the first few magnets. Are the effects of those magnets' magnetic fields on the paper clip as strong as the first magnets?* [No.]

   Point out that the paper clip was affected by the magnetic fields of the first two magnets a lot more than the last two magnets simply because with more magnets added, some had to be farther away from the paper clip. Provide a sentence frame to help students summarize their findings at the bottom of notebook sheet 9.

   • *When magnetic fields are added together, the force of attraction _____. The farther magnets have _____ effect on the force of attraction.* [Increases; less.]

Part 3: Force over Distance

19. Continue the discussion with magnetic fields
Introduce some information about magnetic fields into the sense-making discussion. Tell students,

Magnetic fields are strongest when they are close to the magnet. As an object, like a paper clip, moves farther from a magnet, it is still within its magnetic field, but the force is so small that it will not overcome friction.

In fact, if you travel an infinite distance from a magnet, you are still within its magnetic field. Its magnetic force will be infinitely small, but not zero.

➤ *When you placed two magnets side by side, what happened to the net magnetic force? Why?* [The net force increased because the magnetic fields added together.]

➤ *Why didn't a third or fourth magnet have as strong an effect?* [It was farther away, and its field was not as strong at that distance. The farther magnets are adding less and less to the end of the magnetic field closest to the paper clip.]

20. Test the model further
Ask,

➤ *Based on your model of magnetic fields, how far do you think a paper clip would move if you used five magnets? Six? Seven? Eight?*

Give students time to discuss the question in their groups, and to record their group's prediction on a new page in the notebook labeled "Adding More Magnets."

Then ask groups to share ideas, and to explain the reasoning behind their prediction. The data from experimentation suggests that more magnets will have minimal effect on the net magnetic force. However, accept all ideas, and tell students that they will have a chance to test this with an online simulation.

21. Use online activity
Open "Adding Magnetic Fields" and show students that the workspace is set up like the experiment they did in class with the paper clip and magnets. Now they will be able to test up to eight magnets. Show students how the magnetic field diagrams can be toggled on and off.

Students should develop a data table on their "Adding More Magnets" notebook page. They will collect data for magnets 5–8, using multiple trials, then write up their conclusions.

Distribute laptops or devices to each group or set of partners and show them how to access the online activity.

MATH CONNECTION

This supports Common Core State Standards for Math 6.RP 3 and 7.RP 2.

SCIENCE AND ENGINEERING PRACTICES

Using mathematics and computational thinking

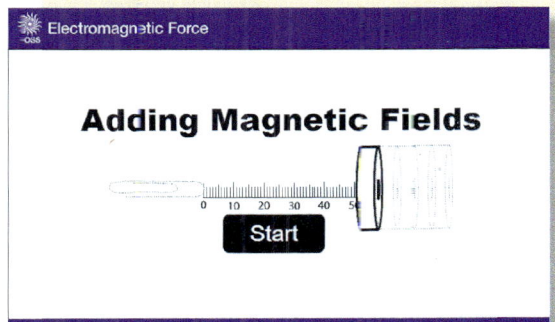

Electromagnetic Force Course—FOSS Next Generation

INVESTIGATION 2 – The Force of Magnetism

CROSSCUTTING CONCEPTS
Patterns
Systems and system models

▶ **NOTE**
Go to FOSSweb for *Teacher Resources* and look for the Crosscutting Concepts and Integration chapter for details on how to engage students with the concept of patterns to integrate content at this grade level.

SCIENCE AND ENGINEERING PRACTICES
Developing and using models

potential energy

E L   N O T E

For students who need support, give them a few minutes to discuss the question and their notebook entries with a partner before writing. You can also provide writing frames such as
One factor that affects magnets' force of attraction is ___ .
For example, when we ___ we found out that ___ . I think this is because ___ .
My model shows that ___ .
I'm wondering if ___ .

---

22. **Discuss conclusions**
    Lead a discussion to help students draw conclusions. Ask,

    ➤ *What patterns did you notice as you added more magnets?* [There were smaller and smaller increases in the jump distance, meaning there were smaller and smaller increases in the magnetic force.]

    ➤ *Why does each new magnet increase the net force less and less?* [The magnetic field extends out from the magnets, but the new magnets are farther and farther away from the paper clip, so they exert less force on the paper clip.]

23. **Revisit the model**
    Ask students to return to their "Multiple Magnets" notebook entries and update them with new information from the class discussion.

24. **Record vocabulary**
    Give students a few moments to review or clarify the vocabulary developed in this investigation. Have students label and/or explain the vocabulary words and definitions in their notebooks if they haven't done so already.

25. **Revisit the focus question**
    Have students draw a line below their original response to the focus question and write a final answer in their notebooks.

    ➤ *What factors affect the force of attraction between magnets?*

    Encourage students to cite evidence derived from data to support their answers.

Part 3: Force over Distance

WRAP-UP

26. Review notebook entries

Ask students to go through their notebook entries and select key points that summarize an important finding from this investigation. They should record these points in their notebooks.

Have students share their key points with their group, selecting one or two key points within the group to share with the class. Create a class chart of key points by recording each group's idea on a piece of chart paper, whiteboard, or document projected from the computer. You might need to help groups rephrase their key points for clarity.

Students should record the key points in their notebooks and reference the page numbers in their notebooks where additional information supports each key point. By using science and engineering practices and exploring core ideas through the lens of crosscutting concepts, students should come forward with these big ideas in the review discussions. These concepts set the stage for learning more about the force of electromagnetism.

- All magnets have two poles, a north pole at one side and a south pole at the other side. Like poles of magnets repel each other, and opposite poles attract. (Planning and carrying out investigations; analyzing and interpreting data; constructing explanations; PS2.B: Types of interactions; patterns, cause and effect.)

- Magnets are surrounded by an invisible magnetic field that acts through space and through most materials. (Asking questions; developing and using models; planning and carrying out investigations; analyzing and interpreting data; engaging in argument from evidence; obtaining, evaluating, and communicating information; PS2.B: Types of interactions, PS3.C: Relationship between energy and forces; patterns; energy and matter.)

- The magnetic force between magnets decreases as the distance between them increases. (Developing and using models; planning and carrying out investigations; analyzing and interpreting data; using mathematics and computational thinking; PS2.A: Forces and motion; PS2.B: Types of interactions; PS3.A: Definitions of energy, PS3.C: Relationship between energy and forces; patterns; energy and matter.)

- Magnetic fields add as they overlap. (Developing and using models; analyzing and interpreting data; using mathematics and computational thinking; constructing explanations; PS2.A: Forces and motion; PS2.B: Types of interactions; PS3.A: Definitions of energy; PS3.C: Relationship between energy and forces; patterns; systems and system models; energy and matter.)

SCIENCE AND ENGINEERING PRACTICES

Asking questions
Developing and using models
Planning and carrying out investigations
Analyzing and interpreting data
Using mathematics and computational thinking
Constructing explanations
Engaging in argument from evidence
Obtaining, evaluating, and communicating information

DISCIPLINARY CORE IDEAS

PS2.A: Forces and motion
PS2.B: Types of interactions
PS3.A: Definitions of energy
PS3.C: Relationship between energy and forces

CROSSCUTTING CONCEPTS

Patterns
Cause and effect
Systems and system models
Energy and matter

INVESTIGATION 2 – The Force of Magnetism

You might ask students to draw a line of learning under their last notebook entry and then to compose a concise statement summarizing what they know about magnetism.

27. Answer the guiding question
Ask students to discuss the investigation guiding question.

➤ *How can we describe magnetic force?*

Ask students to reflect on the different experiences they had with magnets to connect their thinking to the real world. Students can also ask additional questions about magnets that they have not answered yet in class.

28. Extend the investigation with homework
Ask students to test refrigerator magnets at home. Do all refrigerator magnets have the same strength of magnetic force? Students should design a method to test this force, then write their procedures and results. If students don't have magnets at home, considering a lending system in class where students can borrow magnets from you or other students.

SESSION 4   45–50 minutes

29. Assess progress: I-Check
Administer *Investigation 2 I-Check*, asking students to respond to the items on paper or online on FOSSmap. Students should independently answer the questions. When taking the I-Check, students should not use their notebooks, but the notebooks are a good tool to use when students later reflect on their answers.

SESSION 5   45–50 minutes

30. Discuss I-Check results
Code the I-Check items, but do not make any marks on student responses. Note that FOSSmap automatically codes most of the items and provides you with student and class reports. Coding guides can be found on FOSSweb. You can record student results on the *Assessment Record* or download spreadsheets from FOSSmap for recording. Note important points about the items to review with students.

Return the I-Checks to students. Use self-assessment strategies as described in the Assessment chapter for each item to facilitate reflection and clarify student thinking.

> **TEACHING NOTE**
>
> *During or after these next steps with the I-Check, you might ask students to make choices for possible derivative products based on their notebooks for inclusion in a summative portfolio. See the Assessment chapter for more information about creating and evaluating portfolios.*

Extending the Investigation

EXTENDING *the Investigation*

- **Make a compass**
  Students can make a compass using a sewing needle, magnet, plastic-foam chip, and cup of water. They should rub the needle in only one direction several times with the magnet, then stick the needle into the foam chip. They can anchor the chip in the center of a cup of water, using thread and a paper clip.

- **Conduct more force investigations**
  Another way students can test the effect of how much magnetic force is produced by multiple magnets, other than the paper-clip method used in class, is to use the stacked-plastic-cup technique that was used with spacers and a spring scale to determine the effect of distance on magnetic force. Instead of spacers, students can use additional magnets.

- **Explore different magnets**
  Get an assortment of magnets (larger, smaller, bar-shaped, horseshoe). Let students compare the strength of the forces of attraction. Students may bring magnets from home.

- **Investigate polarity of metal objects**
  Students can test stationary metal objects (or at least objects that have spent time in the same orientation) in the classroom for polarity. These objects will generally have north and south poles as indicated by a compass. A file cabinet, a metal table leg, old-fashioned radiators are great, and other similar objects will work. How did these objects end up having polarity? They have resided in one position in the magnetic field of Earth—a good puzzle for students to think about.

> **TEACHING NOTE**
>
> *Encourage students to use the Science and Engineering Careers Database on FOSSweb.*

Electromagnetic Force Course—FOSS Next Generation

INVESTIGATION 2 – The Force of Magnetism

Investigation 3: Electromagnetism

INVESTIGATION 3 – Electromagnetism

PURPOSE

In *Electromagnetism*, students complete an electric circuit. They then explore a new phenomenon: electromagnetism. They build an electromagnet and engineer improvements to increase its strength.

Content

- Energy transfers through an electric circuit from a source to components.
- A magnetic field surrounds a wire through which electric current is flowing.
- The magnetic field produced by a current-carrying wire can induce magnetism in a piece of iron or steel.
- An electromagnet is made by sending electric current through an insulated wire wrapped around an iron core.
- The strength of magnetism induced in the core of an electromagnet increases with the number of winds of wire, the amount of electric current flowing in the wire, and the iron content of the core.

Practices

- Develop and use a model to explain how a magnetic field results from an electric current through a wire.
- Design an electromagnet that will meet specific criteria and constraints.

Part 1
Building a Circuit **206**

Part 2
Building an Electromagnet ... **226**

Part 3
Improving the Design **242**

Guiding question for phenomenon:
How are electricity and magnetism related?

Science and Engineering Practices

- Asking questions and defining problems
- Developing and using models
- Planning and carrying out investigations
- Analyzing and interpreting data
- Using mathematics and computational thinking
- Constructing explanations and designing solutions
- Engaging in argument from evidence
- Obtaining, evaluating, and communicating information

Disciplinary Core Ideas

PS2: How can one explain and predict interactions between objects and with systems of objects?
PS2.B: Types of interactions
PS3: How is energy transferred and conserved?
PS3.A: Definitions of energy
ETS1.A: Defining and delimiting engineering problems
ETS1.B: Developing possible solutions
ETS1.C: Optimizing the design solution

Crosscutting Concepts

- Patterns
- Cause and effect
- Systems and system models
- Energy and matter
- Structure and function

Full Option Science System

INVESTIGATION 3 – *Electromagnetism*

	Investigation Summary	Time	Focus Question for Phenomenon, Practices
PART 1	**Building a Circuit** Students are introduced to electricity and energy. They discover how to make a complete circuit using a D-cell, wires, and a lightbulb. Students discuss the electricity's pathway in the circuit and the function of each of the system's components. They also take a close look at the anatomy of a lightbulb.	**Active Inv.** 2 Sessions* **Reading** 1 Session	**What is required to complete an electric circuit?** **Practices** Developing and using models Planning and carrying out investigations Constructing explanations Obtaining, evaluating, and communicating information
PART 2	**Building an Electromagnet** Students discover that a steel core becomes a magnet when current flows through an insulated wire wound around the steel core.	**Active Inv.** 1 Session **Reading** 1 Session	**How does an electromagnet work?** **Practices** Asking questions Developing and using models Constructing explanations and designing solutions Obtaining, evaluating, and communicating information
PART 3	**Improving the Design** Students brainstorm different variables that might affect the strength of their electromagnet, and then test those variables. Working as a class, they combine their results to determine the best design for an electromagnet.	**Active Inv.** 2 Sessions **Review** 1 Session **Assessment** 1–2 Sessions	**Student-generated question, e.g., How does (student-chosen process) affect the strength of an electromagnet?** **Practices** Asking questions and defining problems Planning and carrying out investigations Analyzing and interpreting data Using mathematics and computational thinking Designing solutions Engaging in argument from evidence

* A class session is 45–50 minutes.

At a Glance

Content Related to DCIs	Literacy/Technology	Assessment
• Energy transfers through an electric circuit from a source to components. • A magnetic field surrounds a wire through which electric current is flowing.	**Science Notebook Entry** *Lighting Bulbs Response Sheet—Investigation 3* **Science Resources Book** "Parts of an Incandescent Lightbulb" "Circuitry and Lightbulbs" "What Is Electricity?" **Online Activity** "Lighting a Bulb"	**Embedded Assessment** Response sheet
• A magnetic field surrounds a wire through which electric current is flowing. • The magnetic field produced by a current-carrying wire can induce magnetism in a piece of iron or steel. • An electromagnet is made by sending electric current through an insulated wire wrapped around an iron core.	**Science Notebook Entry** Answer the focus question **Science Resources Book** "Electromagnetism" **Online Activity** "Kitchen Magnets"	**Embedded Assessment** Science notebook entry
• An electromagnet is made by sending electric current through an insulated wire wrapped around an iron core. • The strength of magnetism induced in the core of an electromagnet increases with the number of winds of wire, the amount of electric current flowing in the wire, and the iron content of the core.	**Science Notebook Entry** *Testing Electromagnet Variables* **Science Resources Book** "Engineering Design Process" "Electromagnetic Engineering" **Online Activity** "Virtual Electromagnet"	**Embedded Assessment** Performance assessment **Benchmark Assessment** *Investigation 3 I-Check* **NGSS Performance Expectations addressed in this investigation** MS-PS2-2 MS-PS2-3 MS-PS2-5 MS-PS3-2 MS-ETS1-1 MS-ETS1-2 MS-ETS1-3 MS-ETS1-4

Electromagnetic Force Course—FOSS Next Generation

INVESTIGATION 3 – Electromagnetism

SCIENTIFIC and Historical Background

In this investigation, students make electric **circuits** that transfer energy to produce light and generate magnetic fields. They encounter an observable phenomenon—a compass moves when current runs through a wire. This indicates that there is a relationship between electricity and magnetism. Students explore the phenomenon of electromagnetism for the rest of the course. The guiding question for this investigation is what is the relationship between electricity and magnetism?

What Is Required to Complete an Electric Circuit?

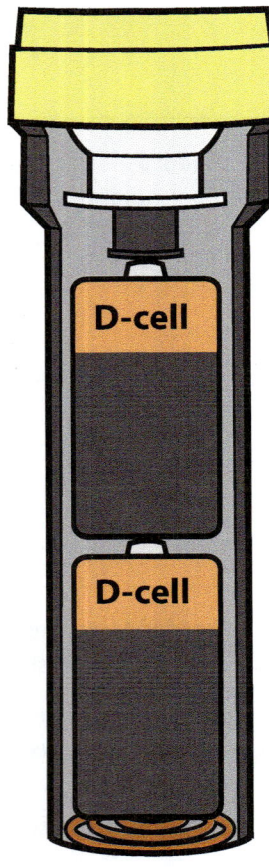

In this investigation, electrical energy in the form of **electric current** starts out in the D-cell, or flashlight **battery**. Scientifically speaking, D-cells are not batteries. Two or more cells must be hooked up to work together to make a battery, like the battery in your car. Although D-cells are technically not batteries, we will honor the colloquial use of the word *battery* with students as the course progresses.

The chemical reactions that take place inside the D-cell to provide electric current are fairly complex, and not important for students to contemplate at this time. Two chemicals are carefully selected for their tendency to react. This particular chemical reaction involves the transfer and sharing of electrons. **Energy transfer** occurs from chemical potential energy to electrical energy throughout the reaction. In the battery, the two chemicals are packaged so the only way they can exchange electrons is through a wire (conductor) connected from one end (terminal) of the D-cell to the other. The movement (flow) of electrons through the system via the wire is electric current, or electrical kinetic energy. If we insert a device that can interact with the flow of electrons, we can put the energy of the moving electrons to use. A D-cell (battery) will push electrons through the wire until the chemical reaction is complete, at which time we say the battery is dead.

Electricity results from a property of matter called charge. Electrons, those minute bits that move around atomic nuclei, have negative charge; protons, major building blocks of the nuclei themselves, have positive charge. Charges in an atom are usually balanced—equal numbers of protons and electrons. When the charges are not balanced, potential energy is available. When charges are separated and not moving to regain balance, we call it static electricity. This is one form of potential energy.

Scientific and Historical Background

When electrons are flowing from a place with an electron excess to a place with an electron deficit, we have kinetic energy, and we call the flow electric current. Whenever matter is in motion, including electrons, the motion energy can be put to work to serve us in many ways.

Electricity performs work when it is channeled into a pathway that connects the two terminals of the battery. We call such a pathway an electric circuit. A circuit is a system, a collection of parts working together. To use the energy of a D-cell (or any other source of electrical energy) to light a lightbulb or operate any other electric device, a pathway must be provided from and to the energy source. The pathway must be through conductive materials like metals and must go from one terminal on the battery through the lightbulb (the **component** of interest in this case) and back to the other terminal of the battery (energy source). It is this complete pathway that is absolutely essential for a lightbulb to light. The movement of charge inside the battery completes the circuit. **Insulation**, such as the plastic coating on a wire, can prevent a circuit from being complete, and its purpose is to prevent movement of electrons to places where we do not want them to go. The light, a form of **electromagnetic radiation**, produced in the complete circuit transfers energy from the circuit system to the environment.

The part of an incandescent lightbulb that makes light is called the **filament**. The filament is a thin wire made of tungsten, which can withstand high temperatures without melting or burning up. The lightbulb produces light when the filament gets so hot that it glows and emits light. The lightbulb is designed to allow electric current to flow through the filament—the filament is actually part of the circuit. The filament is mounted between two support wires inside a protective glass globe. In order to direct the electric current to the filament, the circuit must be connected to two **contact points** on the lightbulb. One of the filament support wires extends down to the metal bead at the very bottom of the lightbulb. The second filament support wire connects to the side of the metal screw case, or lightbulb casing. To place the lightbulb in a circuit, one contact must be made on the metal bead at the very bottom of the lightbulb, and the second contact must be made on the side of the lightbulb casing.

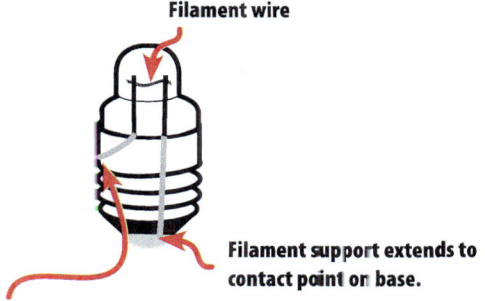

Student preconceptions about circuits. All students come to school with conceptual models of energy. Many of these models are incomplete or naive. As you teach students about energy and how circuitry works, it will be useful for you to know what some of these models are.

INVESTIGATION 3 – *Electromagnetism*

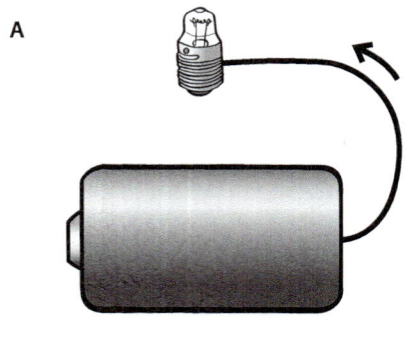

A

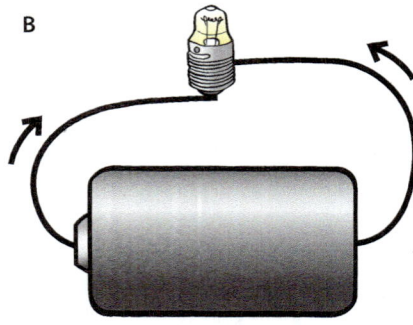

B

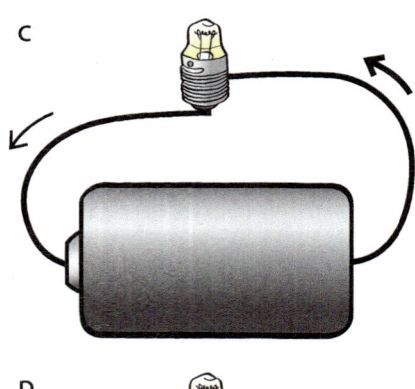

C

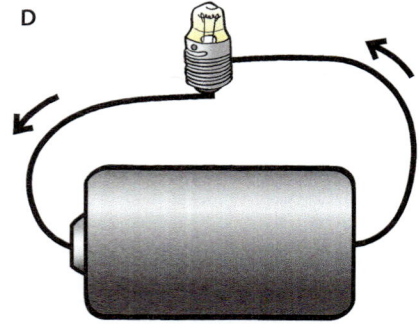

D

In Part 1 of this investigation, you will see that many students have a conceptual model that electricity flows from a cell to the lightbulb to make it light (figure A). These students think that if they touch a wire to the cell and to the lightbulb, the electricity will flow from the cell to the lightbulb. In this model, the student thinks that only one wire is necessary. Most students abandon this model when they try it and fail to light a lightbulb. They test other possibilities with trial and error, eventually replacing their initial conceptual model with a new one.

When students construct a successful circuit, as depicted in figures B through D, they may still have naive notions of what is actually happening in the circuit. For example, some students think that two wires are necessary to light the lightbulb, but their conceptual model is that electricity flows from the cell through both wires and converges at the lightbulb (figure B). The French physicist André-Marie Ampère (1775–1836) believed this, thinking that negative electricity flowed through one wire and positive electricity through the other.

Another view held by some students is that electricity flows to the lightbulb from the cell through one wire and returns through another, but because some electricity gets used up, less electric current flows in the wire through which electricity returns to the cell (figure C).

For this investigation, it is not crucial that students hold the scientists' view—that the direction of the electricity is one-way and that the current flow is uniform throughout the circuit (figure D). However, during discussions, it's desirable to lead students toward this type of understanding.

The activities in this investigation will lead all students toward the scientific view, by developing a functional understanding of circuits. It is not intended that students understand electricity at an atomic level.

Safe electricity. D-cells are generally safe sources of electricity for students to handle in the classroom. Electricity is the movement of charge, usually electrons through a conductor. One characteristic of a flow of electricity is the voltage. Voltage is magnitude of the push moving the charge along. Amperage, the second characteristic, is the quantity of charge per unit time moving through a conductor. A fresh D-cell can muster only 1.5 volts (V) of "push" and less than 1 amp (A) of current, and that really isn't much. The same cannot be said for the electricity available from the electric receptacles in the wall of your classroom. The wall socket provides 110 to 120 V of push and 30 A or more current, and that is enough to cause major disruptions to the vital respiratory and circulatory systems of the human body. Frequently remind students of the danger and admonish them not to put anything into wall sockets during

Scientific and Historical Background

the investigations. However, they should be reassured that they will not get a shock or be otherwise distressed by the modest energy available in a D-cell.

One possible problem is creating a circuit that connects one end of the battery to the other end directly through conducting wire(s) without passing through any component such as a lightbulb or motor. This condition is called a short circuit and has at least four bad outcomes: the wires can get very hot, the battery can get hot, the reacting chemicals in the battery are rapidly depleted, causing the battery to go dead. And then you'll need to buy fresh batteries. Be on the lookout for this condition while students are working with batteries in circuits. Point out that they have created a short circuit and that if they do that, their battery will go dead really fast.

How Does an Electromagnet Work?

Science explains the relationship between magnetism and electricity. These apparently disparate phenomena are actually two expressions of the same fundamental force, both arising from the fundamental property of charge. For this reason, the **electromagnetic force** can shift from one guise to the other, depending on circumstances. Magnetism begets electricity, and electricity begets magnetism. Here's how.

Current flowing through a wire produces a magnetic field around the wire. This can be verified with a magnetic compass, a D-cell, and a wire, assembled as shown. When the circuit is opened and closed, the needle will change orientation as the current starts and stops flowing. Electricity creates a magnetic field.

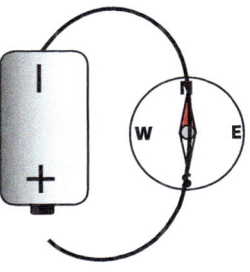
Open circuit

A junkyard crane picks up a jumble of scrap metal and deposits it in a railroad car. Across town a doorbell rings. What do these seemingly unrelated events have in common? Both actions employ an **electromagnet**.

An electromagnet is a device that takes advantage of this phenomenon. When you wrap an insulated wire around a rivet (a piece of steel), the magnetic field created in the current-carrying wire induces magnetism in the steel. The magnetic field produced around the wire is modest, but by winding the wire in a coil around an iron or steel **core**, each little magnetic field adds to the one next to it. When several coils are wrapped around a rivet, the magnetic field is fairly substantial, and a significant magnet can be produced in the steel core in this way. Because the magnetic field is a consequence of the current flowing in the wire, the magnetic field exists only while current is flowing. When the circuit supplying current to the wire coil is opened, the magnetic field collapses.

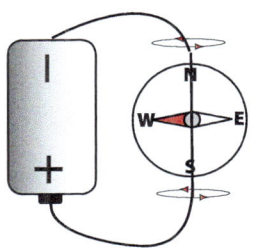
Closed circuit

Electromagnetic Force Course—FOSS Next Generation

INVESTIGATION 3 – Electromagnetism

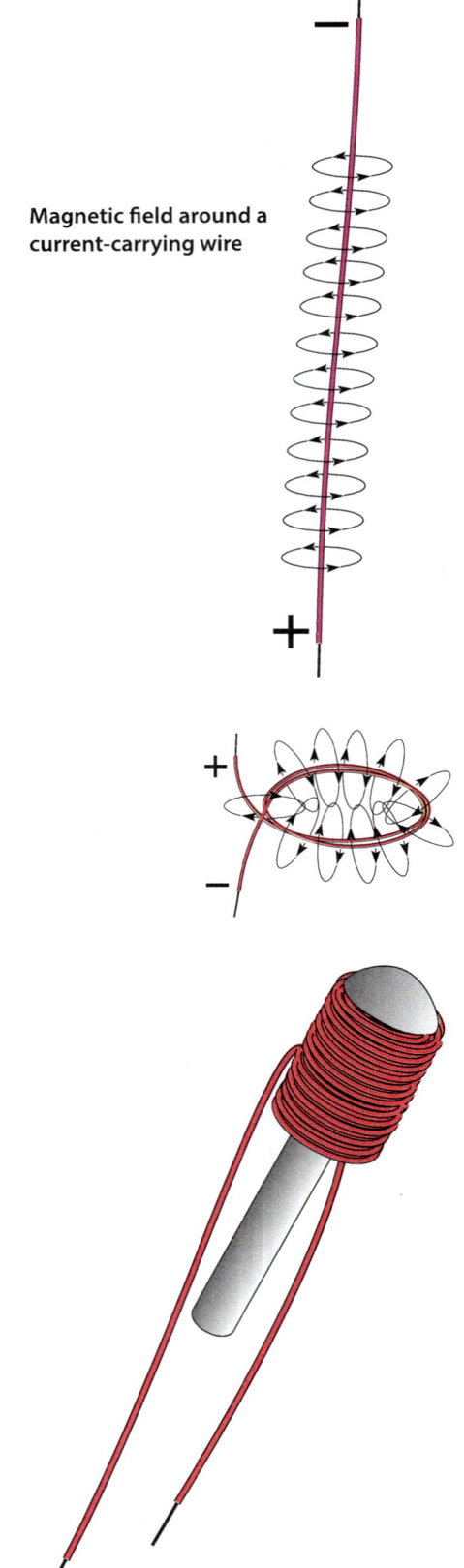

Magnetic field around a current-carrying wire

The induced magnetism in the steel core largely (but not entirely) disappears; the net effect is a magnet that can be turned on and off with a switch.

In 1831, Michael Faraday (1791–1867) showed that the relationship between magnetism and electricity works in the other direction as well. He demonstrated that an electric current can be created by passing a conductor, like a copper wire, through a magnetic field.

Motors and generators are engineered devices that take advantage of these two reciprocal expressions of **electromagnetism**. The design of these devices will be discussed in Investigation 4.

What Modifications to an Electromagnet Will Affect the Strength of Its Magnetic Field?

One design **criteria** of an electromagnet that can be tested is its strength. Careful testing by students, with the design **constraint** of changing only one variable, will reveal ways to increase the strength of an electromagnet. The basic two factors are number of coils per length and amount of current. These two factors result in several testable phenomena. Additional winds of wire increase the strength of the magnetism. Fifty winds on the core can attract more paper clips than 20 winds. Inserting a second D-cell into the circuit in series with the first one will double the voltage, increase the current, and increase the strength of the magnetism. Tight coils will produce a stronger magnet than loose coils. The gauge of the wire also affects the strength of an electromagnet. The larger the wire, the stronger the magnet, given the same number of winds, since larger-diameter wire has less resistance to electric flow, thus allowing more current to flow.

The wire used in the electromagnet is insulated. Why? If you constructed an electromagnet with uninsulated wire, the current would not travel through the long coils of wire, but would instead take the path of least resistance back to the other terminal of the cell, forming a short circuit. Without current flowing all the way around and around the coils of wire, you don't get overlapping fields of magnetism adding to one another.

In a sense, the electromagnet still is a short circuit, since it is a wire connecting the positive and negative ends of the battery. In this case, however, it's a very long wire, and the electromagnet is a circuit component that can do work. Heating elements in electric stoves, ovens, and toasters are also in short circuits manipulated to accomplish useful tasks.

Scientific and Historical Background

Engineers take advantage of these electromagnetic properties. Winding a huge coil with many turns of insulated wire and supplying it with a large electric current can produce a junkyard electromagnet strong enough to lift a 2-metric-ton car (that's 2,000 kg). And a small electromagnet that turns on and off rapidly can alternately attract and release a clapper that rings a doorbell.

Electromagnets have thousands of uses in technologically oriented societies. Electric motors use electromagnets and permanent magnets to produce useful rotational motion. Cars have an electromagnet called the solenoid in the starting system. When you turn your key in the ignition switch, the circuit that is closed activates the solenoid. The solenoid attracts a piece of steel to one of its ends. The steel closes a second circuit—one that carries a lot of electric current directly from your battery to the starter motor, which in turn has coils and magnets. It would be too dangerous to insert your key into the circuit that carries all that electricity, so car starter systems are designed to keep you one circuit away from the battery/starter motor system.

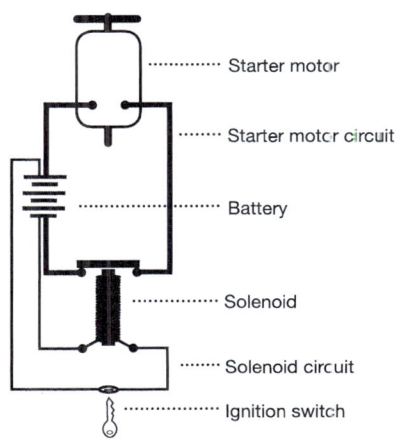

Starter solenoid in circuit

Vocabulary
Battery
Circuit
Component
Constraint
Contact point
Core
Criterion
Electric current
Electromagnet
Electromagnetic force
Electromagnetic radiation
Electromagnetism
Energy transfer
Engineer
Filament
Insulation

Electromagnetic Force Course—FOSS Next Generation

INVESTIGATION 3 – Electromagnetism

TEACHING AND LEARNING about Electromagnetism

NGSS Foundation Box for DCI

PS2.B: Types of interactions

- Electric and magnetic (electromagnetic) forces can be attractive or repulsive, and their sizes depend on the magnitudes of the charges, currents, or magnetic strengths involved and on the distances between the interacting objects. (MS-PS2-3)
- Forces that act at a distance (electric and magnetic) can be explained by fields that extend through space and can be mapped by their effect on a test object (a ball, a charged object, or a magnet, respectively). (MS-PS2-5)

PS3.A: Definitions of energy

- A system of objects may also contain stored (potential) energy, depending on their relative positions. (MS-PS3-2)

ETS1.A: Defining and delimiting engineering problems

- The more precisely a design task's criteria and constraints can be defined, the more likely it is that the designed solution will be successful. (MS-ETS1-1)

ETS1.B: Developing possible solutions

- Sometimes parts of different solutions can be combined to create a solution that is better than any of its predecessors. (MS-ETS1-4)

ETS1.C: Optimizing the design solution

- Although one design may not perform the best across all tests, identifying the characteristics of the design that performed the best in each test can provide useful information for the redesign process—that is, some of those characteristics may be incorporated into the new design. (MS-ETS1-3)

Developing Disciplinary Core Ideas (DCI)

"Magnets and electricity seem like two really different things. One is a black metal and the other you can't even see." The electromagnetic force that produces both electricity and magnetism is not intuitive. There are hints that one force governs both, if you know where to look. This investigation provides those experiences to students and makes undeniable the connection between the two. The full explanation of electromagnetic force at the subatomic level will be left for high school and college.

So how to study the invisible? Students will begin with a basic electric circuit to explore electricity and the concept of energy transfer. Then the question is posed: Does this circuit also have magnetism? Once students discover that it does, the rest of the investigation pulls together that finding with important concepts developed in the last investigation: the weak induced magnetism of the electric circuit can be added many times by coiling the wire so that the magnetic fields overlap. The resulting electromagnet has a strong enough magnetic force to be easily detected.

This investigation also poses an engineering design challenge to students. Once they've built a working electromagnet, they study the system and think of variables that might be changed to improve the design. As a class, they will test multiple variables and combine the data to draw conclusions about the best electromagnet design.

The experiences students have in this investigation contribute to the disciplinary core ideas **PS2.B: Types of interactions**; **PS3.A: Definitions of energy**; **ETS1.A: Defining and delimiting engineering problems**; **ETS1.B: Developing possible solutions**; and **ETS1.C: Optimizing the design solution**.

Teaching and Learning about Electromagnetism

Engaging in Science and Engineering Practices (SEP)

In this investigation, students engage in these practices.

- **Asking questions and defining problems** when thinking about the relationship between magnetism and electricity and how it affects the criteria and constraints of a design challenge.
- **Developing and using models** to explain how a magnetic field results from an electric current through a wire.
- **Planning and carrying out investigations** to try to test an electric circuit for magnetism and modifications to an electromagnet.
- **Analyzing and interpreting data** by reviewing group and class data about electromagnet modifications and drawing conclusions about electromagnet designs.
- **Using mathematics and computational thinking** when comparing the results of electromagnet modifications as measured by the number of paper clips that can be lifted.
- **Constructing explanations and designing solutions** for an electromagnet that will meet specific criteria and constraints.
- **Engaging in argument from evidence** when selecting a design solution based on electromagnet testing.
- **Obtaining, evaluating, and communicating information** about electricity by reading nonfiction texts.

> **NGSS Foundation Box for SEP**
>
> - **Define a design problem** that can be solved through the development of an object, tool, process, or system and includes multiple criteria and constraints, including scientific knowledge that may limit possible solutions.
> - **Develop and/or use a model** to predict and/or describe phenomena.
> - **Plan an investigation individually and collaboratively**, and in the design: identify independent and dependent variables and controls, what tools are needed to do the gathering, how measurements will be recorded, and how many data are needed to support a claim.
> - **Analyze data** to define an optimal operational range for a proposed object, tool, process, or system that best meets criteria for success.
> - **Use digital tools and/or mathematical concepts and arguments** to test and compare proposed solutions to an engineering design problem.
> - **Undertake a design project**, engaging in the design cycle, to construct and/or implement a solution that meets specific design criteria and constraints.
> - **Evaluate competing design solutions** based on jointly developed and agreed-upon design criteria.
> - **Critically read scientific texts** adapted for classroom use to determine the central ideas and/or obtain scientific and/or technical information to describe patterns in and/or evidence about the natural and designed world(s).

INVESTIGATION 3 – Electromagnetism

> **NGSS Foundation Box for CC**
>
> - **Patterns:** Patterns can be used to identify cause-and-effect relationships.
> - **Cause and effect:** Cause-and-effect relationships may be used to predict phenomena in natural or designed systems.
> - **Systems and system models:** Systems may interact with other systems; they may have subsystems and be a part of larger complex systems.
> - **Energy and matter:** Energy may take different forms (e.g., energy in fields, thermal energy, energy of motion).
> - **Structure and function:** Structures can be designed to serve particular functions by taking into account properties of different materials, and how materials can be shaped and used.

Exposing Crosscutting Concepts (CC)

In this investigation, the focus is on these crosscutting concepts.

- **Patterns.** Certain tools will act as magnet detectors because of how they are affected by magnetic fields.
- **Cause and effect.** A completed electric circuit induces a temporary magnetic field.
- **Systems and system models.** An electromagnet is a system that can be measured, studied, and modified.
- **Energy and matter.** Energy transfers in an electric circuit allow chemical potential energy from a D-cell to light a lightbulb.
- **Structure and function.** The configuration of various parts of an electromagnet system affects its magnetic force.

Connections to the Nature of Science

- **Science addresses questions about the natural and material world.** Scientific knowledge is constrained by human capacity, technology, and materials. Science limits its explanations to systems that lend themselves to observation and empirical evidence. Scientific knowledge can describe consequences of actions but is not responsible for society's decisions.

Connections to Engineering, Technology, and Applications of Science

- **Influence of science, engineering, and technology on society and the natural world.** The uses of technologies are driven by people's needs, desires, and values; by the findings of scientific research; and by differences in such factors as climate, natural resources, and economic conditions. Technology use varies over time and from region to region.

Teaching and Learning about Electromagnetism

Conceptual Flow

In this investigation, students explore the phenomenon of electromagnetism. The guiding question is what is the relationship between electricity and magnetism?

The **conceptual flow** starts in Part 1 with students building **circuits** using a **battery**, lightbulb, and **insulated** wires. Students explore the function of each **component** in the circuit and the importance of **contact points** to create a circuit where **electric current** will flow. They learn that **chemical potential energy from the battery transfers to electrical energy in the circuit**, and then electrical energy transfers to light and heat via the **filament**.

Students learn that light is a form of **electromagnetic radiation**, and that **electromagnetic force is one of the fundamental forces of nature**. They test the relationship between magnetism and electricity and learn that **when electric current runs through a wire, it produces a small magnetic field** around the wire.

In Part 2, students further investigate **electromagnetism** by building a simple **electromagnet**. They study the electromagnet components to conclude that by coiling a wire, **the magnetic fields produced when current runs through the wire can overlap**, producing a stronger net magnetic force. Furthermore, this magnetic force can **induce magnetism in a metal core, creating an electromagnet**.

In Part 3, students are challenged with the **criterion** of designing a stronger electromagnet. By using the **constraint** of keeping other variables the same, students design a controlled experiment to test variables that might influence electromagnet strength. They share results as a class to discuss how one could **engineer** the strongest possible electromagnet.

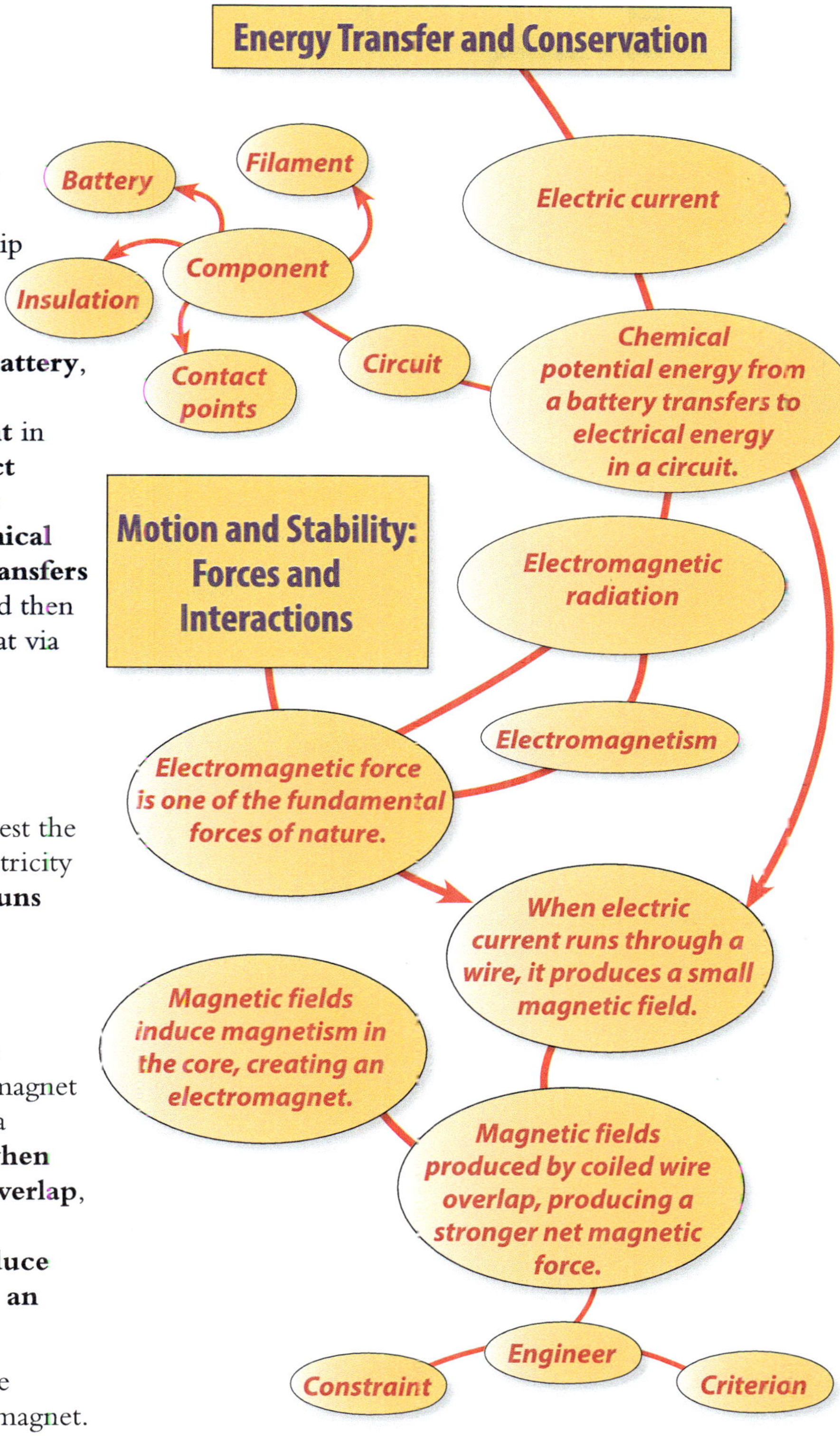

Electromagnetic Force Course—FOSS Next Generation

INVESTIGATION 3 – Electromagnetism

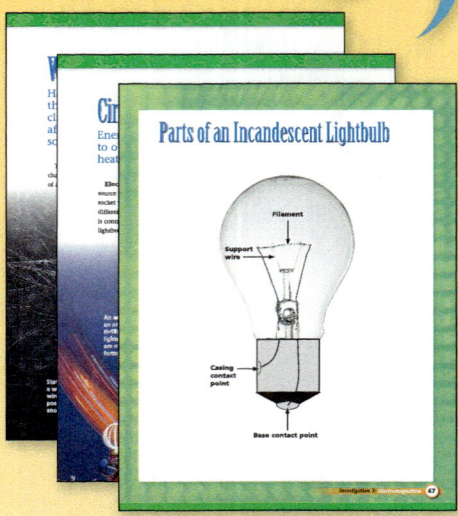

FOSS Science Resources

MATERIALS for
Part 1: Building a Circuit

Provided equipment

For each student
- 1 FOSS Science Resources: Electromagnetic Force
  - "Parts of an Incandescent Lightbulb"
  - "Circuitry and Lightbulbs"
  - "What Is Electricity?"

For each group
- 2 Bulb holders
- 2 D-cells
- 2 Cell holders
- 1 Compass
- 2 Lightbulbs, #222
- 6 Short wires, 20-gauge, 15 cm
- 2 Switches

For the class
- 1 Wire stripper

Teacher-supplied items

For the class
- 1 Metric ruler or meter tape
- 1 Craft stick (optional)
- 1 Screwdriver (optional)
- 1 Bag, paper or plastic (optional)
- 1 Incandescent household lightbulb (optional)

FOSSweb resources

For each student
- 1 Notebook sheet 10, *Lighting Lightbulbs*
- 1 Notebook sheet 11, *Response Sheet—Investigation 3*

For the class
- Online activity, "Lighting a Bulb"

For the teacher
- Teacher master E, *Inside an Incandescent Lightbulb*
- Teacher master F, *New Circuit Challenge*
- *Embedded Assessment Notes*
- Teaching slides, 3.1

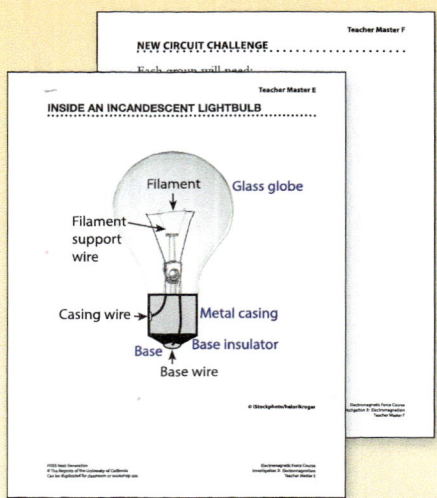

Teacher Masters E and F

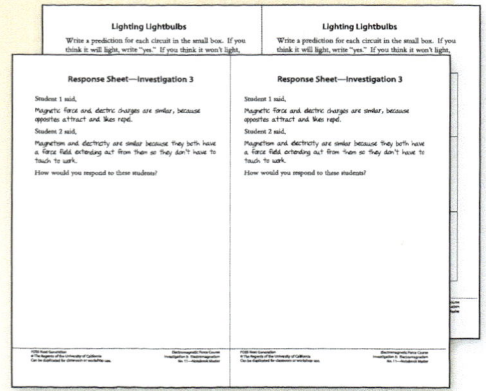

Nos. 10–11—Notebook Masters

Part 1: Building a Circuit

GETTING READY for
Part 1: *Building a Circuit*

Quick Start

Schedule	2 sessions active investigation 1 session reading
Preview	• Preview the FOSSweb Resources by Investigation for this part (such as printable masters, teaching slides, and online activities) • Preview homework reading: "Circuitry and Lightbulbs," Step 12 • Preview the in-class reading: "What Is Electricity?," Step 13
Print or Copy	**For each student** • Notebook sheets 10, 11 **For the teacher** • *Embedded Assessment Notes*
Prepare Material	• Prepare connecting wires **A** • Prepare a demonstration lightbulb (optional) **B** • Plan for safety **C** • Practice using cell holders **D** • Set up a materials station each day
Plan for Assessment	• Review Step 16, "What to Look For" in the response sheet

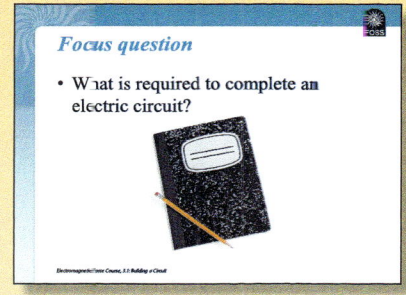

▶ **NOTE**
Preview the teaching slides on FOSSweb for this part.

Day 1 Materials Station
- lightbulbs
- short wires
- D-cells

Day 3 Materials Station
- lightbulbs
- short wires
- D-cells
- cell holders
- switches
- lightbulb holders

Electromagnetic Force Course—FOSS Next Generation

INVESTIGATION 3 – Electromagnetism

Preparation Details

A ▶ Prepare connecting wires

Each pair of students will need two wires to connect their D-cell to a lightbulb. Prepare 48 short wires for this part, if they have not already been cut. This needs to be done only once.

Use the thicker 20-gauge wire, with the red insulation.

a. Use the wire stripper to cut 48 pieces 15 cm long.

b. Strip about 1 cm insulation from both ends of each wire. Adjust the set screw on the wire stripper, so that when it is clamped shut, the notch cuts through the insulation but not through the wire. With the tool clamped shut, pull on the wire to slip the insulation off the end of the wire.

You might consider enlisting the assistance of a student or two for this task.

B ▶ Prepare a demonstration lightbulb (optional)

If possible, procure a household incandescent lightbulb. Place the lightbulb in a plastic or paper bag and gently but firmly tap it with the blade of a screwdriver to break the glass. Carefully remove the glass globe to expose the filament. Filaments are fragile and may not be intact, but will still suffice for the demonstration.

C ▶ Plan for safety

Some students may be fearful about working with electricity. Be prepared to reassure them that D-cells are safe to handle, but wall sockets are not. As students try lighting the lightbulb, they may find that the wires or D-cells become hot; most likely they have unintentionally created a short circuit.

D ▶ Practice using cell holders

Practice loading a D-cell into a cell holder by pushing the battery between the springs. It is easiest to slide the negative terminal (flat end) of the battery in first, then push the positive terminal down. The positive end of the battery does not really have to be pushed all the way down in the cell holder, as long as the spring is touching any of the metal surface on the positive end of the battery. You can also use a craft stick to compress the positive spring before you insert the battery, making it easier to snap into place when you remove the stick.

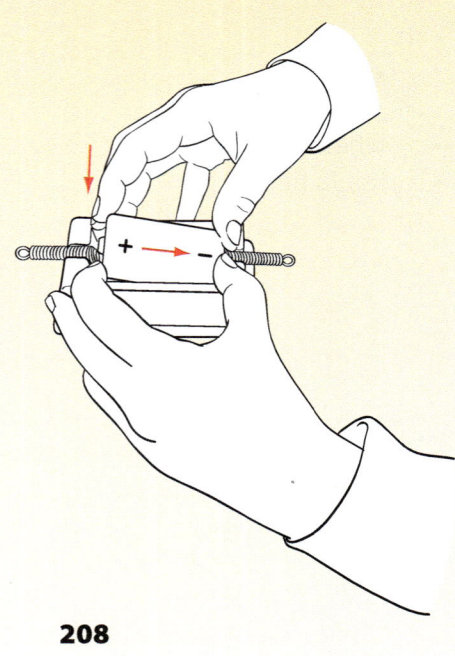

These cell holders make it easy for students to connect wires to the battery by sticking a wire end anywhere into the spring at either end of the battery. Bend the spring downward, and gaps will appear. Insert a wire, let go of the spring, and the spring will hold the wire tightly.

Part 1: Building a Circuit

GUIDING the Investigation
Part 1: Building a Circuit

SESSION 1
Students will . . .
- Think about energy and circuits (Steps 1–3)
- Create circuits and discuss them in terms of energy transfers and components (Steps 4–11)
- Extend the investigation with homework (Step 12)

SESSION 2
Students will . . .
- Read about electricity (Steps 13, 14)
- Write ideas about magnetism and electricity (Step 15)
- Assess progress on the response sheet (Step 16)

SESSION 3
Students will . . .
- Create a circuit with new components (Steps 17, 18)
- Think about energy in the circuit (Step 19)
- Learn about electromagnetism and explore the circuit for evidence of electromagnetic force (Steps 20–22)
- Review vocabulary and answer the focus question (Steps 23, 24)
- Review notebook entries (Step 25)

FOCUS QUESTION
What is required to complete an electric circuit?

TEACHING NOTE
A battery is made of two or more cells. A D-cell, which is made of a single cell, is therefore not technically a battery. However, the colloquial use is ubiquitous and we will use the terms interchangeably.

EL NOTE
Give students a few minutes to discuss what they know about electricity. If necessary, project or provide images involving electricity.

SESSION 1   45–50 minutes

▶ SAFETY NOTE
Be alert for **short circuits**. If students complain that the wire or D-cell is getting hot, tell them to disconnect all their wires immediately and try something else. The heat is evidence of a short circuit. In a short circuit, current flows from one end of the D-cell directly to the other end of the cell without flowing through any other component other than a wire.

1. **Activate prior knowledge about energy**
   Hold up a D-cell and tell students,

   *Energy is always required to make things happen. Energy is present in many places. Energy can be stored in a D-cell **battery**. This D-cell is a source of potential energy in the form of chemicals.*

   ➤ *What could we do with that chemical potential energy?* [The battery could make an electric device work, such as a radio making sound, a toy car moving, or a flashlight producing light.]

   Tell students,

   The D-cell is a source of potential energy to make flashlights and radios work. It is a very safe source of energy for us to work with. But the energy from wall sockets is another story. Wall sockets have dangerous levels of electrical energy. We will not put any of these materials into wall sockets at any time.

   Your challenge is to find out how to get energy from this source, the D-cell, to a lightbulb.

Electromagnetic Force Course—FOSS Next Generation

INVESTIGATION 3 – Electromagnetism

2. **Introduce the lightbulb**
   Hold up a lightbulb. Tell students,

   *This is the lightbulb we will use. It is the kind of lightbulb you might find in a flashlight. A lightbulb will light up when it is connected to an energy source in an electric **circuit**. Your challenge today is to figure out how to set up an electric circuit to light the lightbulb.*

3. **Focus question: What is required to complete an electric circuit?**
   Write or project the focus question on the board.

   ➤ *What is required to complete an electric circuit?*

   Have students write this in their notebooks. Tell students that there is a D-cell for each pair of students and a supply of wires for the class. Have Getters go to the materials station to get two lightbulbs, two D-cells, and four wires for their groups.

4. **Monitor student progress**
   Walk among the pairs as they try to light their lightbulbs. It may be several minutes before every pair has successfully lit the lightbulb; holding wires to make contacts can be clumsy. Resist the temptation to show students what to do.

5. **Review successes**
   When everyone has succeeded in lighting the lightbulb, tell students to pause and draw a diagram in their notebooks, showing how they were able to light the lightbulb. Ask a few students to share their method for producing light. Guide the discussion with questions.

   ➤ *To get the light to shine, how did you connect to the D-cell?* [One wire on each end of the cell.]

   ➤ *Where did you connect to the lightbulb?* [One wire touches the bump at the very bottom of the metal part. The other wire connects to the side of the metal case of the lightbulb.]

   ➤ *What happens when you connect to the glass part of the lightbulb?* [Nothing.]

   Open the online activity, "Lighting a Bulb," and have students direct you as to where to place the wire tips to light the lightbulb.

6. **Discuss the circuit**
   Give students a few moments to think about how energy transfers throughout the circuits they made. Have them add an explanation to their diagrams. Discuss using arrows to represent the transfer of energy. Give students time to share their diagrams with a partner. Then make or project a diagram (or ask for a volunteer) on the board and illustrate as you explain,

SCIENCE AND ENGINEERING PRACTICES
Planning and carrying out investigations

TEACHING NOTE
It's also possible to light the lightbulb by touching the metal lightbulb base to one end of the battery and using only one wire to connect to the other end of the battery. If students do not discover this now, they will in Step 7.

CROSSCUTTING CONCEPTS
Energy and matter

Part 1: Building a Circuit

When the lightbulb lit up, you completed an electric circuit. The wires, D-cell, and lightbulb are all part of the circuit. **Energy transfers** occur throughout the circuit. Electricity moves the stored chemical potential energy of the D-cell to the lightbulb. The light produced by the lightbulb moves energy out into the environment surrounding the lightbulb and D-cell system in the form of light. But the lightbulb system produced light only when the parts were connected just right to form a circuit in an unbroken loop.

7. **Introduce notebook sheet**

   Distribute notebook sheet 10, *Lighting Lightbulbs*. Ask students to study the arrangements of D-cells and lightbulbs and to predict which arrangements will light up. Have students record their predictions in the small boxes at the bottom left of each drawing. Encourage students to discuss and explain their predictions in their groups.

   Students should use their D-cells and bulbs to check systems about which they disagree or are uncertain. Encourage students to write observations (e.g., no light; lightbulb works) to the right of the prediction box for each system they test.

8. **Introduce circuit vocabulary**
   Discuss the systems that produced light. Ask students to be specific about the locations on the D-cell and lightbulb where they connected the wires. (Students may not have paid close attention to the specific places where the wire touched the lightbulb.) Allow time for retesting and clarification of contact points.

   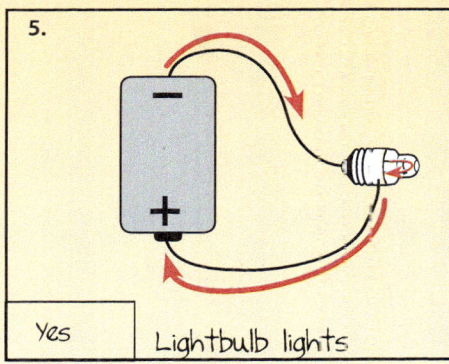

   Project the notebook sheet so you can zoom in on system 5. Use arrows to trace the path taken by the electricity from the negative end of the D-cell through the wire to one contact point on the base of the lightbulb, through the filament, to the second contact point (silver-colored metal casing of the lightbulb), and back to the positive end of the D-cell. Explain,

   *The flow of electricity through the wires is called **electric current**. Where there is electric current, there is energy available to do work. An electric circuit is the pathway through which electric current flows from the D-cell through the lightbulb and back to the cell. The circuit must form a complete pathway from one end of the D-cell back to the other end of the D-cell for the electricity to flow. We call the individual items in the circuit **components**.*

   Electric current transfers energy from component to component. This system has four components: a D-cell, a lightbulb, and two wires. The specific places where the wires need to touch the components are called

> **TEACHING NOTE**
>
> Electric current is one example of electricity. Static electricity and lightning are other examples.

> **EL NOTE**
>
> As you explain, add these words to the circuit diagram on chart paper.

Electromagnetic Force Course—FOSS Next Generation

INVESTIGATION 3 – Electromagnetism

CROSSCUTTING CONCEPTS
Energy and matter

EL NOTE

Give students a moment to draw and label the lightbulb.

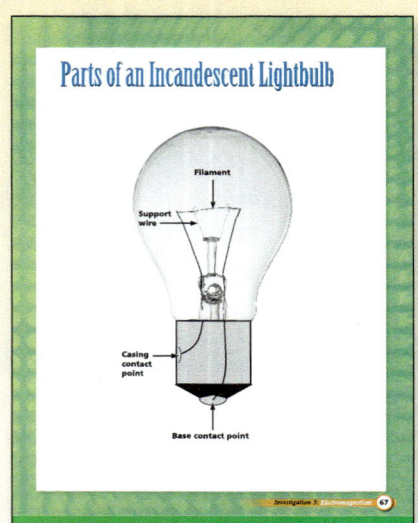

FOSS Science Resources

---

contact points. Notice that the ends of the wires are bare. The rest of the wire is covered in **insulation** that does not allow electricity to flow through it, so that portion of the wire is not a contact point.

Tell students that the electric current flows from the negative end of the D-cell (the flat terminal), through the circuit, and to the positive end (the terminal with the bump).

Add the new words to diagram 5 on the notebook sheet.

9. **Study the lightbulb filament**
   Tell students,

   *The part of the lightbulb that produces light is the **filament**. When electricity flows through the filament, the electrical energy transfers to heat and light energy. The filament gets so hot that it glows. This is called incandescence. The glowing filament gives off visible light and feels warm, both of which are evidence that energy transfer has occurred.*

   Study the lightbulb circuit very carefully, including how electricity goes through the wires and the filament itself. The electricity goes into the lightbulb through one contact point, flows through the filament, and goes out through the other contact point.

   If you have a household lightbulb with the glass removed, call the class around for a close look at the connections and how the support wires connect to the lightbulb base, go through the filament, and return to the lightbulb casing.

   If a demonstration lightbulb is not available, project teacher master E, *Inside an Incandescent Lightbulb*, for the discussion. Distribute *FOSS Science Resources* to each student and have them turn to "Parts of an Incandescent Lightbulb."

   After 1 minute of close observation, ask students to discuss in their groups how the current goes through the circuit. They should be sure to discuss the pathway through which the current flows, including the contact points on the casing (side) and base of the lightbulb and the filament.

10. **Discuss circuit principles**
    After students have studied and discussed their lightbulb circuits, discuss a few of the circuit principles.

    ➤ *When you connect a D-cell in a circuit, what contact points do you use?* [One contact point on the top of the cell; a second contact point on the bottom of the cell.]

    ➤ *How do you connect a lightbulb in a circuit? What contact points do you use to make a complete circuit to move energy?* [Contact point on the metal tip at the base; a second contact point anywhere on the side of the metal lightbulb casing.]

Part 1: Building a Circuit

➤ *How can you get a lightbulb to light with only one wire?*

Let students work on this challenge and share their successes (system 4 on notebook sheet 10).

11. Clean up

Ask Getters to collect all the materials and return them to their proper places at the materials station.

READING *in Science Resources*

12. Extend the investigation with homework

The article "Circuitry and Lightbulbs" can be assigned as homework to reinforce ideas from the class discussion. To support reading comprehension, suggest that students follow this procedure:

- Preview the text by analyzing the illustrations and thinking about what you already know about circuits and lightbulbs. Focus on the diagrams and trace the pathways of electricity. Read the captions and compare your interpretations to what the text says. Read the subtitles and think about how the article is organized. Ask yourself what you will learn from reading this article.

- Set up your notebook for note-taking using a structure such as Cornell Notes. Write the focus question at the top of two columns as a guide for note taking: What is required to complete an electric circuit?

- Write down key words, questions, and main ideas in the left column, and in the right column write down definitions, diagrams, and thoughts you have for each of the subtitles. Include labeled drawings of the circuits and lightbulbs to show how electricity flows. When you finish, make a space at the bottom to write a summary.

- Use the information in your Cornell Notes to answer the Think Questions at the end of the article. Make sure to include evidence from the text to support your answers.

➤ *How do you know when electric current is flowing in a lightbulb circuit?* [The lightbulb lights up.]

➤ *Describe the path taken by electricity through an incandescent lightbulb.* [Electricity flows into the lightbulb through a contact point in the casing. It flows through an inner wire to the filament, through the filament, then through another inner wire to a contact point in the base.]

➤ *What are some ways in which modern lightbulbs help save energy?* [They use less energy to light up, and they heat up less.]

Electromagnetic Force Course—FOSS Next Generation

SCIENCE AND ENGINEERING PRACTICES

Obtaining, evaluating, and communicating information

FOSS Science Resources

ELA CONNECTION

These suggested strategies address the Common Core State Standards for ELA for literacy.

RST 7: Integrate quantitative or technical information expressed in words in a text with a version of that information expressed visually.

RST 5: Analyze the structure an author uses to organize a text.

RST 2: Determine the central ideas or conclusions of a text; provide an accurate summary.

WHST 8: Gather relevant information from print.

RST 1: Cite evidence to support analysis of science texts.

INVESTIGATION 3 – Electromagnetism

SESSION 2 45–50 minutes

READING in Science Resources

13. Read "What Is Electricity?"

Tell students that the article "What Is Electricity?" will help them determine if their ideas about electricity are supported by scientific evidence. Distribute a copy of *FOSS Science Resources* to each student.

Have students preview the text by discussing the images and diagrams with a partner, including personal connections, what they know, and what questions they have about electricity. Call on a few volunteers to share their or their partner's ideas about what electricity is and record this on the board or chart paper.

14. Use a reading comprehension strategy

Use an Anticipation Guide. Choose a few of the statements from the class chart or use these as the "agree" or "disagree" statements:

- Electrically charged objects can attract or repel.
- Lightning is caused by clouds rubbing together.
- Copper is a good conductor of electricity.
- Batteries have electricity inside them.

Have students set up a chart in their notebooks such as the one shown here and tell them to write "A" if they agree with the statement and "D" if they disagree. As they read, they should record evidence that supports or refutes their ideas. They should also jot down any unknown words or phrases, or questions they have.

Anticipation Guide for "What Is Electricity?"		
(Agree or Disagree)	Supports my idea	Refutes my idea
1		
2		
3		
4		

When students are finished reading, give them a few minutes to discuss in their groups any difficulties they had with the reading and to review the evidence they found for and against their anticipation guide statements. (For those who finish early, have them start writing their responses to the Think Questions.) Call on the Reporters for each group to share the evidence they found from the text and questions they have. Encourage students to build on and/or challenge the ideas of others. Use the following guide to continue leading a whole-class discussion about the reading.

FOSS Science Resources

SCIENCE AND ENGINEERING PRACTICES

Obtaining, evaluating, and communicating information

Part 1: Building a Circuit

What Is Electricity?

Have you ever rubbed a balloon on your hair to hang the balloon on the wall? Have you ever felt "static cling" in your clothes? Have you ever felt a shock after walking across a carpet and then touching something?

A These experiences involve a **static** electric charge. Electric charge is a basic property of all matter. Even atoms, which make up everything, have electric charge. Thinking about what is happening at the atomic level helps us understand electricity.

Static electricity is giving this girl a wild hairstyle! Especially in dry winter weather, hairs become positively charged and repel one another, or stand on end.

A

Connect to real life: Pause to let students share their experiences with static electricity. Discuss why they think the author begins the article with these examples. Point out that these examples are evidence that electric charge is a property of all matter, an important idea they should record in their notebooks. Ask,

➤ *Can you think of other examples?*

ELA CONNECTION

This suggested strategy addresses the Common Core State Standards for ELA for literacy.

RST 6: Analyze the author's purpose in providing an explanation, describing a procedure, or discussing an experiment in a text.

Electromagnetic Force Course—FOSS Next Generation

INVESTIGATION 3 – Electromagnetism

Summarize key points: Confirm that here the text states that electrically charged objects can attract or repel. Discuss the similarities and differences between this property in magnets and in electrically charged objects. [Magnets have north and south poles, whereas charge is negative and positive. Both can attract and repel objects.]

Analyze photograph and diagram: Focus on the photograph and ask students to visualize what is happening with the atoms in the balloon and the woman's hair according to the explanation in the text. Then ask students to compare their ideas with the diagram at the bottom of the page.

Review invisible forces: Point out the last sentence and ask students to review the other invisible forces in the universe. Suggest they record this idea in their notebooks if they haven't done so already.

ELA CONNECTION

This suggested strategy addresses the Common Core State Standards for ELA for literacy.

RST 7: Integrate quantitative or technical information expressed in words in a text with a version of that information expressed visually.

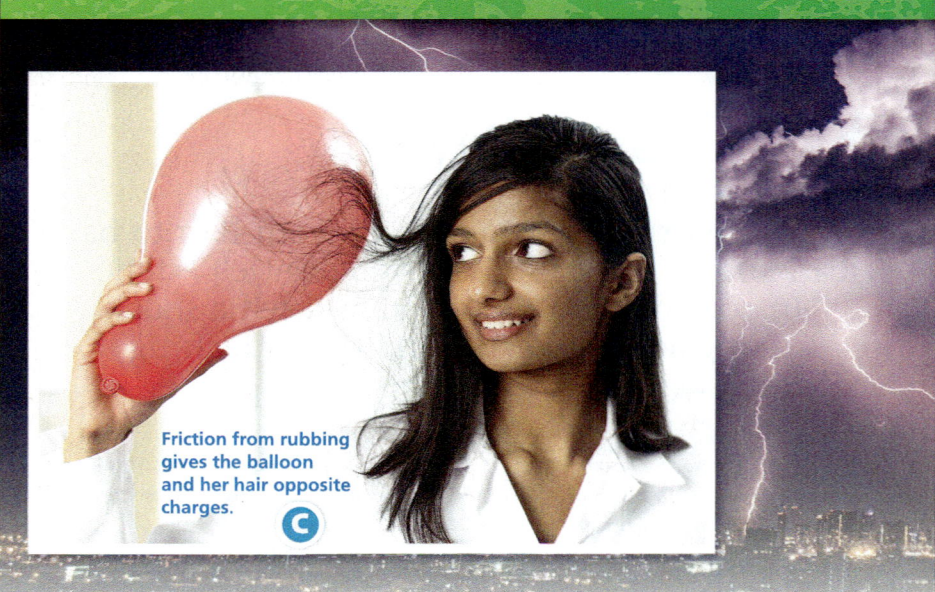

Friction from rubbing gives the balloon and her hair opposite charges.

Electric Charge

Electrons form the outer part of the atom. Each electron has a negative electric charge. If an electron breaks away from an atom, that atom is left with a positive electric charge.

When you rub a balloon on your hair, some electrons break away from the balloon's atoms. Now the balloon has a slightly positive electric charge. Where do the electrons go? They join the atoms of your hair. They give your hair a slightly negative electric charge.

Just as magnetic poles attract or repel, electrically charged objects can attract or repel.

- Opposite charges attract. Things with opposite charges, like your hair and the balloon, attract each other.
- Like charges repel. Things with negative charges repel each other. Things with positive charges repel each other.

When your hair sticks up because of static electricity, the hairs are positively charged. Each hair is being repelled by the other hairs!

The force between two charged objects is an **electric force**, another of the invisible forces of nature like gravity and magnetism.

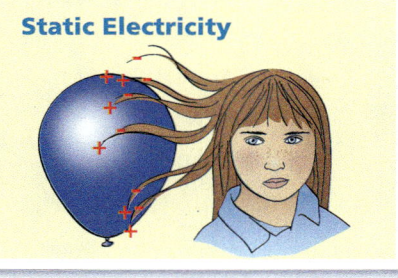

Static Electricity

When electrons move from the balloon to the hair, the balloon is left with a positive charge and the hair gains a negative charge. Now the balloon and the hair attract each other!

32

SCIENCE AND ENGINEERING PRACTICES

Developing and using models

Part 1: Building a Circuit

Lightning is a spectacular discharge of electricity in the atmosphere, usually during thunderstorms. Scientists estimate that 44 lightning bolts strike Earth's surface every second.

Electric Current

Electric charge can be static, which means not moving. Electric charge can move, which is called electric current. Remember getting a shock after walking on a carpet and touching an object? As you walk, static electric charge builds up on your body. If you have enough static electric charge, a spark will jump from your finger to the object. The spark is actually moving electric charges.

Remember your work with the lightbulb, battery, and wire? Electric charges will not move unless there is a complete circuit. Think of electric force as a push. The force pushes electrons through the circuit's pathway. If the circuit is not complete, the electric current will not flow.

Lightning is also a short-lived electric current, but on a huge scale. The bottoms of clouds build up negative charges, and the ground builds up positive charges. The lightning bolt is a giant spark as the electric current moves to balance the charges. This powerful spark is very dangerous for anyone in its path.

> **Did You Know?**
>
> It's best to seek shelter at the start of a storm, before lightning begins. Electricity travels at the speed of light, which is nearly 300 million meters per second!

Investigation 3: *Electromagnetism* 33

E

Develop vocabulary:
Point out the word *static*.

➤ Why do you think it is called static electricity? What is not moving? [The electric charge is not moving until you touch something and it moves in a spark.]

F

Summarize phenomenon: Confirm that here the text refutes the idea that lightning is caused by clouds rubbing together; rather, it occurs when the positive and negative electric charges within a cloud separate in different parts of the cloud. Reread this section and pause for students to visualize what that might look like. They may want to draw a model in their notebooks.

ELA CONNECTION

This suggested strategy addresses the Common Core State Standards for ELA for literacy.

RST 1: Cite evidence to support analysis of science texts.

Electromagnetic Force Course—FOSS Next Generation

INVESTIGATION 3 – Electromagnetism

Develop concept: Confirm that here the text supports the statement that copper is a good conductor. Discuss why it is. Make sure students understand that it is the electrons (matter) in the wire that are moving to conduct electricity (energy).

Analyze photograph: Have students examine the photo of the wires and discuss what they notice and can infer.

▶ *Why are the wires metal on the inside and plastic on the outside?* [The metal inside is a conductor, and the plastic outside insulates the wire.]

▶ *What does the structure have to do with its function?* [The outer material is designed to insulate the wire inside, so it wraps around the metal except for areas where the wire must touch other conductors.]

CROSSCUTTING CONCEPTS
Energy and matter
Structure and function

SCIENCE AND ENGINEERING PRACTICES
Constructing explanations

ELA CONNECTION
This suggested strategy addresses the Common Core State Standards for ELA for literacy.

RST 1: Cite evidence to support analysis of science texts.

Using Electricity

We use electricity every day to power lightbulbs, TVs, computers, light-rail trains, and electric cars. This electricity consists of electrons moving through wires. The wires are typically made of the metal copper. They are coated with insulating material such as plastic.

We use wires to connect an electrical energy source to a device. The source could be a battery or an electric outlet. The electric force is instantly felt throughout the wire, pushing electrons along the path. Electrons flow through the circuit, creating an electric current.

Why is copper used to make electric wires? The arrangement of electrons in copper atoms makes it easy for them to produce an electric current. Other metals, like silver, gold, steel, and tin, have the same property. They also conduct electricity well. Nonmetals have different electron arrangements and may conduct electricity poorly (called **semiconductors**). Some do not conduct at all (**insulators**). The plastic coating on a copper wire is a good insulator.

Out of sight behind walls, ceilings, and floors is a network of wires and cables that make your world run smoothly. To carry current safely, the metal conductors are wrapped inside plastic insulators.

Part 1: Building a Circuit

Battery Structure

A battery is an energy source. Energy cannot be created or destroyed. But it can transfer from one form to another or from one place to another. Batteries change chemical energy into electrical energy.

The most common disposable batteries have these essential parts.

- The positive (+) terminal touches a graphite rod surrounded by a chemical mixture (electrolyte).
- The negative terminal (–) is a zinc container.
- The electrolyte transfers electric charge between the positive and negative terminals.
- A thin layer of paper or fabric separates the electrolyte from the zinc container.

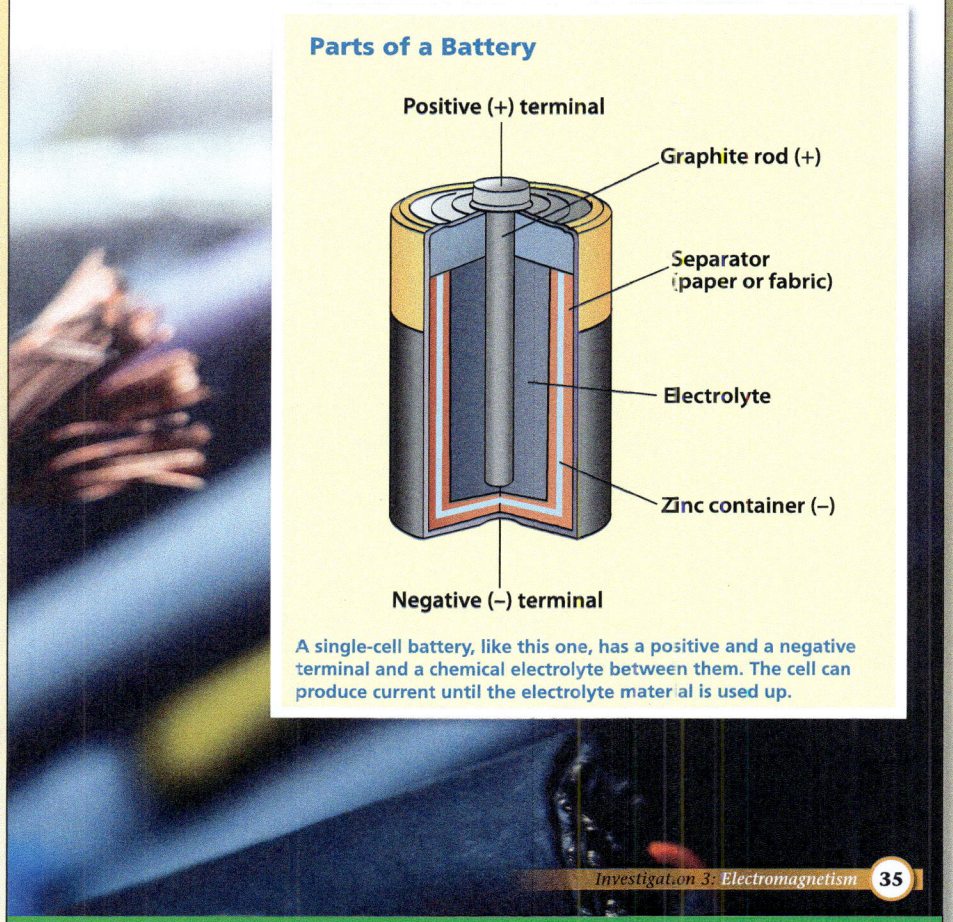

Parts of a Battery

- Positive (+) terminal
- Graphite rod (+)
- Separator (paper or fabric)
- Electrolyte
- Zinc container (–)
- Negative (–) terminal

A single-cell battery, like this one, has a positive and a negative terminal and a chemical electrolyte between them. The cell can produce current until the electrolyte material is used up.

Investigation 3: Electromagnetism 35

Summarize key points: Confirm that batteries don't have electricity inside them; rather, they are an energy source. Read the first paragraph aloud and point out to students that this is a big idea in science—energy cannot be created or destroyed.

CROSSCUTTING CONCEPTS
Energy and matter

ELA CONNECTION

This suggested strategy addresses the Common Core State Standards for ELA for literacy.

RST 8: Distinguish among facts, reasoned judgment based on research findings, and speculation in a text.

Electromagnetic Force Course—FOSS Next Generation

INVESTIGATION 3 – Electromagnetism

Develop vocabulary:
Review with students what a chemical reaction is and how it relates to the potential energy in the battery. [The stored chemicals represent chemical potential energy in the battery. The flow of electrons (electrical energy) occurs when the circuit is closed and chemical reactions can occur.]

The electrolyte inside most single-use disposable batteries is alkaline, which means it has a high pH. If a battery breaks open or leaks, the chemicals can cause severe damage to skin and eyes.

How a Battery Works

A typical D-cell has two terminals, positive (+) and negative (–). These terminals must be connected to complete a circuit with the battery. The chemical reaction inside the battery will not start until the circuit is complete.

When a wire connects two terminals of a battery to complete a circuit, a chemical reaction takes place. The reaction releases electrons from the zinc atoms. Electrons have a negative charge, so they flow through the circuit toward the positive terminal. Electric current passes through the entire circuit, including components like lightbulbs, which light up as the current passes through.

As the reaction progresses, the chemicals get used up. Eventually, the chemical reaction stops. The electric current stops flowing. The battery is dead and ready for proper disposal.

Rechargeable batteries are used in smartphones, cameras, laptop computers, electric cars, and many other devices. The most common rechargeable batteries today are lithium ion batteries.

36

ELA CONNECTION

This suggested strategy addresses the Common Core State Standards for ELA for literacy.

RST 3: Follow precisely a multistep procedure.

Part 1: Building a Circuit

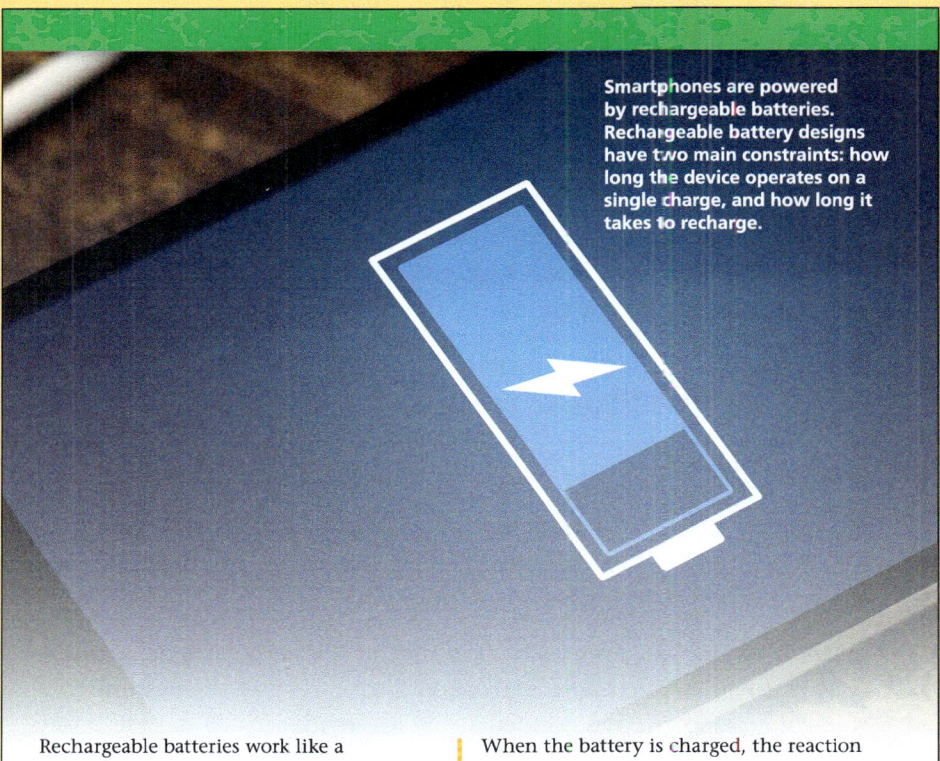

Smartphones are powered by rechargeable batteries. Rechargeable battery designs have two main constraints: how long the device operates on a single charge, and how long it takes to recharge.

Rechargeable batteries work like a disposable battery. However, connecting a rechargeable battery to an electrical energy source reverses the chemical reaction.

When the battery is charged, the reaction can take place again. Rechargeable batteries eventually wear out, but only after hundreds of recharging cycles.

Did You Know?

All batteries contain chemicals that can harm the environment. A discarded battery breaks down over time and can pollute the local ecosystem and ground water. Many stores and community organizations accept used batteries for safe disposal or recycling. Find out where to recycle batteries in your community.

Think Questions

1. If you rubbed two balloons on your hair to charge them electrically, would the two balloons attract or repel one another?
2. If you rub a balloon on your hair, you can hang the balloon on the wall. Why does the balloon stick to the wall?
3. Do all materials conduct electricity equally well?
4. Why are insulators important?

Investigation 3: *Electromagnetism* 37

Connect to real life: Discuss what the options are for battery disposal in your community.

Review Think Questions: Give students time to work on the Think Questions in their groups and then call on Reporters to share their groups' ideas. If you have balloons handy, consider letting students test their ideas.

▶ *If you rubbed two balloons on your hair to charge them electrically, would the two balloons attract or repel one another?* [Each balloon would have a slightly positive charge, so they would repel one another.]

▶ *If you rub a balloon on your hair, you can hang the balloon on the wall. Why does the balloon stick to the wall?* [The balloon would be left with a slightly positive charge. When you put it near the wall, it could attract electrons in the wall's atoms, so it can stick to the wall.]

▶ *Do all materials conduct electricity equally well?* [No. It depends on their arrangement of atoms. Metals are the best conductors.]

▶ *Why are insulators important?* [They do not conduct electricity, so they let us build safe circuits that direct electricity exactly where we want it to go, and not into other places like our hands if we touch a wire.]

ELA CONNECTION

This suggested strategy addresses the Common Core State Standards for ELA for literacy.

SL 1: Engage in collaborative discussions.

INVESTIGATION 3 – Electromagnetism

15. Record circuit ideas
Distribute a copy of notebook sheet 11, *Response Sheet—Investigation 3*, to each student. Encourage students to review their notebook entries as they write their responses.

16. Assess progress: response sheet
Collect the response sheets. Select a sample of responses from across your classes to assess students' thinking. The sample should give you a snapshot of the range of student understanding at this point in time.

What to Look For

- *Student 1 is correct: There are similarities between magnetic forces and electric charges in how they attract and repel.*

- *Student 2 is not correct: There are differences between magnetism and electricity in that electric components need to touch, whereas magnets have a force field extending out from them.*

Plan to spend 15 minutes reviewing the selected student responses. Using *Embedded Assessment Notes* as a tool, review the responses, record any alternative concepts that are evident, and decide if any next-step strategies are required before moving forward.

After your review, return the notebook sheets to students to be taped or glued into their science notebooks.

SESSION 3   45–50 minutes

17. Introduce new components
Tell students they will have a chance to build a new circuit today, and that you have a few new tools that will make their circuit construction a little easier. Hold up the lightbulb holder and demonstrate how to screw in a lightbulb. Hold up a cell holder and demonstrate how to insert a D-cell. Then show how to insert wires into the ends of the cell holder. Hold up a switch and demonstrate how to open and close the connection.

18. Complete a new circuit
Project teacher master F, *New Circuit Challenge*, and review the list of materials and the task. Each group should send a Getter to the materials station to pick up materials for their group. Each pair of students will set up a working circuit. Students will need about 5 minutes to complete a circuit using the new components.

> **TEACHING NOTE**
>
> *The lightbulbs can be a little tricky to screw in and out. Consider having your first period leave the lightbulbs and D-cells in their holders for later classes to use.*

Part 1: Building a Circuit

19. Discuss the circuit
Ask,

➤ *When the switch was closed, what evidence did you have that the circuit was completed?* [The lightbulb lit up.]

➤ *You can't see electrical energy in the circuit. What evidence do you have that electrical energy is present?* [When electrical energy transferred to the lightbulb, the lightbulb lit up and heated up.]

➤ *What other forms of energy are in the system?* [Chemical potential energy, light, heat.]

20. Introduce *electromagnetic force*
Tell students that the light they saw is a form of **electromagnetic radiation**. Poll the class to find out how many students have heard of electromagnetism before. Point out the roots of the word, that it pertains to both electricity and magnetism. Tell students,

*We are going to study the force of **electromagnetism**, which is one of the fundamental forces of nature. It is known as **electromagnetic force**. We can't observe this force as directly as a push or a pull with your hand or other physical object, but we can look for evidence of its presence and we can find ways to measure it.*

Ask,

➤ *What evidence have we seen of electrical energy?* [It caused the lightbulb to light up when the circuit was complete.]

➤ *Have we seen any evidence of magnetism through our circuit? How could we test for this?*

Give students a few moments to share their ideas, but don't confirm or deny any ideas at this time. Tell students that you think they should explore the question, and ask what tools they think might be helpful. When someone suggests using a compass, ask students to review what a compass might help them do (determine the orientation of a magnetic field because it contains a tiny magnet that can swivel).

21. Explore electromagnetism
Outline a procedure.
a. Set up a circuit with a switch and D-cell, leaving the switch open.
b. Place a compass on top of one of the wires in the circuit, in the middle of the wire. Hold it as steady as possible and wait for the needle to stop moving.
c. Close the switch and watch the compass needle.
d. Take turns opening and closing the switch until you can determine a pattern.

SCIENCE AND ENGINEERING PRACTICES
Planning and carrying out investigations

CROSSCUTTING CONCEPTS
Patterns
Cause and effect
Systems and system models

TEACHING NOTE
If some groups aren't noticing a change, ask students to share techniques that helped them see a difference. Students will eventually notice the pattern that a wire parallel to the resting compass needle will produce a more noticeable effect than one that is perpendicular.

Electromagnetic Force Course—FOSS Next Generation

INVESTIGATION 3 – Electromagnetism

Students will need to watch very closely to see the compass needle respond, as it is subtle. They will be able to identify a small shift (about 3–5 degrees) when the electric circuit is complete and electricity is passing through the wire.

22. Summarize findings

Ask groups to work together to develop an explanation of any relationship between electricity and magnetism. They should record diagrams in their notebooks to describe their results.

Ask groups to share their results with the class, and allow time for retesting as needed. Summarize the findings.

It looks like there is some relationship between electricity and magnetism, because when an electric current passes through a wire, we can observe evidence of a magnetic field. We will explore this relationship further in the next class session.

23. Record vocabulary

Give students a few moments to review and clarify the vocabulary developed in this part. Suggest that they add the vocabulary words to their diagrams and make sure they understand their meanings. This is also a good time to update their vocabulary indexes if they haven't already done so.

If students need further support, have them work together in groups to construct a concept map.
- Write the vocabulary words on self-stick notes.
- Organize the words on a large piece of paper according to how they relate.
- Draw lines connecting the words and on those lines, write a few words to explain how they relate to each other.

When students are finished, post their charts on the wall. If time permits, let them examine the different ways each group organized the concepts. Keep the concept maps handy for students to revisit with new vocabulary words. They can also copy them into their notebooks.

24. Answer the focus question

Have students answer the focus question in their notebooks.

▶ *What is required to complete an electric circuit?*

Challenge students to come up with a general statement as to what constitutes an electric circuit, to use as many of their new vocabulary words as possible, and to use diagrams where appropriate.

Magnetic field around a current-carrying wire

battery
circuit
component
contact point
electric current
electromagnetic force
electromagnetic radiation
electromagnetism
energy transfer
filament
insulation

EL NOTE

For students who need support, you can also provide sentence frames such as
To build an electric circuit you need ___.
It's important to ___.
Evidence that the circuit is complete is ___.
An electric circuit means ___.
For example, this diagram shows ___.

Part 1: Building a Circuit

WRAP-UP/WARM-UP

25. Review notebook entries

Give students a few minutes to review and share their notebook entries with a partner. Have them take turns explaining their diagrams to each other. Encourage them to give each other constructive feedback and to revise their entries if needed. This is also a good opportunity to have students discuss how the concept of cause and effect helps them understand circuits.

INVESTIGATION 3 – Electromagnetism

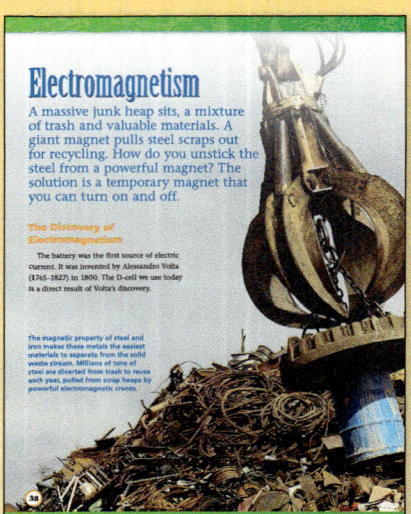

FOSS Science Resources

MATERIALS for
Part 2: Building an Electromagnet

Provided equipment
For each student
- 1 *FOSS Science Resources: Electromagnetic Force*
  - "Electromagnetism"

For each group
- 1 Rivet
- 1 Electromagnet wire, 24-gauge, 150 cm
- 1 Wire, 20-gauge, 15 cm
- 1 D-cell
- 1 Cell holder
- 1 Switch
- • Paper clips, 1/2 box
- 1 Plastic cup
- 1 Magnet, doughnut-shaped

For the class
- 1 Wire stripper

Teacher-supplied items
For the class
- 1 Metric ruler or meter tape

FOSSweb resources
For the class
- • Online activity, "Kitchen Magnets"

For the teacher
- • Teacher master G, *Electromagnet Setup*
- • *Embedded Assessment Notes*
- • Teaching slides, 3.2

Teacher Master G

226   **Full Option Science System**

Part 2: Building an Electromagnet

GETTING READY for
Part 2: Building an Electromagnet

Quick Start

Schedule	1 session active investigation 1 session reading
Preview	• Preview the FOSSweb Resources by Investigation for this part (such as printable masters, teaching slides, and online activities) • Preview the in-class reading: "Electromagnetism," Step 13 • Plan for homework: online activity, Step 19
Print or Copy	**For the teacher** • *Embedded Assessment Notes*
Prepare Material	• Cut new wires **A** • Conserve D-cells **B** • Practice new way to connect wires **C** • Check rivet washers **D** • Check D-cells **E** • Put 1/2 box paper clips in each cup
Plan for Assessment	• Review Step 18, "What to Look For" in the notebook entry

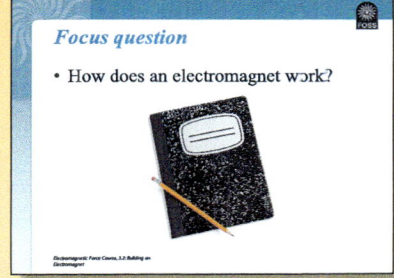

Teaching slides, 3.2

Electromagnetic Force Course—FOSS Next Generation

INVESTIGATION 3 – Electromagnetism

Preparation Details

A ▸ Cut new wires

Two different wires are used in this investigation, the 20-gauge wires from Part 1 (15 cm) and new 24-gauge electromagnet wires (150 cm).

For each group, cut one 150 cm electromagnet wire from the thinner 24-gauge insulated wire, usually yellow in this kit. (The larger the gauge number, the thinner the wire.) Strip about 2 cm of plastic insulation from each end of the electromagnet wires.

To store the wires so they will not get tangled, wrap each wire loosely around four fingers of one hand. Slide the loop off your hand, place the index finger of each hand inside the loop, and give the loop a half twist to make a figure 8.

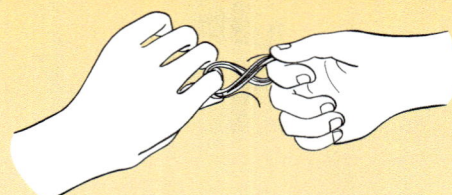

B ▸ Conserve D-cells

Electromagnets consume enormous amounts of electricity. An electromagnet can drain the D-cell's power in minutes. You know this is happening if a cell gets warm. Students should keep the switch open except when conducting a test. Have students get in the habit of keeping the switch in a wide open position with the switch lever as high as possible, so you can check from a distance that the battery is not being accidentally drained.

C ▸ Practice new way to connect wires

Throughout this investigation, use a slightly different technique with the battery holders. To ensure consistency in testing, students should connect the wires to the D-cell holder springs by inserting each wire as close to the cell terminal as possible. To do this, push the D-cell toward one of the springs in the holder, compressing that spring and opening up the spring at the other terminal end. At the "open" spring, insert the bare end of the wire into the coil as close to the terminal as possible. Repeat this and insert the second wire at the other terminal.

Wires inserted at other distances, such as the far end of the coil, will decrease the strength of the electromagnet and affect the test results in this part and Part 3. Encourage students to be consistent, and check for this as you circulate among groups.

Part 2: Building an Electromagnet

D **Check rivet washers**

The steel rivet (iron core) has three rubber washers on the shaft. The washer closest to the rivet head serves as a boundary for the wire coils. Students wind the wire between the rivet head and the first washer. The other two washers are not used. Check the locations of these washers in the illustration in the sidebar.

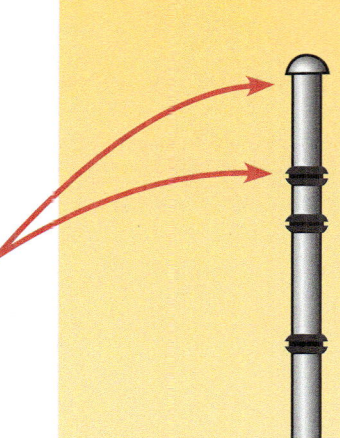

E **Check D-cells**

If you started this module with used D-cells, or if they have been used a lot, you might want to test them before launching into this investigation. Cells that fail to pass should be retired to the recycling box. Replace them with fresh alkaline D-cells. Test the cells as follows:

a. Leaving about 10 cm wire free at the end, make an electromagnet by wrapping one of the 150 cm electromagnet wires 40 times in the same direction tightly around a rivet, between the head and the first rubber washer.

b. Put the electromagnet into a circuit, using one D-cell in a holder and a switch. Connect the wires near the battery terminals for the best results.

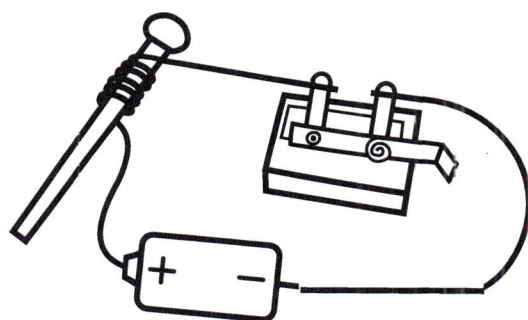

c. Open a box of paper clips.
d. Close the switch to complete the circuit and pick up paper clips with the rivet-head end of the electromagnet.

Retire any cell that fails to pick up at least five paper clips. Provide each group with one of the strong D-cells to make an electromagnet.

Electromagnetic Force Course—FOSS Next Generation

INVESTIGATION 3 – Electromagnetism

FOCUS QUESTION
How does an electromagnet work?

GUIDING the Investigation
Part 2: Building an Electromagnet

SESSION 1
Students will . . .
- Review ideas about electromagnetism (Step 1)
- Think about how to make an electromagnet (Steps 2–5)
- Build and analyze electromagnets (Steps 6–11)

SESSION 2
Students will . . .
- Review principles of electromagnet design (Step 12)
- Read about electromagnetism (Steps 13, 14)
- Have a sense-making discussion about the electromagnet design (Step 15)
- Record vocabulary and answer the focus question (Steps 16–18)
- Extend the investigation with homework and review notebook entries (Steps 19, 20)

SESSION 1   45–50 minutes

1. **Review magnetic fields in circuits**
   Give students a few minutes to share their notebook entries from the last session with a partner. Then ask,

   ➤ *We know that a magnetic field surrounds a magnet. What did you learn about magnets and electricity in the last part of the investigation?* [The compass showed a magnetic field when electricity ran through a wire, but there was no measurable magnetic field when the circuit was incomplete.]

   Ask students to share questions they have about the relationship between electricity and magnetism. Add that you have some ideas for how you think they could explore this relationship further.

2. **Introduce the challenge**
   Tell students,

   I was thinking about an old junkyard crane that I once saw. The crane used a huge magnet to lift cars and put them in a giant crusher. The crane operator turned the magnet off to drop the cars.

   ➤ *Can you make a magnet that turns on and off?*

SCIENCE AND ENGINEERING PRACTICES
Asking questions

EL NOTE
Project or provide an image of a junkyard crane. Give students a few minutes to discuss what they know about these machines.

Part 2: Building an Electromagnet

3. **Review magnetic interactions**

   Use a magnet, a steel rivet, and one cup of paper clips to demonstrate the following.

   a. Use a doughnut-shaped permanent magnet to pick up some paper clips from the cup. Ask students to describe what is happening. [The magnet attracts the paper clips because they are steel, but you can't turn the magnet off.]

   b. Introduce the rivet as a new tool, and use the magnet to pick up the rivet. Ask students what they can tell about the rivet by seeing the demonstration. [The rivet sticks, so it must be made of steel or iron.] Confirm that the rivet is made of steel.

   c. Use the rivet stuck to the magnet to pick up some paper clips. Ask students to describe what is happening. [Temporary magnetism is created in the rivet by the magnet, and you can't turn it off without removing the magnet.]

   d. Try to use the rivet by itself to pick up paper clips. [No paper clips stick to the steel rivet because it is not a magnet.]

4. **Discuss strength of magnetic field**

   Ask,

   ➤ *When you tested a complete circuit with a compass, how strong was the magnetic field surrounding the wire?* [Quite weak.]

   ➤ *What ideas do you have to make the magnetic field surrounding the wire much stronger?*

   Give students time to talk in their groups and come up with ideas. After several minutes, give this hint.

   ➤ *What experiments have we done in class that resulted in a stronger magnetic field?* [Adding magnets.]

   Give groups another few minutes to think about how this concept could be adapted to the wire challenge. Solicit ideas in a class discussion. Guide students to these conclusions through the discussion.

   - Magnetic fields can overlap to create a stronger force.
   - Wrapping or coiling the wire could add magnetic fields together and create a stronger magnetic force.

   SCIENCE AND ENGINEERING PRACTICES
   Designing solutions

5. **Focus question: How does an electromagnet work?**

   Tell students that coiling up wire forms an electromagnet. That is what they will build and learn about today. Write or project the question on the board, and have students record it in their notebooks.

   ➤ *How does an **electromagnet** work?*

INVESTIGATION 3 – Electromagnetism

> **NOTE**
> Remind students often to keep the circuits *open* except when actually conducting a test.

SCIENCE AND ENGINEERING PRACTICES
Constructing explanations

6. **Build electromagnets**
   Project teacher master G, and walk through the setup by having students read the instructions out loud as you model. Have Getters pick up the long wires and other materials. Do not distribute the doughnut-shaped magnets at this time. Give students time to work in their groups to make an electromagnet that turns on and off.

   Remind students to leave their switches in the off position with the switch lever as high as possible when they are not testing, so they will keep the batteries from accidentally draining too quickly.

   Visit each group as they work and show them the new way to connect the D-cell so the wires are as close to the terminal of the cell as possible. (This was described in Preparation Details.)

7. **Discuss electromagnet designs**
   When students have successfully constructed electromagnets, call for attention and ask them to *make sure their switches are open*. Call on individual students to share their discoveries. Ask,

   ➤ *What can you tell me about your system?*

   ➤ *What details of the design were important to get the electromagnet working?*

   ➤ *What does wrapping the wire around the* **core** *accomplish?*

   Students may offer these ideas.

   - The rivet becomes a magnet that can be used to pick up paper clips.
   - The rivet is a magnet only while the circuit is closed. The magnetism goes away when the switch is open.
   - The wire must be wrapped around the rivet. Wrapping the wire adds many weak fields on top of one another.
   - The bare wire ends must be in a circuit with a switch and the D-cell.

8. **Define** *electromagnet*
   Tell students,

   You made an electromagnet. An electromagnet is a magnet made using the flow of electricity through an insulated wire to produce a magnetic field. The magnetic field gets stronger when you wrap the wire around a piece of iron or steel, which becomes a temporary magnet when the magnetic field of the wire induces magnetism in the core. The piece of steel around which the wire is wrapped is the core of the electromagnet. The wrapped wire is called a coil.

   Have students draw their electromagnets. It is important that they make detailed illustrations so that they can label each component in the next step.

Part 2: Building an Electromagnet

9. **Label the components**
   With students reviewing their diagrams, ask,

   ➤ *What are the components of this electromagnet circuit?* [Switch, wire, steel rivet/core, D-cell, cell holder.]

   Have students label each component in their diagrams.

10. **Explore interactions with permanent magnets**
    Tell students that they will now have a chance to explore the interaction between their electromagnet and a permanent magnet. Distribute one doughnut-shaped magnet to each group.

    With the electromagnet on, give students a chance to explore the interactions between the permanent magnet and the rivet head. Ask groups to open the switch and share findings with the class. Students will notice attraction (and may be able to notice repulsion) of the magnet, depending on how they position the permanent magnet. Give students a chance to retest until all groups can confirm that the electromagnet attracts or repels the permanent magnet, depending on its position.

    Students should then reverse the direction of current flow in the electromagnet and observe what happens to the polarity of the electromagnet.

11. **Clean up**
    Ask Getters to disassemble their electromagnets (including uncoiling the wire and bundling it as it was at the beginning of class) and return all the materials to the materials station. In your last class, keep one electromagnet for reference the next day. The cups of paper clips can be nested for easy storage. They will be used in Part 3.

    > **TEACHING NOTE**
    >
    > This knowledge will support students' understanding of electric motors in Investigation 4.

    > **TEACHING NOTE**
    >
    > Note that depending upon the charge of the battery, the repulsion phenomenon may be very subtle. It is easier to observe if the magnet is held and moved toward the electromagnet.
    >
    > Students can think of this as a net force interaction. The attraction of the permanent magnet may be stronger than the repulsion of the electromagnet.

    SESSION 2 45–50 minutes

    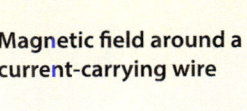

12. **Discuss magnetic force**
    Ask students to think back to their experience with the compass and electric circuit.

    ➤ *How would you compare the magnetic force of a single wire in a circuit with an electromagnet coil?* [The coil has a much stronger magnetic force.]

    ➤ *What makes the magnetic force of the electromagnet coil so much stronger?* [The wire is coiled so the magnetic field of the wire is added together many times.]

    Highlight this last point. It is the additive effect of magnetic fields that gives an electromagnet its strong magnetic force.

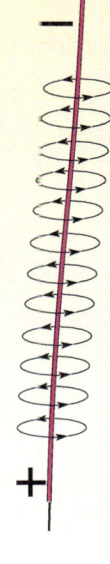

Magnetic field around a current-carrying wire

INVESTIGATION 3 – Electromagnetism

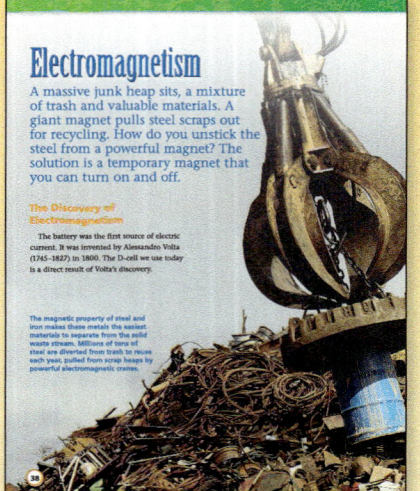

FOSS Science Resources

READING *in Science Resources*

13. Prepare to read "Electromagnetism"

Tell students that the article "Electromagnetism" will give them a chance to think in more detail about the relationship between electricity and magnetism. Distribute a copy of *FOSS Science Resources* to each student.

14. Use a reading comprehension strategy

Have students preview the text by discussing the illustrations with a partner. They should also take note of the subtitles and words in bold. Suggest that students read this article with the Think Questions in mind. Have them set up two columns in their notebooks to record their notes and ideas as they read. In the first column they jot down notes from the article that pertain to the Think Questions. In the second column they record the Think Questions leaving space in between for writing down their own thinking about the question based on the information from the text. Encourage them to include at least one new question they have for each section.

Notes (information related to the question)	Think Questions (plus my new ideas and questions)
	What was Ørsted's historical discovery?
	How do you make an electromagnet?
	How could you make an electromagnet stronger?

Once most students have finished reading and taking notes, use the following guide to lead an in-class discussion of the article.

SCIENCE AND ENGINEERING PRACTICES

Obtaining, evaluating, and communicating information

ELA CONNECTION

This suggested strategy addresses the Common Core State Standards for ELA for literacy.

SL 4: Present claims and findings.

Part 2: Building an Electromagnet

Electromagnetism

A massive junk heap sits, a mixture of trash and valuable materials. A giant magnet pulls steel scraps out for recycling. How do you unstick the steel from a powerful magnet? The solution is a temporary magnet that you can turn on and off.

The Discovery of Electromagnetism

The battery was the first source of electric current. It was invented by Alessandro Volta (1745–1827) in 1800. The D-cell we use today is a direct result of Volta's discovery.

The magnetic property of steel and iron makes these metals the easiest materials to separate from the solid waste stream. Millions of tons of steel are diverted from trash to reuse each year, pulled from scrap heaps by powerful electromagnetic cranes.

A

Connect to real life: If students have not observed a junkyard crane, have them visualize what it might look like, sound like, and the amount of force it takes to lift heavy metal objects like cars. You might want to search online for a video of one in action.

B

Share prior knowledge: Give students a moment to share any prior knowledge they have about Volta and the history of batteries.

ELA CONNECTION

This suggested strategy addresses the Common Core State Standards for ELA for literacy.

RST 9: Compare and contrast the information gained from experiments, simulations, video, or multimedia sources with that gained from reading a text on the same topic.

INVESTIGATION 3 – Electromagnetism

Analyze diagrams: Have students analyze and discuss these diagrams.

➤ *What are the parts in this system?*

➤ *What is the function of each of these parts?*

➤ *What is different in the second panel?*

➤ *How does this diagram compare to our investigations in class?*

Summarize text: Call on a few volunteers to share their responses to the first Think Question, including any new questions they'd like to investigate about electromagnets.

SCIENCE AND ENGINEERING PRACTICES
Asking questions

ELA CONNECTION

This suggested strategy addresses the Common Core State Standards for ELA for literacy.

RST 7: Integrate quantitative or technical information expressed in words in a text with a version of that information expressed visually.

Hans Christian Ørsted (1777–1851) was a Danish physics professor in the late 1700s. He was fascinated by Volta's battery. Ørsted conducted many experiments with electric current.

In 1820, Ørsted was demonstrating that electric current makes wires hot. When he closed the electric circuit, the needle of a compass on the lecture table rotated. Some people think that Ørsted had planned to show the relationship between electric current and magnetism that day. Others think it was just a lucky accident. We will never know for sure.

Here is what might have happened. Ørsted had a thin wire connected to a battery and a switch. A compass needle was right under one of the wires forming the circuit.

When Ørsted closed the circuit to deliver electric current to the thin wire, the needle rotated.

When Ørsted made this discovery, he conducted more experiments. Four months later, he wrote about his findings. He concluded that a flow of electric current produces a magnetic field.

This important discovery resulted in hundreds of inventions in the years that followed. One was the **electromagnet**, a magnet that can be turned on and off.

The Discovery of Electromagnetism

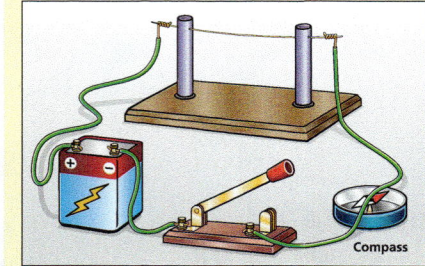
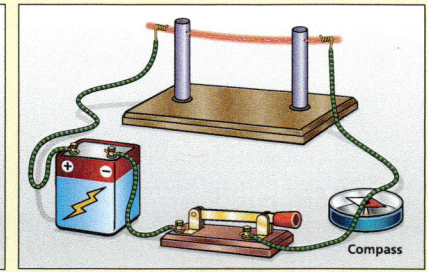

Whether by accident or by design, Ørsted discovered the relationship between electricity and magnetism. Both are caused by the electromagnetic force.

Part 2: Building an Electromagnet

Electromagnetism

The wire you have been using to make circuits is made of copper. Copper is not magnetic. There is no magnetic field around a copper wire. You can confirm or prove this by bringing a compass close to a copper wire. The compass needle does not move.

Things change when you connect a copper wire to a source of electricity, such as a D-cell. While electric current flows through the wire, a magnetic field surrounds it. When you bring a compass close to the wire, the compass needle rotates slightly. When you break the circuit, the magnetic field disappears. The compass needle points north again.

The magnetic field around a wire that has electric current flowing through it may not be very strong. But if you put two magnetic fields together, the magnetism becomes stronger. That is what happens when you coil up a wire. The magnetic field around each loop of wire adds to the fields from other loops. The greater the number of loops, the stronger the total magnetic field is.

Electric Current and Magnetic Field

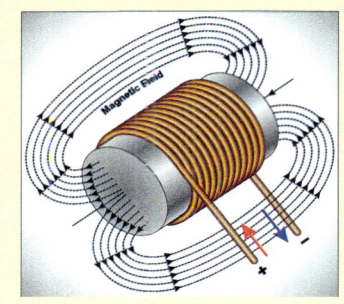

Copper itself is not magnetic. But the flow of electric current through a copper wire creates a magnetic field around the wire.

Magnetic Fields of Electromagnets

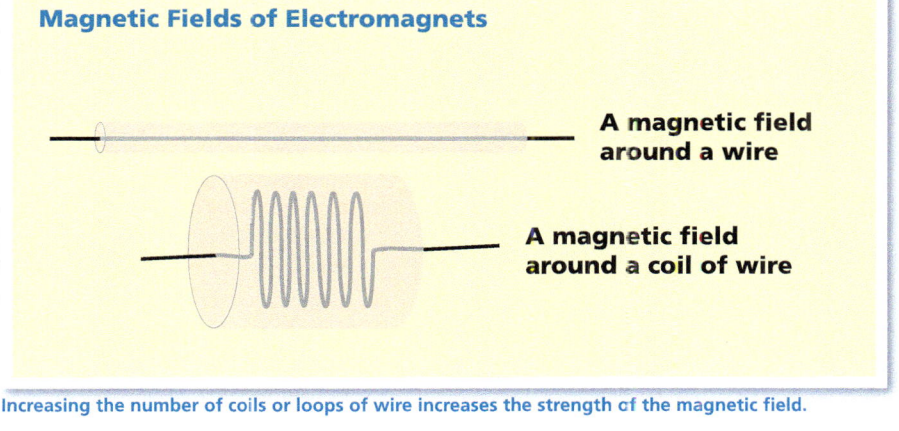

A magnetic field around a wire

A magnetic field around a coil of wire

Increasing the number of coils or loops of wire increases the strength of the magnetic field.

40

E

Summarize text: Ask students to share with a partner the main idea of this section.

▶ *How do the diagrams illustrate this point?* [Both diagrams show that adding coils to an electromagnet increases its magnetic field strength.]

▶ *What other evidence can you provide that this is true?* [In class, we tested a number of coils and learned that it affects the strength of an electromagnet.]

ELA CONNECTION

This suggested strategy addresses the Common Core State Standards for ELA for literacy.

RST 9: Compare and contrast the information gained from experiments, simulations, video, or multimedia sources with that gained from reading a text on the same topic.

INVESTIGATION 3 – Electromagnetism

Compare and contrast: Have students compare the junkyard crane to the electromagnet they built in class.

➤ How are they the same?
➤ How are they different?
➤ Why do you think the author used this example?

Review Think Questions:
Give students time to work on the Think Questions in their groups and then call on Reporters to share their groups' ideas.

➤ What was Ørsted's historic discovery? [He realized that an electric circuit produced a magnetic field.]

➤ How do you make an electromagnet? [You run electric current through a long wire, and coil the wire around a core. The magnetic field surrounding each wire wrap adds together for a stronger magnetic net force.]

➤ How do you think you could make an electromagnet stronger? [Accept all ideas. Students will test this in the next part of the investigation.]

ELA CONNECTION

This suggested strategy addresses the Common Core State Standards for ELA for literacy.

RST 6: Analyze the author's purpose in providing an explanation, describing a procedure, or discussing an experiment in a text.

Steel is the world's most recycled material, more than paper, plastic, glass, and aluminum combined. Yesterday's cars and toasters may be tomorrow's bridges and skyscrapers.

What happens when the coil wraps around a steel **core**, like a rivet? The strong magnetic field induces magnetism in the steel. The steel becomes a temporary magnet as long as the electric circuit is complete. And when you open the switch, the magnetism turns off. This is **electromagnetism**.

Not long after Ørsted's discovery, Michael Faraday (1791–1867) discovered that magnetism could be used to create electric current. From then on, it was clear that one force was behind both magnetism and electricity. That force is the **electromagnetic force**.

Now you know how metal objects can quickly be sorted for recycling. Strong electromagnets are used in recycling centers for separating some metals (mostly iron and steel) from other scrap metal. Aluminum cans, for example, are left behind because they are not attracted to magnets. Turn on a large electromagnet over a junk heap, and watch as it lifts steel parts from the pile. Move the electromagnet over your collection bin. Then break the circuit. When the current stops flowing, the electromagnet no longer has induced magnetism. The steel falls into the bin below.

Think Questions

1. What was Ørsted's historic discovery?
2. How do you make an electromagnet?
3. How do you think you could make an electromagnet stronger?

Investigation 3: Electromagnetism 41

Part 2: Building an Electromagnet

15. Discuss the magnetic field

Ask students to think about their electromagnets. Ask,

➤ *In an electromagnet, is electricity flowing through the wire? What is your evidence?* [Yes. The magnet turns on when the circuit is complete.]

➤ *Is electricity flowing into the core? Why or why not?* [No, because the part of the wire that is touching it is covered in a rubber/plastic material (insulation).]

Tell students,

When electric current flows through a wire, a magnetic field is produced around the wire. You can detect this magnetic field on a straight wire, but when you coil the wire around a core, the magnetic fields of the wire coils overlap and add, so the magnetic force intensifies. This produces an electromagnet.

The wire is covered in insulation, so electricity doesn't travel into the steel rivet (the core), but the magnetic field does. Because the core (rivet) is now in a strong magnetic field, induced magnetism makes the core a temporary magnet that you can control by turning on and off the flow of electric current.

Ask a few more questions to probe for understanding.

➤ *Is the core a magnet? Why or why not?* [When the circuit is complete, the core is a magnet. It could pick up metal items when the electric current flowed.]

➤ *Can magnetic fields pass through materials like the plastic insulation on the wire?* [Yes. We have evidence from this experiment that it can pass through plastic. Magnetic fields pass through most materials.]

➤ *What is happening to the core when the magnetic field around the core is present?* [It is a temporary induced magnet while the electric current flows.]

16. Record vocabulary

Give students a few moments to review or clarify the vocabulary developed in this part. Tell students that these words should be included in their diagrams and explained in their answer to the focus question. This is also a good time to update their vocabulary indexes if they haven't already done so.

17. Answer the focus question

Have students answer the focus question in their notebooks.

➤ *How does an electromagnet work?*

SCIENCE AND ENGINEERING PRACTICES
Developing and using models
Constructing explanations

CROSSCUTTING CONCEPTS
Systems and system models

core
electromagnet

Electromagnetic Force Course—FOSS Next Generation

INVESTIGATION 3 – Electromagnetism

EL NOTE

For students who need support, suggest they begin by describing the electromagnet activity. You can also provide sentence frames such as:
We are trying to find out ___.
We explored this question by ___.
We found out that ___.
This is how an electromagnet works: First, ___. Next, ___. Finally, ___.
What I found most surprising was ___. It makes me think about ___.
One question I have is ___.

Ask students to discuss answers in their small groups and share with the class, so that students who are stuck will get some support from classmates.

Students can use evidence from class to start the answer to this question: magnetic fields are present when an electric current flows, and electric current can induce magnetism in an iron core. However, students will be left with some unanswered questions. These questions will be addressed in greater depth in their high school and college physics classes.

18. **Assess progress: notebook entry**

    After students complete their responses to the focus question, collect a sample of notebooks from each class. The sample should give you a snapshot of the range of student understanding at this point in time.

    ### What to Look For

    - *Students explain that electric current running through a wire creates a small magnetic field around the wire.*
    - *Students explain that the coil of an electromagnet adds together the magnetic field of each wire wrap when current runs through the system.*
    - *Students explain that the coil induces magnetism in the core, causing it to become a temporary magnet.*

    Plan to spend 15 minutes reviewing the selected student responses. Using *Embedded Assessment Notes* as a tool, review the responses, record any alternative concepts that are evident, and decide if any next-step strategies are required before moving forward.

19. **Extend the investigation with homework**

    Students can explore the online activity "Kitchen Magnets" at home, then look for items with electromagnets in their own home, and submit a list of them.

Part 2: Building an Electromagnet

WRAP-UP/WARM-UP

20. Review notebook entries

Give students a few minutes to share responses to the focus question with someone from a different group. Encourage them to give each other constructive feedback and to revise and/or add ideas to their responses under a line of learning.

INVESTIGATION 3 – Electromagnetism

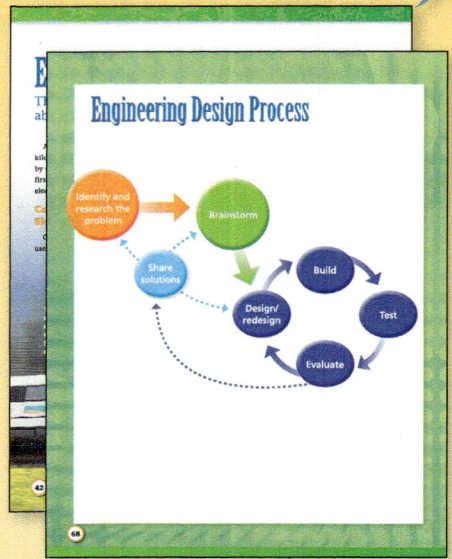

FOSS Science Resources

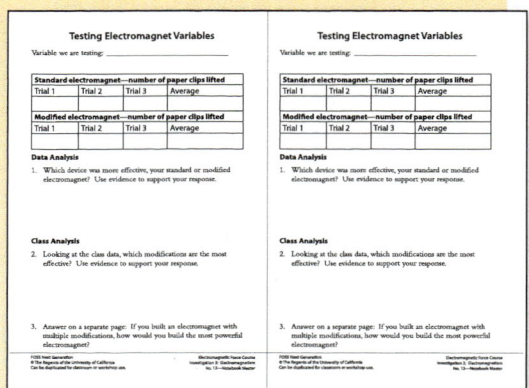

No. 12—Notebook Master

Teacher Master H

MATERIALS for
Part 3: Improving the Design

Provided equipment

For each student
- 1 FOSS Science Resources: Electromagnetic Force
  - "Engineering Design Process"
  - "Electromagnetic Engineering"

For each group
- 1 Rivet
- 1 Electromagnet wire, 24-gauge, 150 cm
- 2 Wires, 20-gauge, 15 cm
- 2 D-cells
- 2 Cell holders
- 1 Switch
- • Cup of paper clips from Part 2

For the class
- 1 Wire stripper
- 2 Wires, 20-gauge, 150 cm
- 2 D-cells
- 2 Cell holders
- 4 Wires, 20-gauge, 15 cm
- 2 Paper clips

Teacher-supplied items

For each student
- 1 Self-stick note
- 1 Scissors

For the class
- 2 Pens or pencils
- 2 Nails, 5 cm or longer

Part 3: Improving the Design

FOSSweb resources

For each student
1. Notebook sheet 12, *Testing Electromagnet Variables*
1. *Investigation 3 I-Check*

For the class
- Online activity, "Virtual Electromagnet"

For the teacher
- Teacher master H, *Electromagnet Variables—Class Data*
- *Performance Assessment Checklist*
1. *Assessment Record*
- Teaching slides, 3.3

INVESTIGATION 3 – Electromagnetism

GETTING READY for
Part 3: Improving the Design

Quick Start

Schedule	2 sessions active investigation 1 session review 1–2 sessions assessment
Preview	• Preview the FOSSweb Resources by Investigation for this part (such as printable masters, teaching slides, and online activities) • Plan for homework: Online activity: "Virtual Electromagnet," Step 15 Reading: "Electromagnetic Engineering," Step 18
Print or Copy	**For each student** • Notebook sheet 12 • *Investigation 3 I-Check*, or schedule it on FOSSmap **For the teacher** • *Performance Assessment Checklist*
Prepare Material	• Organize materials for testing **A**
Plan for Assessment	• Review Step 10, "What to Look For" in the performance assessment • Plan for benchmark assessment, Step 19, *I-Check 3*

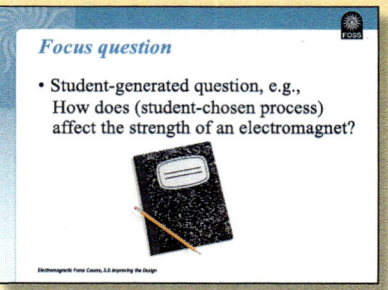

Teaching slides, 3.3

Part 3: Improving the Design

Preparation Details

A▶ Organize materials for testing

In this part, students will brainstorm ways to improve the electromagnet design, and then test their ideas. Each group will retest the standard design from Part 2, then test just one modification to the design. Depending on what ideas students come up with, you might want to provide additional materials. Here are some examples of what students might suggest and test.

- Decrease number of winds (same wire, wind less times)
- Increase number of winds (same wire, wind more times)
- Different wire (wrap 20-gauge wire around core instead of 24-gauge)
- More D-cells (students connect two or more D-cells in series)
- Different core material (wrap wire around a pen or pencil)
- Different core diameter (wrap wire around a nail or straightened paper clip)

Each group will investigate only one variable. Depending on the ideas that the class brainstorms, and how realistic they are to test, you might have two groups test the same variable.

INVESTIGATION 3 – Electromagnetism

GUIDING *the Investigation*
Part 3: *Improving the Design*

FOCUS QUESTION

Student-generated question, e.g., How does (student-chosen process) affect the strength of an electromagnet?

SESSION 1

Students will . . .
- Think about possible modifications to electromagnets (Steps 1–3)
- Define the engineering problem (Steps 4–6)
- Build and test modified electromagnets (Steps 7, 8)

SESSION 2

Students will . . .
- Combine class results and analyze data (Steps 9–11)
- Use results to design next electromagnet modifications (Step 12)
- Record vocabulary and answer the focus question (Steps 13, 14)
- Extend the investigation with homework (Step 15)

SESSION 3

Students will . . .
- Review notebook entries (Step 16)
- Answer the guiding question (Step 17)
- Extend the investigation with homework (Step 18)

SESSIONS 4–5

Students will . . .
- Demonstrate understanding on *I-Check 3* (Step 19)
- Review I-Check items through next-step strategies (Step 20)

SESSION 1 *45–50 minutes*

1. **Consider the electromagnet design**
   Have students open their notebooks to the electromagnet diagram they drew and quickly review the components and their functions. Tell students that their challenge for the day is to improve upon the design of the electromagnet.

2. **Discuss ideas in groups**
   Have students talk with their groups for 3 minutes to make a list of several variables they think might affect the strength of magnetism of an electromagnet. They can record this list under their focus-question response in their notebooks.

Part 3: Improving the Design

3. **Share ideas**

   Go around the room, asking each group to share one idea from their list, as you record a class list on the board. Repeat the process until there is a comprehensive list on the board.

   Tell students,

   You've generated a list of variables that might affect the strength of an electromagnet. Some of these ideas might not be realistic to test in the classroom. (Give an example from the list if applicable.) But some of these we can test today.

   Show students the materials you have provided, and ask them which idea they might test with each material. For example, when you hold up the electromagnet wire, you could make a note on the board next to "change wire thickness," if that is an idea that students have come up with.

   You might have to help students identify which ideas are realistic to test, and you might have to hint at new ideas if their class list is meager.

   - Decrease number of winds (same wire, wind less times)
   - Increase number of winds (same wire, wind more times)
   - Different wire (wrap 20-gauge wire around core instead of 24-gauge)
   - More D-cells (students connect two or more D-cells in series)
   - Different core material (wrap wire around a pen or pencil)
   - Different core diameter (wrap wire around a nail or straightened paper clip)

   Cross ideas off the list if there are no materials to test them, so that you are left with a class list of viable candidate variables for testing.

SCIENCE AND ENGINEERING PRACTICES
Planning and carrying out investigations

INVESTIGATION 3 – Electromagnetism

SCIENCE AND ENGINEERING PRACTICES

Defining problems

Planning and carrying out investigations

TEACHING NOTE

You may need to tell students that *criterion* is the singular form of of *criteria*, as they are likely more familiar with the latter.

4. **Discuss how to test variables**
   Tell students,

   In the last session, we worked with a standard design for an electromagnet. Each group will retest the standard design, and each group will modify the electromagnet design to see how it affects the strength of the electromagnet. We have identified a list of variables that we want to test, and that we can practically test in the classroom today.

   Ask,

   ➤ *What are some **constraints** of this challenge?* [Adhere to the standard design, and modify only one variable.]

   ➤ *What is the **criterion** we are looking for?* [Whether a modification to the electromagnet design changes the strength of its magnetic field.]

   ➤ *What will happen if a group creates a new design that changes three variables?* [They might have a better electromagnet, but they won't know which variable is responsible.]

   ➤ *How can we make sure to keep track of which variables are improving the design?* [Test only one variable at a time to know how it affects the strength of the electromagnet.]

5. **Student-generated question, e.g., How does (student-chosen process) affect the strength of an electromagnet?**
   Tell students that the entire class will act as an engineering project team. Each group will test just one variable to see how it affects an electromagnet. In the end, they will share their findings with the rest of the class and combine data so they can design the most effective electromagnet.

   Lead a class discussion to figure out which one variable each group will test. It is fine for more than one group to test a variable. Students should record their choice in the focus question in their notebooks.

   ➤ *How does (student-chosen process) affect the strength of an electromagnet?*

6. **Discuss trials**
   Distribute notebook sheet 12, *Testing Electromagnet Variables*. Students should fill in their group's variable at the top of the page.

   Review the data table. Students will need to see how many paper clips they can lift with each design, the standard (original) and modified design. They will collect data for three trials, then average their data. Review this process with the class.

248 Full Option Science System

Part 3: Improving the Design

7. **Begin experimentation**
   Students can pick up the materials they will need to create the basic electromagnet, and any materials they will need for their modification, then get to work building and testing.

   As students work, circulate among the groups and make sure students are setting up complete circuits and collecting data from multiple trials.

8. **Clean up**
   At the end of class, or when the experiment is done, ask Getters to disassemble their devices and return all the materials to the materials station. Keep the paper clips in the plastic cups.

   SESSION 2 45–50 minutes

9. **Analyze results**
   Give groups time to calculate their averages and work as a group on question 1 on notebook sheet 12. Remind students to include evidence in their responses.

   Reporters should come to the front of the room and fill in their group's data on teacher master H, *Electromagnet Variables—Class Data*.

10. **Assess progress: performance assessment**
    As students conduct the investigation and analyze their data, listen to the group discussions and observe how they work together to assess their three-dimensional learning. Note student progress on the *Performance Assessment Checklist*.

    What to Look For

    - *Students conduct an investigation in which they control all variables but one. (Planning and carrying out investigations.)*
    - *Students use precision in their calculations and numerical comparison of results. (Analyzing and interpreting data; using mathematics and computational thinking; systems and system models.)*
    - *Students use collected data to formulate conclusions about design performance. (Analyzing and interpreting data; designing solutions; engaging in argument from evidence; ETS1.C: Optimizing the design solution; cause and effect.)*

> **TEACHING NOTE**
> If any group selected testing multiple batteries, they may need help setting up a circuit with the batteries in series. The diagram shows one way they can do so.

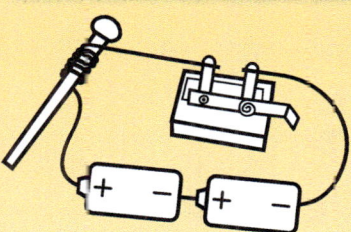

> **MATH CONNECTION**
> This supports Common Core State Standards for Math 7.NS 1.

SCIENCE AND ENGINEERING PRACTICES

Planning and carrying out investigations

Analyzing and interpreting data

Using mathematics and computational thinking

Designing solutions

Engaging in argument from evidence

DISCIPLINARY CORE IDEAS

ETS1.C Optimizing the design solution

CROSSCUTTING CONCEPTS

Cause and effect

Systems and system models

INVESTIGATION 3 – Electromagnetism

CROSSCUTTING CONCEPTS

Cause and effect

Systems and system models

▶ **NOTE**
Go to FOSSweb for *Teacher Resources* and look for the Crosscutting Concepts and Integration chapter for details on how to engage students with the concept of cause and effect to integrate content at this grade level.

TEACHING NOTE

Here are some of the major ideas about electromagnet design that may come out of the discussion.

Thicker wire around the core increases strength of magnetism.

More winds increase strength of magnetism.

A steel core is more effective than a plastic or wood core.

More batteries in series increase strength of magnetism.

CROSSCUTTING CONCEPTS

Structure and function

TEACHING NOTE

Go to FOSSweb for *Teacher Resources* and look for the Science and Engineering Practices chapter for details on how to engage students with the practice of engaging in argument from evidence.

11. Review class data

When all groups have transcribed their data on teacher master H, ask the class to review the data. Read aloud any confusing words or numbers, and ask groups to confirm data if there are any apparent outliers.

Ask a student to read question 2 from the notebook sheet.

▶ *Looking at the class data, which modifications are the most effective? Use evidence to support your response.*

Ask a few students to share ideas about what might be helpful evidence (the number of paper clips lifted, as recorded on the teacher master).

Give students a few minutes to talk it over and record their responses to question 2. Lead a class discussion, asking students to defend their responses with evidence. Work toward a class consensus about which modifications were the most effective and which were the least effective.

Students may need help interpreting the data. If they are stuck, consider providing sentence frames such as "As the number of winds around an electromagnet _____ , the magnetic force _____ ."

As a final review, ask,

▶ *How can you make an electromagnet stronger?* [Add more coils of wire, increase the current by adding batteries (in series), and increase the thickness of the wire.]

12. Work on the next design

Ask a student to read question 3 out loud. Point out that this question requires the class to work as a team and look at all the data from the class, not just at the variable their group tested. Which modifications would they incorporate in a final design, when they can modify multiple variables?

Ask students to answer question 3 on a separate page in the notebook. Give students 5–8 minutes to craft a detailed response.

Then, ask a few volunteers to read their responses. Other students should ask the reader questions as needed to understand which modifications they are suggesting and why. Encourage students to engage in argument from evidence to explain why they agree or disagree with the proposed modifications.

Part 3: Improving the Design

Point out to students that continually improving a design by incorporating new scientific findings is an important part of thinking like an **engineer**. Distribute a copy of *FOSS Science Resources* to each student and have them turn to the "Engineering Design Process." Give groups a few minutes to discuss which parts of the process they engaged in during this part, then ask groups to share ideas. During the class discussion, focus on how important it was for the class to share ideas so that they would be able to build the strongest electromagnet.

13. **Record vocabulary**
    Give students a few moments to review and/or clarify the vocabulary developed in this investigation. Have students add vocabulary words and explanations to their diagrams and update their indexes to their notebooks if they haven't done so already.

14. **Revisit the focus question**
    Ask students to record and answer the focus question in their notebooks.

    ▶ *Student-generated question, e.g., How does (student-chosen process) affect the strength of an electromagnet?*

    Encourage students to cite evidence derived from the class data to support their answers.

15. **Extend the investigation with homework**
    The online activity "Virtual Electromagnet" on FOSSweb allows students to explore electromagnet variables beyond what they tested in class. Students can manipulate the simulation and then write a summary of any additional findings of how to modify the strength of electromagnets that they discovered in the online activity.

SESSION 3   45–50 minutes

SCIENCE AND ENGINEERING PRACTICES

Asking questions
Analyzing and interpreting data
Designing solutions
Engaging in argument from evidence

 constraint
criterion
engineer

EL NOTE

For students who need support, give them a few minutes to discuss their response with a partner before writing. You can also provide sentence frames such as We wanted to find out ___. We set up our investigation by ___. We found out that ___. Next time, I want to see if ___.

Electromagnetic Force Course—FOSS Next Generation

INVESTIGATION 3 – Electromagnetism

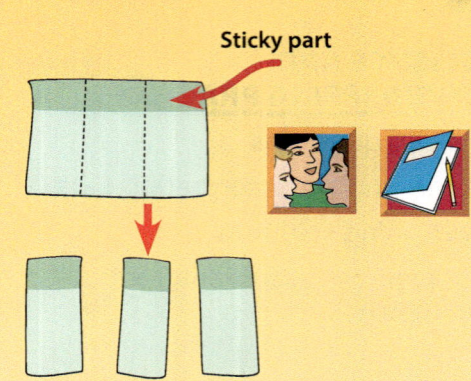

SCIENCE AND ENGINEERING PRACTICES

Asking questions and defining problems

Developing and using models

Planning and carrying out investigations

Analyzing and interpreting data

Using mathematics and computational thinking

Constructing explanations

Engaging in argument from evidence

Obtaining, evaluating, and communicating information

DISCIPLINARY CORE IDEAS

PS2.B: Types of interactions

PS3.A: Definitions of energy

ETS1.A: Defining and delimiting engineering problems

ETS1.B: Developing possible solutions

ETS1.C: Optimizing the design solution

CROSSCUTTING CONCEPTS

Patterns

Cause and effect

Systems and system models

Energy and matter

Structure and function

WRAP-UP

16. Review notebook entries

Distribute one self-stick note to each student. Ask students to cut the note into three pieces, making sure to cut so that each piece has a sticky end.

Ask students to take 3 minutes to look back through their notebook entries to find the three most important things they learned in this investigation. They should tab those pages with the three notes. They might use a highlighter or colored pencils to call out the key point.

Students sometimes list what they did, instead of what they learned. Encourage them to reflect on their findings from the activities and discussions.

After students tag their three key ideas (no more), give them 3 minutes for group discussion to share the ideas they value most in this investigation. You might need to help groups rephrase their key points for clarity. By using science and engineering practices and exploring core ideas through the lens of crosscutting concepts, students should come forward with these big ideas in the review discussions. These concepts set the stage for learning more about the the relationship between electricity and magnetism.

- An electric circuit is complete when current can flow through the circuit and transfer energy to components. (Planning and carrying out investigations; developing and using models; constructing explanations; obtaining, evaluating, and communicating information; PS2.B: Types of interactions; PS3.A: Definitions of energy; systems and systems models; energy and matter.)

- A magnetic field surrounds a wire through which electric current is flowing. (Asking questions; planning and carrying out investigations; developing and using models; constructing explanations; PS2.B: Types of interactions; patterns; cause and effect; systems and system models.)

- Increasing the number of winds, using a thicker wire, or adding more current will make an electromagnet stronger. (Asking questions and defining problems; planning and carrying out investigations; analyzing and interpreting data; using mathematics and computational thinking; engaging in argument from evidence; ETS1.A: Defining and delimiting engineering problems; ETS1.B: Developing possible solutions; ETS1.C: Optimizing the design solution; cause and effect; systems and system models; structure and function.)

You might ask students to draw a line of learning under their last notebook entry and then to compose a concise statement summarizing what they know about electromagnetism.

Part 3: Improving the Design

17. Answer the guiding question
Ask students to discuss the investigation guiding question.

➤ *How are electricity and magnetism related?*

You might use an image from the *FOSS Science Resources* book (such as the spread on pages 38 and 39 or pages 42 and 43) to connect their thinking to the real world. Students can also ask additional questions about the phenomena of electromagnetism.

READING *in Science Resources*

18. Extend the investigation with homework
The article "Electromagnetic Engineering" can be assigned as homework to reinforce ideas from the class discussion. To support reading comprehension, suggest that students follow this procedure.

Tell students,

Before reading, think about the things you know of that use electromagnets. Preview the text by looking at the illustrations and reading the captions and subtitles. As you read, annotate the text by using self-stick notes to record your thoughts and questions.

Here are some symbols students can use.

★	interesting	W	wondering
?	question	S	surprising
L	learning something new		

After they finish reading, have them record responses to the *Think Questions* in their notebook. Allow a few minutes before the next session for students to share one of their self-stick notes and discuss the Think Questions with their table group.

➤ *How has use of electromagnetic technology changed over the years?* [Electromagnets have been made stronger and put into many new technologies like heating and MRI machines.]

➤ *List an engineering constraint or criterion that would be important to consider in designing such a device.* [Answers will vary, but may include constraints such as expense, size, or materials use, or criteria such as strength or function.]

➤ *What did you learn from this article that could make your electromagnetic design stronger?* [Answers may include using more coils of wire, using more electric current, using thicker wire, or supercooling the wires.]

ELA CONNECTION

This suggested strategy addresses the Common Core State Standards for ELA for literacy.

WHST 8: Gather relevant information from multiple print and digital sources.

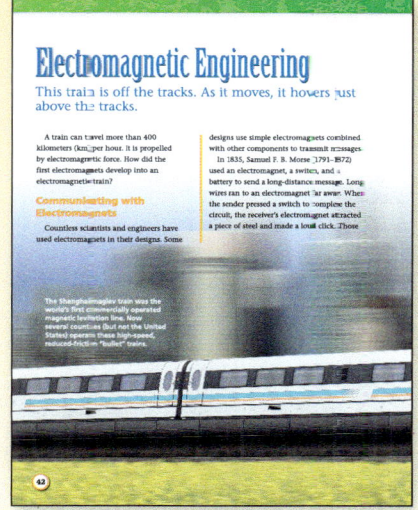

FOSS Science Resources

SESSION 4 45–50 minutes

Electromagnetic Force Course—FOSS Next Generation

INVESTIGATION 3 – Electromagnetism

19. Assess progress: I-Check

Administer *Investigation 3 I-Check*, asking students to respond to the items on paper or online on FOSSmap. Students should independently answer the questions. When taking the I-Check, students should not use their notebooks, but the notebooks are a good tool to use when students later reflect on their answers.

SESSION 5 45–50 minutes

TEACHING NOTE

During or after these next steps with the I-Check, you might ask students to make choices for possible derivative products based on their notebooks for inclusion in a summative portfolio. See the Assessment chapter for more information about creating and evaluating portfolios.

20. Discuss I-Check results

Code the I-Check items, but do not make any marks on student responses. Note that FOSSmap automatically codes most of the items and provides you with student and class reports. Coding guides can be found on FOSSweb. You can record student results on the *Assessment Record* or download spreadsheets from FOSSmap for recording. Note important points about the items to review with students.

Return the I-Checks to students. Use self-assessment strategies as described for each item in the Assessment chapter to facilitate reflection and clarify student thinking.

Extending the Investigation

EXTENDING *the Investigation*

- **Make a rheostat**

    Graphite, the black substance used as pencil lead, is a form of carbon. Graphite is a pretty good conductor, but not as good as most metals. This is because graphite imposes greater resistance to the movement of current. Therefore, the greater the distance a current flows through graphite, the lower the current.

    A lightbulb shines brightest when the circuit imposes low resistance to the flow of current. When resistance is added, the current goes down, and the brightness of the lightbulb decreases accordingly. One device that adds resistance to a circuit is a rheostat.

    Students can make rheostats (light dimmers) with graphite pencils, by cutting the wood away on one side, or by drawing lines on paper with a graphite (woodless) pencil, available at office-supply stores or art stores. This project would be good for a group of students who finish quickly with their other investigations.

- **Build the ultimate electromagnet**

    Students may want to build the final class design they imagined in Part 3. Consider providing materials and time for students to build these designs and compare them with other students' electromagnet designs. They could continually improve the design until they are satisfied with it. Remind students that some batteries may be weaker than others, so they should use the same battery when comparing two designs.

> **TEACHING NOTE**
>
> Encourage students to use the Science and Engineering Careers Database on FOSSweb.

Electromagnetic Force Course—FOSS Next Generation   **255**

INVESTIGATION 3 – Electromagnetism

Investigation 4: Energy Transfer

INVESTIGATION 4 – Energy Transfer

Part 1	
Electric Motors	270
Part 2	
Electric Generators	281
Part 3	
Force and Energy	303

Guiding question for phenomenon:
How do humans use energy?

Science and Engineering Practices
- Asking questions
- Developing and using models
- Planning and carrying out investigations
- Analyzing and interpreting data
- Constructing explanations
- Engaging in argument from evidence
- Obtaining, evaluating, and communicating information

PURPOSE

In *Energy Transfer*, students investigate the phenomena of human energy use. They describe motor and generator designs in terms of energy transfer. They consider electricity use, generation, and implications for renewable and nonrenewable energy use.

Content
- An electric motor is designed with a commutator that acts as a switch, turning on and off an electromagnet.
- Electric generators transfer energy from kinetic energy to electrical energy.
- Energy cannot be created or destroyed, only transferred.
- Every energy use can be described as a sequence of energy transfers.
- Energy sources can be categorized as renewable or nonrenewable.

Practices
- Analyzing and interpreting data to compare the components and function of motors and generators.
- Developing and using models to explain energy transfers within a system.
- Obtaining, evaluating, and communicating information about energy sources for human use, including renewable and nonrenewable sources, and their environmental consequences.

Disciplinary Core Ideas

PS3: How is energy transferred and conserved?

PS3.B: Conservation of energy and energy transfer

PS3.C: Relationship between energy and forces

ESS3: How do Earth's surface processes and human activities affect each other?

ESS3.A: Natural resources

ESS3.C: Human impacts on Earth systems

Crosscutting Concepts
- Cause and effect
- Scale, proportion, and quantity
- Systems and system models
- Energy and matter
- Structure and function
- Stability and change

Full Option Science System

INVESTIGATION 4 — Energy Transfer

	Investigation Summary	Time	Focus Question for Phenomenon, Practices
PART 1	**Electric Motors** Students operate an electric motor in a circuit, dissect a motor, and explain how it works after analyzing its components. They describe its design and function in terms of its components and energy transfers.	**Active Inv.** 2 Sessions*	**How does an electric motor work?** **Practices** Developing and using models Planning and carrying out investigations Analyzing and interpreting data Constructing explanations Engaging in argument from evidence
PART 2	**Electric Generators** Students observe a generator and compare its components and function to a motor. They explain the interactions in terms of energy transfer. They consider energy sources for human electricity use and use solar cells to power an electric motor. Students read about human energy sources, including resource limitations and consequences.	**Active Inv.** 2 Sessions **Reading** 1 Session **Assessment** 1–2 Sessions	**How can we generate electrical energy?** **Practices** Asking questions Developing and using models Planning and carrying out investigations Analyzing and interpreting data Constructing explanations Engaging in argument from evidence Obtaining, evaluating, and communicating information
PART 3	**Force and Energy** Students consider key points from the entire course to prepare for the final benchmark assessment. They revisit the *Entry-Level Survey* and improve their responses.	**Review** 1 Session **Assessment** 1 Session	**What is the relationship between magnetic and electrical forces?** **Practices** Constructing explanations Obtaining, evaluating, and communicating information

* A class session is 45–50 minutes.

At a Glance

Content Related to DCIs	Literacy/Technology	Assessment
• An electric motor is designed with a commutator that acts as a switch, turning on and off an electromagnet. • Every energy use can be described as a sequence of energy transfers.	**Science Notebook Entry** Answer the focus question **Science Resources Book** "Motor Dissection A" "Motor Dissection B" **Online Activity** "Kitchen Magnets"	**Embedded Assessment** Science notebook entry
• Electric generators transfer energy from kinetic energy to electrical energy. • Energy cannot be created or destroyed, only transferred. • Every energy use can be described as a sequence of energy transfers. • Energy sources can be categorized as renewable or nonrenewable.	**Science Notebook Entry** Energy Transfers **Science Resources Book** "Generator Dissection" "The Rebirth of Electric Cars" "Where We Get Energy" **Video** Generator Dissection	**Embedded Assessment** Performance assessment **Benchmark Assessment** Investigation 4 I-Check
• Energy cannot be created or destroyed, only transferred. • Every energy use can be described as a sequence of energy transfers. • Energy sources can be categorized as renewable or nonrenewable.	**Science Notebook Entry** Key-Points Summary	**Benchmark Assessment** Posttest **NGSS Performance Expectations addressed in this investigation** MS-PS3-5 MS-ESS3-3 (foundational) MS-ESS3-4 (foundational)

Electromagnetic Force Course—FOSS Next Generation

INVESTIGATION 4 – *Energy Transfer*

SCIENTIFIC *and Historical Background*

With a basic understanding of force, energy, and electromagnetism, students are ready to pull all the pieces together to consider energy transfers that power human lifestyles. Students explore the phenomenon of human energy use by studying relatively simple electrical designs: a motor and a generator. Students investigate a motor for evidence of electromagnetism and identify the energy transfers involved. They then identify the energy transfers in a generator before turning their attention to the sources that provide energy for human use. The guiding question for this investigation is how do humans use energy?

How Does an Electric Motor Work?

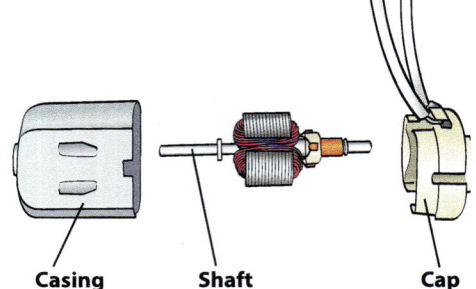

Electricity creates a magnetic field. **Motors** and generators take advantage of the two reciprocal expressions of electromagnetism. The electric motor used in this course has a steel casing with a couple of permanent magnets stuck inside. A **shaft** extends through the center of the casing. Attached to the shaft are three coils of wire wrapped around iron cores. The coils of wire are connected to the wire leads extending out of the motor.

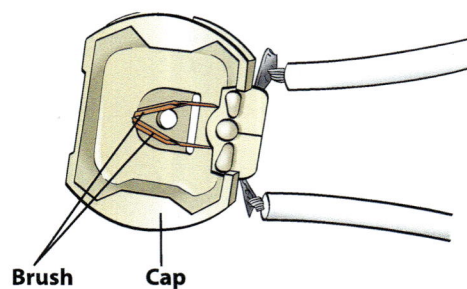

When current is supplied to the motor, it flows through one or two of the coils, making them electromagnets that interact with the two permanent magnets in the steel can. The three electromagnets in the motor don't turn on all at once—they cascade.

It was a significant engineering challenge to get electricity to flow from stationary wires outside the motor to the coils of wire that are **rotating** inside the motor. This challenge was solved by having the ends of the wires outside the motor attached to pieces called **brushes** that slide over sections of metal, called a **commutator**, attached to the coils of wire that are rotating. The brushes sliding over the commutator stay in contact well enough to provide a good connection for electric current to flow into the rotating coils of wire.

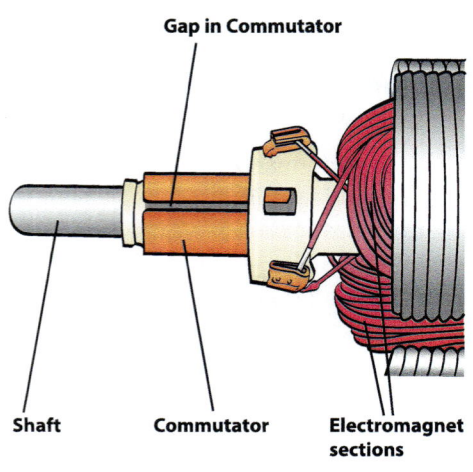

Electromagnet 1 turns on briefly, then turns off. Just as electromagnet 1 goes off, electromagnet 2 turns on, then electromagnet 3, and the sequence repeats. This sequence rotates the motor shaft. Electrical energy transfers to kinetic energy.

More sophisticated motor designs, such as those used at power plants, do not use brushes, which can wear out over time. Those motors use electronic controllers and sensors that can detect rotor position to control which electromagnets are turned on. However, in this course students will focus only on the more simple brush design.

Electricity is turned into motion with an electric motor. By using electricity to create magnetism in coils of wire, which in turn applies a force between the coils and permanent magnets to rotate a shaft, we can perform a universe of mechanical tasks—transportation, tools, toys, music reproduction, air circulation, industrial machinery, on and on.

Scientific and Historical Background

How Can We Generate Electrical Energy?

In the electromagnet, the wire wrapped around a steel rivet creates magnetism in the steel when the wire carries electric current. In 1831, Michael Faraday (1791–1867) showed that the relationship between magnetism and electricity worked in the other direction as well. He demonstrated that an electric current could be created by passing a conductor, like a copper wire, through a magnetic field. While the wire was passing through the magnetic field, current flowed in the wire. This is how a hand-crank **generator** works.

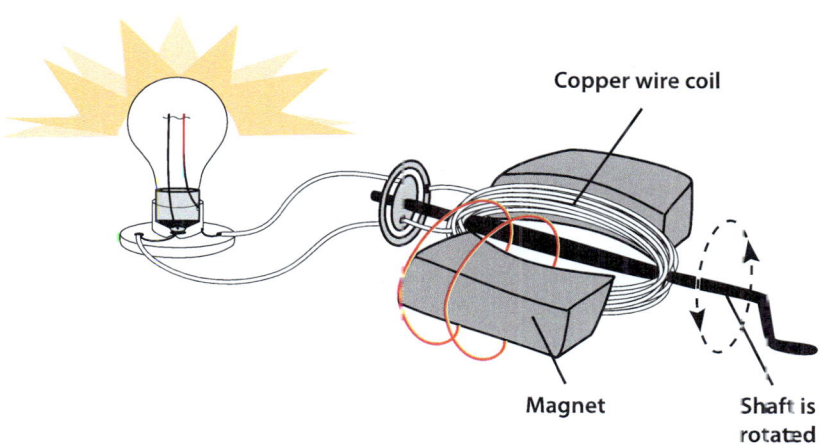

Inside the plastic housing is a coil of wire positioned between two permanent magnets. The magnets produce continuous magnetic fields. By rotating the coil with a crank, the wires move through the lines of the magnetic field. Each interaction with a line of the magnetic field adds a little push to the electrons in the copper wires, which results in electric current flowing through the wire. Kinetic energy (from the motion of the coil) transfers to electrical energy.

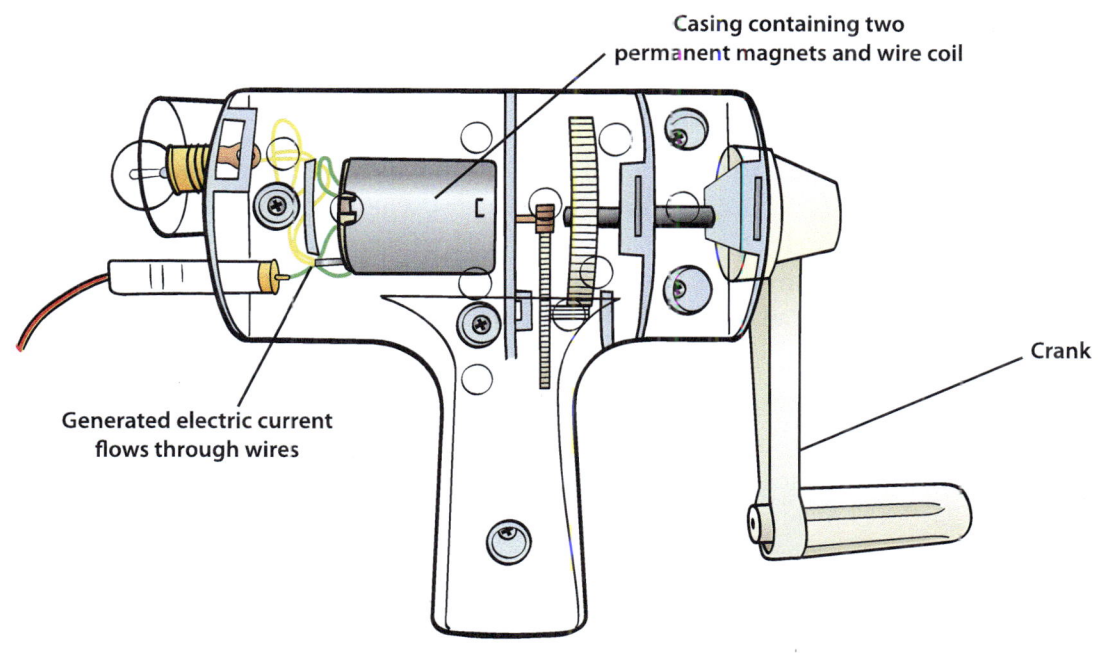

Electromagnetic Force Course—FOSS Next Generation

INVESTIGATION 4 – Energy Transfer

The generator has the same engineering problem as the motor: stationary wires outside the generator must connect to the rotating coils of wire inside. The solution is the same as with the motor: brushes sliding over a commutator.

What would happen, however, if you turned the equation around and ran electric current into the wires leading out of the generator? Would the generator crank turn by itself? The answer is yes, and the generator in this instance is called an electric motor.

Soon engineers were mounting large coils of wire on cranks. They placed powerful magnets close to the coils. When the crank turned, the wire coils passed continuously through the magnetic fields. As long as the coils turned, electric current flowed through the coils, through commutator and brushes, and into a lightbulb or other electric component.

This simple hand-operated device was the first electricity generator. As time passed, generators became larger and more efficient. New and more powerful energy sources were employed to turn the shaft, including **renewable** energy sources such as falling water and windmills as well as **nonrenewable** energy sources such as diesel engines and coal-fired steam turbines.

Sources of energy for human use. In the last part of this course, students reflect on one of the biggest questions facing society: Where can we get our energy? **Fossil fuels** are substances that were created from organic materials such as plants and animals. The materials were buried and transformed over millions of years into the substances we know as fossil fuels. These substances store chemical potential energy in the form of solids (coal and peat), liquids (oil), and natural gas.

The use of peat for fuel began in the 17th century and continued at an increasing rate until the mid-20th century, when other fossil fuels became more accessible. We have whole economies based on extraction of fossil fuels from the earth, with the result that we've come to depend on abundant, cheap energy from fossil fuels.

But use of fossil fuels has serious drawbacks in the long run. Burning fossil fuels results in emission of the greenhouse gas carbon dioxide as well as many noxious pollutants. The increasing amount of carbon dioxide in Earth's atmosphere is driving global temperatures upward and altering Earth's climate. A finite amount of fossil fuels is waiting to be mined from Earth, so someday there won't be enough left for us to run things as we are used to.

> "In the last part of this course, students reflect on one of the biggest questions facing society: where we get our energy from."

Scientific and Historical Background

Most of our electricity comes from power plants that burn fossil fuels to heat water and make high-temperature, high-pressure steam that drives a turbine, a machine like a fan that has many blades, which in turn drives an electric generator. The electricity goes to businesses and homes via high-voltage wires.

In nuclear power plants, nuclear reactions using uranium heat water to get high-pressure steam to run turbines to generate electricity. They produce virtually no greenhouse gases that would contribute to global warming, but they do have a serious problem of radioactive waste products that must be safely stored for many thousands of years. Also, uranium is mined from the ground and is a finite resource like fossil fuels.

© momente/Shutterstock
Giant generators produce electricity in power plants.

Geothermal power plants also run turbines using steam, but it is steam that comes from deep underground where conditions are naturally hot. They do not contribute any greenhouse gases, but do not contribute much electricity in the United States because there are few suitable locations.

Solar thermal plants use radiant energy from the Sun to create steam that can run turbines. These plants are designed to concentrate the Sun's rays and heat up a fluid to high temperatures. The fluid circulates and heats water to produce steam. They do not generate greenhouse gases but work best over a large area and with direct sunlight.

© ssuaphotos/Shutterstock
Wind turbines transfer the wind's kinetic energy to electrical energy.

There are ways to make a turbine spin without steam: turbines in a dam generate hydroelectric power and produce no greenhouse gases, but a dam has a limited lifetime (several decades) before the lake behind the dam fills up with silt and the water pressure drops. Hydroelectricity is a prevalent power source in the Pacific Northwest. Engineers are working on other types of water turbines to harness power from rivers, ocean waves, and tides, but these are not yet ready to contribute significantly to our energy need.

With wind turbines, energy in wind transfers into electricity. Wind itself is driven by heating from the Sun's radiant energy. Wind turbines account for about 7 percent of electricity in the United States. One drawback of wind-electric power is that it is available only when there is enough wind.

Electromagnetic Force Course—FOSS Next Generation

INVESTIGATION 4 – Energy Transfer

Wind-generated electricity supplements other sources of electricity by connection to a power grid.

What each of these technologies has in common is that spinning turbines form part of a generator designed to transfer kinetic energy into electrical energy for human use. The energy source that provides the force needed to make the turbines move could be chemical potential energy (as in the case of fossil fuels), nuclear energy, thermal energy (as in the case of geothermal heating), potential and kinetic energy (as in the case of hydroelectric dams), or kinetic energy (as in the case of wind turbines).

Solar power. Not all electricity is generated by transferring kinetic energy to electrical energy. Our star, Sol (the Sun), is the most powerful source of energy in the solar system. Bountiful energy in the form of a wide range of radiation streams to Earth continuously. If you were to place a motor in the sunshine, it would get warm, but the shaft would not rotate. The Sun can be used to operate a motor if an intervening technology is employed. The device commonly called a **solar cell** (more precisely a photovoltaic cell) uses a technology that produces electric current when it interacts with light from the Sun (or any other source of light).

© Frederico Rastagno/Shutterstock

"When photons of light strike a photovoltaic cell, radiant energy from the Sun transfers to electrical energy, which can in turn transfer to other forms of energy."

If a motor is connected to a solar cell that is exposed to direct solar radiation, it will operate. A solar cell is typically made of silicon with small amounts of impurities. When photons of light strike a photovoltaic cell, radiant energy from the Sun transfers to electrical energy, which can in turn transfer to other forms of energy. Solar cells do not store energy like a D-cell. They only function while light is hitting their surface.

Solar panels are perfect as a geographically distributed energy source that can be put on the roofs of schools, businesses, and homes. They are also starting to be installed over parking lots, shading the cars and providing electric power. Solar electric power does not work at night or on cloudy days. It must be stored or used to supplement other sources of electricity. Storage can be in rechargeable batteries, though this is not yet cost effective in many places. In 2016, less than 1 percent of electricity in the United States came from solar panels, but the solar industry is growing rapidly.

What Are the Big Ideas about Electromagnetic Force?

This course began with the most simple definition of force: force is a push or a pull. Students have analyzed combinations of forces that result in a net force. Most forces we deal with on Earth are also accompanied by an opposing frictional force.

Scientific and Historical Background

The electromagnetic force is not observable in the same way as a poke or prod with a spring scale, but it is a force nonetheless, one of the fundamental forces in the universe. When a magnet pulls a paper clip closer to it, that's an electromagnetic force. When a battery lights a bulb, that's evidence of an electromagnetic force.

Force and energy are inextricably linked. This investigation connects an electric generator with an electric motor: they are the reverse of each other. In a generator, a wire moving in the magnetic field of a permanent magnet creates an electric force in the wire that pushes electrons through the wire, making electric current. Kinetic energy is transferring into electrical energy. In a motor, electric current in a wire establishes a magnetic field that creates a force between it and permanent magnets, causing the coil of wire to spin. Electrical energy is being transferred into kinetic energy.

At the culmination of this course, students will have a developmental understanding of energy transfers, and a solid foundational understanding that while energy can be transferred, it cannot be created or destroyed.

Vocabulary
Brush
Commutator
Fossil fuel
Generator
Motor
Nonrenewable
Renewable
Rotate
Shaft
Solar cell

INVESTIGATION 4 – Energy Transfer

TEACHING AND LEARNING about *Energy Transfer*

Developing Disciplinary Core Ideas (DCI)

"Energy makes my phone charge and powers my laptop. All I have to do is plug them in." Human energy consumption is so rampant in the 21st century that students take it for granted. Only when one stops to consider that energy cannot be created (or destroyed), but only transferred from one source or form to another, is the human reliance on cheap, abundant electrical energy recognized as an engineering marvel.

However, the limitations of our current energy sources are apparent. Many of our fuel sources are finite; many of our fuel sources release pollutants into the atmosphere that change the planet's climate. Your students' generation will play a critical role in determining whether society can develop sustainable energy systems.

Students start with analyzing energy sources and transfers within systems, and move into a discussion about implications of humans using various energy sources. Our societal dilemma of what to do about energy systems that are unsustainable is something that students will continue to face.

The experiences students have in this investigation contribute to the disciplinary core ideas **PS3.B: Conservation of energy and energy transfer**; **PS3.C: Relationship between energy and forces**; **ESS3.A: Natural resources**; and **ESS3.C: Human impacts on Earth systems**.

NGSS Foundation Box for DCI

PS3.B: Conservation of energy and energy transfer
- When the motion energy of an object changes, there is inevitably some other change in energy at the same time. (MS-PS3-5)

PS3.C: Relationship between energy and forces
- When two objects interact, each one exerts a force on the other that can cause energy to be transferred to or from the object. (MS-PS3-2)

ESS3.A: Natural resources
- Humans depend on Earth's land, ocean, atmosphere, and biosphere for many different resources. Minerals, fresh water, and biosphere resources are limited, and many are not renewable or replaceable over human lifetimes. (MS-ESS3-1)

ESS3.C: Human impacts on Earth systems
- Typically as human populations and per-capita consumption of natural resources increase, so do the negative impacts on Earth unless the activities and technologies involved are engineered otherwise. (MS-ESS3-3, MS-ESS3-4)

Teaching and Learning about Energy Transfer

Engaging in Science and Engineering Practices (SEP)

In this investigation, students engage in these practices.

- **Asking questions** about electric cars before learning about how they are designed.
- **Developing and using models** to describe energy transfers within a system.
- **Planning and carrying out investigations** when testing solar panels in a circuit.
- **Analyzing and interpreting data** to compare the components and function of a motor and generator.
- **Constructing explanations** to describe how energy is transferred within various systems.
- **Engaging in argument from evidence** to explain how energy transfers through a system, but cannot be created or destroyed.
- **Obtaining, evaluating, and communicating information** when reviewing notebook entries and synthesizing key points from the entire course.

NGSS Foundation Box for SEP

- **Ask questions** that can be investigated within the scope of the classroom, outdoor environment, and museums and other public facilities with available resources and, when appropriate, frame a hypothesis based on observations and scientific principles.
- **Develop and/or use a model** to predict and/or describe phenomena.
- **Conduct an investigation** and/or evaluate and/or revise the experimental design to produce data to serve as the basis for evidence that meet the goals of the investigation.
- **Analyze and interpret data** to determine similarities and differences in findings.
- **Apply scientific ideas, principles, and/or evidence** to construct, revise, and/or use an explanation for real-world phenomena, examples, or events.
- **Construct, use, and/or present an oral and written argument** supported by empirical evidence and scientific reasoning to support or refute an explanation or a model for a phenomenon or a solution to a problem.
- **Communicate scientific and/or technical information** (e.g., about a proposed object, tool, process, system) in writing and/or through oral presentations.

Electromagnetic Force Course—FOSS Next Generation

INVESTIGATION 4 – Energy Transfer

> **NGSS Foundation Box for CC**
>
> - **Cause and effect:** Cause-and-effect relationships may be used to predict phenomena in natural or designed systems.
> - **Scale, proportion, and quantity:** Time, space, and energy phenomena can be observed at various scales using models to study systems that are too large or too small.
> - **Systems and system models:** Systems may interact with other systems; they may have subsystems and be a part of larger complex systems.
> - **Energy and matter:** The transfer of energy can be tracked as energy flows through a designed or natural system.
> - **Structure and function:** Structures can be designed to serve particular functions by taking into account properties of different materials, and how materials can be shaped and used.
> - **Stability and change:** Stability might be disturbed either by sudden events or gradual changes that accumulate over time.

Exposing Crosscutting Concepts (CC)

In this investigation, the focus is on these crosscutting concepts.

- **Cause and effect.** Motors and generators function to transfer energy in specific ways to achieve their design purpose.
- **Scale, proportion, and quantity.** Nonrenewable energy sources form on Earth at a time scale too slow for human renewing.
- **Systems and system models.** Models of systems can help explain energy flow and transfers through the systems.
- **Energy and matter.** Energy cannot be created or destroyed, only transferred.
- **Structure and function.** Motors and generators are designed with special components whose shape and materials support design goals of energy transfer within a moving system.
- **Stability and change.** Human burning of fossil fuels releases pollutants into the atmosphere that can cause climate change.

Connections to the Nature of Science

- **Science is a human endeavor.** Men and women from different social, cultural, and ethnic backgrounds work as scientists and engineers. Scientists and engineers rely on human qualities such as persistence, precision, reasoning, logic, imagination, and creativity. Scientists and engineers are guided by habits of mind, such as intellectual honesty, tolerance of ambiguity, skepticism, and openness to new ideas. Advances in technology influence the progress of science, and science has influenced advances in technology.

Connections to Engineering, Technology, and Applications of Science

- **Influence of science, engineering, and technology on society and the natural world.** All human activity draws on natural resources and has both short- and long-term consequences, positive as well as negative, for the health of people and the natural environment. The uses of technologies are driven by people's needs, desires, and values; by the findings of scientific research; and by differences in such factors as climate, natural resources, and economic conditions. Technology use varies over time and from region to region.

Teaching and Learning about Energy Transfer

Conceptual Flow

In this investigation, students investigate the phenomenon of human energy use. The guiding question for the investigation is how do humans use energy?

The **conceptual flow** starts in Part 1 when students figure out how a **motor rotates when electric current runs through it**. They analyze the external structure and function of the device, and then they look at what's inside. After studying the internal components, including the **brush**, **commutator**, permanent magnets, electromagnet, and **shaft**, students develop a model that explains how **the motor transfers electrical energy to kinetic energy**.

In Part 2, students explore a **generator** in terms of energy transfers. They realize that a **generator has the same components as a motor**, but transfers energy the opposite way, **from kinetic energy to electrical energy**. They then use a **solar cell to transfer light energy to electrical energy**. This leads to a discussion about human energy sources, including **nonrenewable** sources such as **fossil fuels**, and **renewable** sources such as solar and wind power. Students consider the implications of the fact that **energy cannot be created, only transferred**, and think about the options that humans have to minimize energy use, including **new technology** developments in transportation such as the modern electric car.

In Part 3, students summarize key points from the course, including the major themes of **force**, **electromagnetism**, and **energy transfer**. Students then take the *Posttest*.

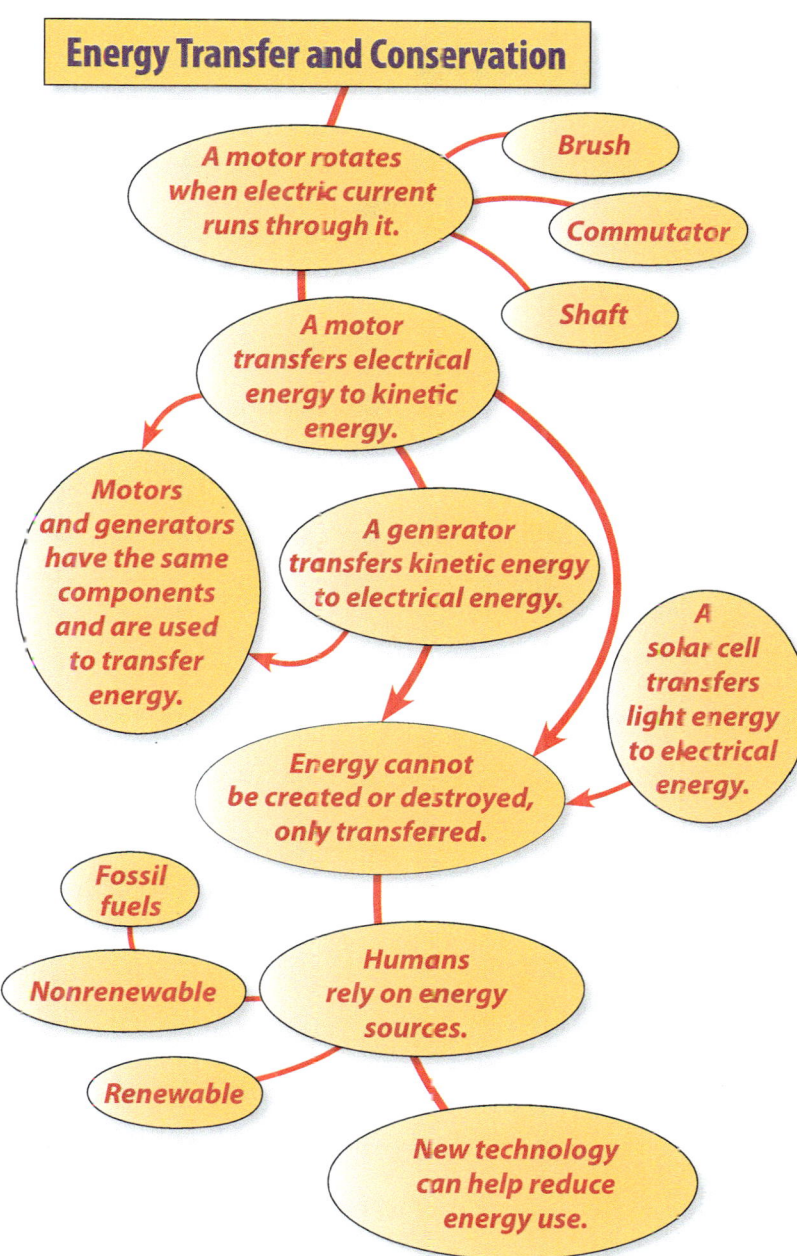

Electromagnetic Force Course—FOSS Next Generation

INVESTIGATION 4 – Energy Transfer

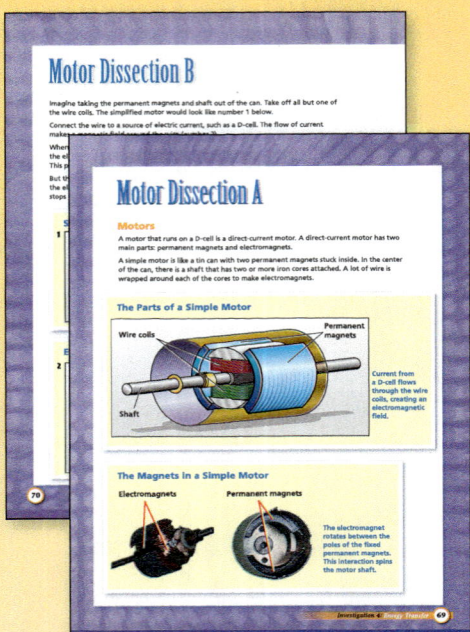

FOSS Science Resources

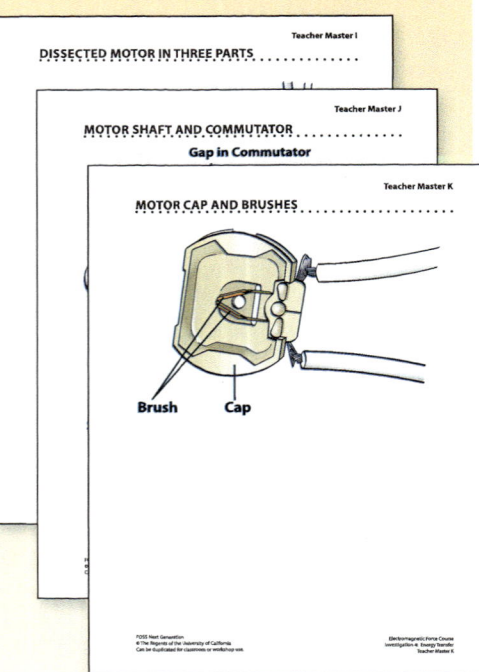

Teacher Masters I–K

MATERIALS for
Part 1: Electric Motors

Provided equipment
For each student
- 1 FOSS Science Resources: Electromagnetic Force
  - "Motor Dissection A"
  - "Motor Dissection B"

For each group
- 1 D-cell
- 1 Cell holder
- 1 Compass
- 1 Motor
- 1 Motor, dissected
- 1 Paper clip

For the class
- Masking tape

Teacher-supplied items
For each student
- 1 Piece of white paper, 22 × 28 cm (8.5" × 11")

For each group
- 1 Piece of chart paper

For the class
- 1 Safety goggles
- 1 Scissors or craft knife
- 1 Sturdy work gloves
- 1 Small screwdriver, approximately 3 mm blade

FOSSweb resources
For the class
- Online activity, "Kitchen Magnets"

For the teacher
- Teacher master I, *Dissected Motor in Three Parts*
- Teacher master J, *Motor Shaft and Commutator*
- Teacher master K, *Motor Cap and Brushes*
- *Embedded Assessment Notes*
- Teaching slides, 4.1

Part 1: Electric Motors

GETTING READY for
Part 1: *Electric Motors*

Quick Start

Schedule	2 sessions active investigation
Preview	• Preview the FOSSweb Resources by Investigation for this part (such as printable masters, teaching slides, and online activities) • Plan for homework: online activity, Step 19
Print or Copy	**For the teacher** • *Embedded Assessment Notes*
Prepare Material	• Dissect motors **A** • Put tape on motor shafts **B**
Plan for Assessment	• Review Step 18, "What to Look For" in the notebook entry

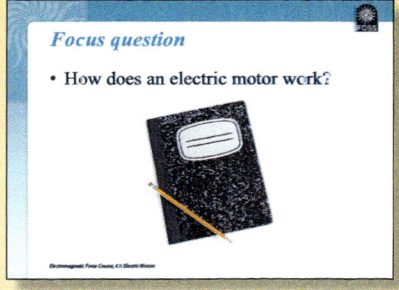

▶ **NOTE**
Preview the teaching slides on FOSSweb for this part.

Electromagnetic Force Course—FOSS Next Generation

INVESTIGATION 4 – Energy Transfer

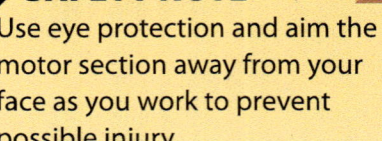

▶ **SAFETY NOTE**
Use eye protection and aim the motor section away from your face as you work to prevent possible injury.

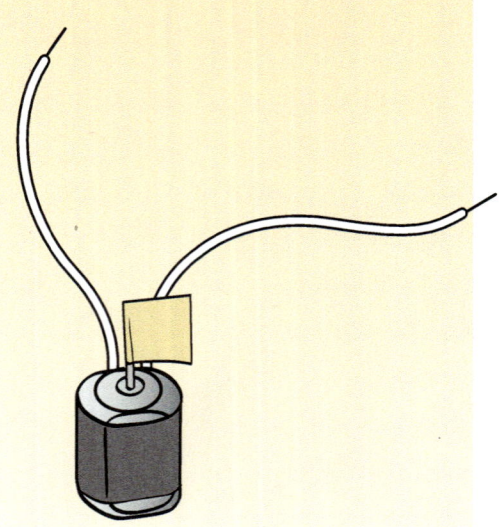

Preparation Details

A ▶ Dissect motors

You will open eight motors for students to see the inner works. Leave the remaining motors unmodified for use in class.

Use scissors or a craft knife to cut and remove the black plastic sleeve around the motor casing. You will see a white plastic cap attached to the metal case. The metal case is crimped into several small dimples. Wearing sturdy gloves to protect your hands, use a tiny flat-headed screwdriver to loosen the two locations where the metal has been crimped into slots in the plastic cap. A 3 mm screwdriver inserted below the crimp and rotated with a twisting motion works well.

Once the metal casing has been uncrimped, you should be able to slide it off the plastic cap, revealing the inner works of the motor. You can then slide the rotor (a shaft with three electromagnets attached) out of the casing. Preview teacher master I, *Dissected Motor in Three Parts*, and see the three parts of the motor after dissection. Reassemble the casing and slide the casing back onto the plastic head for distribution in class.

B ▶ Put tape on motor shafts

Put tape on the shafts of all the undissected motors, to help show when the shaft is spinning. Do not tape the shaft to the casing. Make sure the shaft still moves freely.

Part 1: Electric Motors

GUIDING the Investigation
Part 1: Electric Motors

FOCUS QUESTION
How does an electric motor work?

SESSION 1

Students will . . .
- Review properties of electromagnetism (Step 1)
- Consider and test a motor's function (Steps 2–7)
- Look inside a motor to identify its components (Steps 8–11)

SESSION 2

Students will . . .
- Analyze motor design (Step 12)
- Develop a model that explains energy transfer in the motor system and have a sense-making discussion (Steps 13–15)
- Review vocabulary and revisit the focus question (Steps 16–18)
- Extend the investigation with homework and review notebook entries (Steps 19, 20)

SESSION 1   45–50 minutes

EL NOTE
Start a word wall for this investigation and add the words in bold.

1. **Review properties of electromagnetism**
   Ask,

   ➤ *What are some things you have learned about the relationship between electricity and magnetism?* [Magnetic fields are present when an electric current is running through a wire. Electricity flowing through a wire coil can create a temporary magnet, called an electromagnet.]

   Students might not remember the compass test at first. If necessary, prompt them to remember that experience, look in their notebooks, and review their findings by asking them,

   ➤ *What happens when you bring a compass near a wire with electric current running through it?* [The compass needle moves when an electric current is flowing through a wire.]

2. **Introduce** *motor*
   Tell students that their focus in this part will be to explore another electric device, called a **motor**. Show them a motor, and ask if they recall any experiences they've had using this component. Ask students if they've ever wondered how this electric device works. Suggest they do some investigating to find out.

Electromagnetic Force Course—FOSS Next Generation

INVESTIGATION 4 – Energy Transfer

3. **Focus question: How does an electric motor work?**
   Ask students to consider this question.

   ➤ *How does an electric motor work?*

   Have students record the focus question in their notebook and record their preliminary ideas. Ask a few students to share their ideas with the class.

4. **Observe a motor**
   Distribute one undissected motor to each group, and ask them to take a moment to look at the outside of the motor and to identify any parts that they can. After a few moments, ask groups to share their ideas. They will probably identify wires, a metal body (case), and a metal piece (**shaft**) sticking out of one end.

   Ask,

   ➤ *How can we get information about the inside of the motor, without taking it apart?* [Use a compass to see if there are any magnetic parts inside.]

5. **Data from compasses**
   When the idea of using a compass has been suggested, distribute one compass to each group. Give students a few moments to explore with the compass. Have them share their observations, inferences, and questions. If necessary, use these questions to guide the discussion.

   ➤ *What can you determine by using the compass as a tool?* [The compass needle moves strongly when it comes near the metal case, so there is probably a magnet inside.]

   ➤ *Could the compass needle be moving because there is an electrical current in the motor? Why not?* [No, the motor is currently not hooked up to any energy source like a battery.]

   ➤ *What can you conclude about the internal structure of this motor?* [It must contain a magnet.]

6. **Complete a motor circuit**
   Tell students that they will now connect the motor in an electric circuit to see what it does. Distribute a D-cell and cell holder to each group, and let students figure out how to create a circuit. When the motor is running, they will be able to hear it, and might be able to see and feel the shaft turning.

   Call the class to attention, and introduce the term shaft to describe the rotating metal part extending from the end of the motor. If tape has come off the motor shaft, show students how to affix a small piece of masking tape on the shaft so they can better see the shaft turning.

TEACHING NOTE

Students may suggest hooking the motor up to electricity. They will test that soon, but ask them to think about any other tools that might give them information about what is inside the component. Suggest a compass if students don't come up with it themselves.

EL NOTE

Make or project a diagram on the board as you explain. Emphasize the cause-and-effect interactions.

CROSSCUTTING CONCEPTS

Cause and effect
Structure and function

Part 1: Electric Motors

Once all groups have completed a circuit and seen the motor spin, ask them to disassemble the circuit and place all materials in the center of their table for a class discussion.

Ask groups to describe what the motor does when it is turned on. Students may describe that when an electric current runs through the motor, the shaft turns. Introduce the term **rotate** to describe the motion of the shaft.

Collect the motor from each group.

7. View dissected motor

Tell students that now they will have a chance to look inside a motor to learn how it is constructed. Distribute a prepared motor (with the black plastic cover removed and casing uncrimped) to each group. Show students how to remove the white cap and then slide out the internal parts by pushing and/or pulling on the shaft. Project teacher master 1, *Dissected Motor in Three Parts*, so students will see the three pieces they are going to end up with.

Once students remove the head and slide the shaft out of the case, they will see three distinct parts: the plastic cap with wires, the shaft with coils of wire and a metal core, and the case with magnets inside. Students should not continue to dissect the motor: for example, no cutting or uncoiling of wire, or removing of magnets from the case.

Give students 5 minutes to analyze all the subsystems they can see and discuss in their groups what they think makes the motors work. Call the class to attention and ask,

➤ *What parts can you identify, and what do you think they might do?*

Answers will vary by class, but students are likely to come up with some of the following:

- The coiled wires look like they could be electromagnets.
- Magnets are attached to the inside of the metal casing.
- Thin, flattened wires under the white cap look like they bring the electricity inside from the wires outside.

8. Confirm findings

Ask students to focus on one part at a time, starting with the permanent magnets.

➤ *You mentioned seeing some magnets. Where are these permanent magnets?* [On the inside of the metal casing.]

➤ *How can you test whether these are magnetic?* [Hold up the compass near them, or use another steel item like a paper clip to confirm attraction.]

EL NOTE

Suggest students make a structure-and-function table in their notebooks and add the parts when they are introduced.

Motor part	Structure (describe the shape and composition)	Function (how does it work and how is that related to its structure?)
Shaft		
Permanent magnets		
Coil		
Commutator		
Brush		

SCIENCE AND ENGINEERING PRACTICES

Constructing explanations

Engaging in argument from evidence

Electromagnetic Force Course—FOSS Next Generation

INVESTIGATION 4 – Energy Transfer

CROSSCUTTING CONCEPTS

Structure and function

Energy and matter

Distribute one paper clip to each group so students can confirm the location of the permanent magnets.

Ask students to focus on the small wires coiled around the shaft section. Give students a moment to think about and discuss the structure and function of this component. If necessary, ask,

➤ *What does this thin, coiled wire indicate?* [It's probably an electromagnet.]

➤ *Where is the core of the electromagnet?* [There might be three cores, because there are three coils of wire. Each one is wrapped around a mushroom-shaped metal structure that must be steel or iron.]

Point out that these cores are shaped differently from the rod-shaped cores they used in their electromagnets, but the cores are still a metal (steel or iron) with coiled wire around them, so they might be able to act as an electromagnet. Leave it ambiguous whether there is one electromagnet or three, as students will test this in the next steps.

Ask,

➤ *Through what pathway does the electromagnet get its energy from the battery?* [On the shaft, the electromagnet wires connect to a round copper structure at the end of the shaft. This copper section comes into contact with the ends of the wire that run in from the battery in the plastic cap.]

9. **Introduce** *commutator*
   Ask students to take a close look at that copper section on the shaft. Tell students that the name for that section is the commutator [COM-you-ta-tor]. After a moment, ask,

   ➤ *What do you notice about the **commutator** when you look closely?* [It has three sections.]

   Tell students that the commutator acts as a switch for the electromagnet. Their task is to see if they can figure out how the design acts as a switch.

   Project teacher master J, *Motor Shaft and Commutator*, to help students see the break between sections of the commutator.

10. **Discuss the plastic cap**
    Ask students to look inside the plastic cap of the motor, where the wires connect. Ask,

    ➤ *What is the shape of those wires at the contact point?* [Flattened and broad, sort of like a paintbrush or a paddle.]

    ➤ *How might the shape of the wires relate to their function?* [A broad area will have better contact with other components.]

CROSSCUTTING CONCEPTS

Structure and function

Part 1: Electric Motors

Project teacher master K, *Motor Cap and Brushes*, and tell students that the term for those flat ends of wire is **brush**. Point out that the current runs in through the wires from the battery, through the brush, and to the commutator at the contact between the brush and commutator. Continue the discussion, using these questions as a guide.

➤ *How many wires bring current through the motor cap?* [Two.]

➤ *How many sections of the commutator are there?* [Three.]

➤ *Is it possible for all three sections of the commutator to receive current at the same time?* [Not really, because the brushes provide only two contact points.]

➤ *What will happen if only two sections of the commutator receive current at one time?* [Only two sections of the electromagnet will work.]

Depending on where the commutator is in the rotation, it's touching only two contact points (brushes), so two parts will be switched on and one will be switched off.

11. Test the dissected electromagnet

Tell students they will now find out what happens if there are only *two* places for the current to enter the motor, but there are *three* commutator contact points. Assist students with these steps.

- Show students how to carefully reattach the cap on the shaft piece by sliding the shaft and commutator between the brushes of the cap.
- The brushes must be in contact with the commutator. Students should not add the case at this time.
- Students can set up the circuit with the battery and test each section of the electromagnet, using the paper clip as a tool for detecting magnetic fields.

Give groups several minutes for reassembly and testing. Encourage students to document their cause-and-effect observations in their notebooks. Students should be able to observe that the magnetism in the two sections of the electromagnet is activated. The third section may have some magnetism, but will be weaker. Which two sections are magnetized will change as the shaft turns in the cap. Students can rotate the commutator bit by bit to confirm that the strength of each electromagnet section depends on which sections of the commutator are in contact with the two brushes.

SCIENCE AND ENGINEERING PRACTICES
Constructing explanations

SCIENCE AND ENGINEERING PRACTICES
Planning and carrying out investigations

Analyzing and interpreting data

SESSION 2   45–50 minutes

Electromagnetic Force Course—FOSS Next Generation

INVESTIGATION 4 – Energy Transfer

SCIENCE AND ENGINEERING PRACTICES
Developing and using models
Constructing explanations

CROSSCUTTING CONCEPTS
Structure and function

TEACHING NOTE

Refer to the Sense-Making Discussions for Three-Dimensional Learning chapter in Teacher Resources on FOSSweb for more information about how to facilitate this with students.

12. Review implications

Help students make connections between what they have tested and the function of the motor. Point out that the shaft of the motor is designed with three sections of electromagnet, only two of which turn on at one time.

Ask,

➤ *What happens to each electromagnet section when a current runs through that section?* [The electromagnet turns on.]

➤ *How will the electromagnet interact with the permanent magnet inside the metal casing?* [It will be attracted or repelled by the permanent magnet adjacent to it inside the metal case.]

Now it is time to make a big connection. Give students a few minutes to discuss the following question in their groups.

➤ *Why would the motor be designed so only two of the three electromagnet sections are turned on at any one time?*

Have each group make a model on chart paper of what they think is happening inside the motor.

13. Have a sense-making discussion

Gather together for a sense-making discussion, with each group bringing their chart paper models and notebooks. Review the norms for a class discussion, and ask groups to share their models and ideas about how an electromagnet works. Remind students to build on others' ideas and to ask clarifying questions as they develop a working model of an electromagnet together.

When all groups have shared, provide more information as needed to help students understand the electric motor design. Tell students,

When two sections of electromagnets are turned on, and one section is not, those two "on" sections exert a force on the permanent magnets inside the case. As the "on" sections attract or repel the permanent magnets, the force causes the shaft of the motor to rotate. But as the shaft rotates, the commutator also rotates into a new position. Suddenly, the section that was "off" is turned "on," and one of the previously "on" coils turns off.

Ask students,

➤ *What happens to the electromagnet when a section that was off is turned on?*

Have students discuss ideas with a partner before letting them share ideas with the class. After hearing student thinking, provide more information as needed.

The electromagnets exert a force again, rotating the shaft again. This process repeats over and over and over, creating an electric motor with a rotating shaft that could drive a toy car, spin a washing machine basin, run a blender, or do countless other jobs humans might dream of.

Part 1: Electric Motors

The brush and commutator system is a kind of switch. The rotation of the shaft opens and closes the circuit, turning the electromagnets on and off. The design of the commutator switches on and off the electromagnets at exactly the right times to keep the shaft rotating.

14. Retest motors and consider energy transfer

Distribute the working (nondissected) motors and D-cells in holders and let students create a circuit. Distribute the dissected motors so students can look at the inner parts of the motor as they watch the working motor run, focusing on how the motor works. Ask students to think about how energy is being transferred in this system.

Have students return to their group models and add arrows and labels to show transfer of energy through the circuit. To focus students, ask,

➤ *What evidence do we have of energy in this system?* [There's evidence of kinetic energy, because we can see the shaft turning.]

➤ *Where did the energy come from that transferred to the shaft to make it move?* [From the electrical energy in the circuit.]

➤ *Where did the electrical energy in the circuit come from?* [The chemical potential energy in the battery.]

15. Analyze diagrams

Distribute a copy of *FOSS Science Resources* to each student, and have them turn to "Motor Dissection A" in the Images and Data section. Tell students that this diagram and the next pages, "Motor Dissection B," will help students as they prepare to answer the focus question.

Give students about 5 minutes to work in their groups to analyze both diagrams and the accompanying text. Students should explain the diagrams to each other in their groups, and call you for help if there are any remaining questions.

16. Record vocabulary

Take a few moments to review the vocabulary developed in this part. Ask students to add definitions to their notebooks, and update their vocabulary indexes if they haven't already done so.

17. Revisit the focus question

Have students return to the focus question.

➤ *How does an electric motor work?*

Have students answer on a separate piece of white paper. Ask them to draw and label a diagram of a dissected electric motor and include it with their explanation. In their response, students should describe the role of electric current, permanent magnets, electromagnets, and the shaft.

SCIENCE AND ENGINEERING PRACTICES
Developing and using models

CROSSCUTTING CONCEPTS
Energy and matter

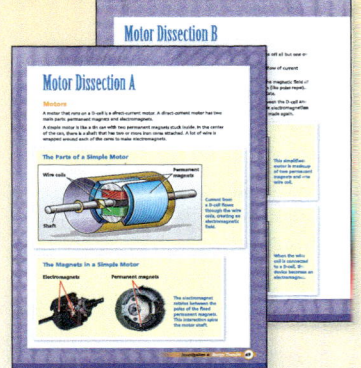

FOSS Science Resources

brush
commutator
motor
rotate
shaft

INVESTIGATION 4 – Energy Transfer

18. Assess progress: notebook entry
Collect the sheets and use a sample to consider students' thinking about how electric motors work.

What to Look For

- *Electric current travels into the motor through long wires that connect to the brushes.*
- *The brushes make contact with two sections of the commutator at one time.*
- *The commutator is a switch that turns electromagnets on and off.*
- *Only two sections of the electromagnet are turned on at one time; these sections repel from the permanent magnets in the case, causing the shaft to rotate.*
- *As soon as the electromagnet sections rotate, the commutator is in a new position and one section will turn off while another turns on. The cycle will continue, turning the shaft over and over again.*

Plan to spend 15 minutes reviewing the selected student responses. Using *Embedded Assessment Notes* as a tool, review the responses, record any alternative concepts that are evident, and decide if any next-step strategies are required before moving forward.

After your review, return the sheets to students to be taped or glued into their science notebooks.

19. Extend the investigation with homework
Students can go back to the online activity "Kitchen Magnets" they explored in Investigation 3. Now they will be able to identify which items might use electromagnets as part of an electric motor. Students should describe which of the featured objects they think use that technology and why.

WRAP-UP/WARM-UP

20. Review notebook entries
Give students a few minutes to share their notebook entries with a partner. Have them take turns explaining their diagrams to each other. Encourage them to give each other constructive feedback and to revise their entries if needed. Students can also compare their structure-and-function charts.

Part 2: Electric Generators

MATERIALS for
Part 2: *Electric Generators*

Provided equipment

For each student

1   *FOSS Science Resources: Electromagnetic Force*
 - "The Rebirth of Electric Cars"
 - "Where We Get Energy"
 - "Generator Dissection"

For each group

1   Poster, *FOSS Outdoor Safety*
1   Solar cell
1   Motor

For the class

1   Hand-crank generator
1   Motor
2–3   D-cells
2–3   Cell holders
1–2   Wires, 20-gauge, 15 cm

Teacher-supplied items

For the class

1   Incandescent lightbulb (optional)
1   Lamp (optional)

FOSSweb resources

For each student

1   Notebook sheet 13, *Energy Transfers*
1   Notebook sheets 14–20, *Where We Get Energy*
1   Investigation 4 I-Check

For the class

- Video, *Generator Dissection*

For the teacher

- Teacher master L, *Hand-Crank Generator*
- Performance Assessment Checklist
- Assessment Record
- Teaching slides, 4.2

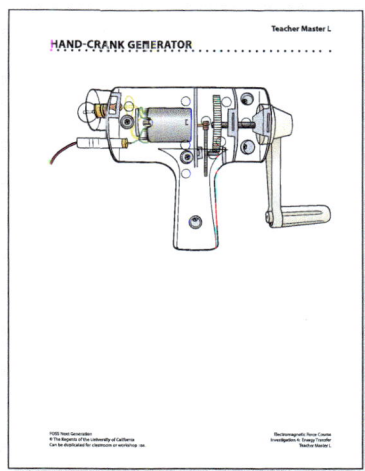

Teacher Master L

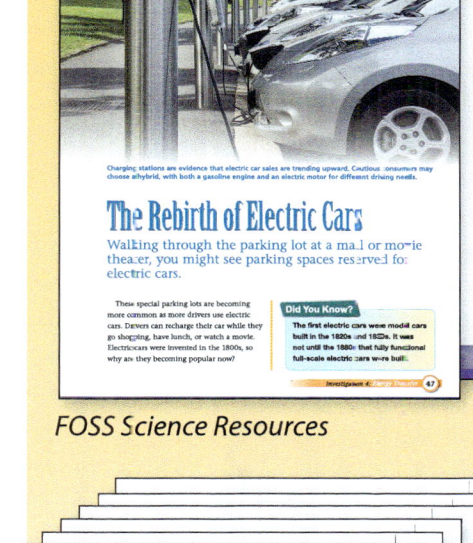

FOSS Science Resources

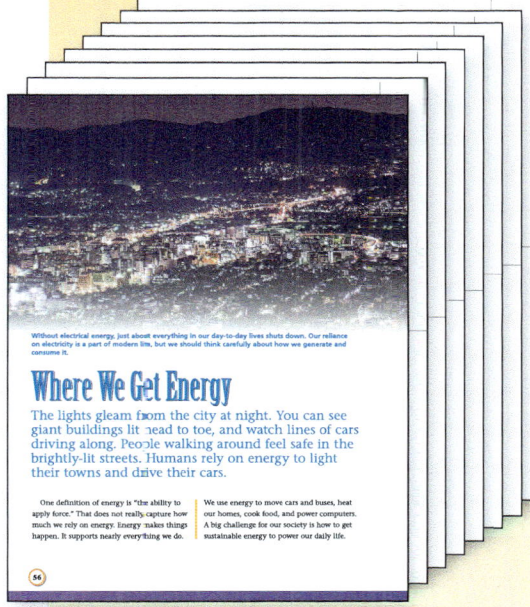

FOSS Science Resources and Nos. 14–20—Notebook Masters

No. 13—Notebook Master

INVESTIGATION 4 – Energy Transfer

GETTING READY for
Part 2: Electric Generators

Quick Start

Schedule	2 sessions active investigation 1 session reading 1–2 session assessments and next steps
Preview	• Preview the FOSSweb Resources by Investigation for this part (such as printable masters, teaching slides, and online activities) • Preview the video: *Generator Dissection*, Step 7 • Plan homework reading: "The Rebirth of Electric Cars," Step 15 • Preview the in-class reading: "Where We Get Energy," Step 23
Print or Copy	**For each student** • Notebook sheets 13–20 • *Investigation 4 I-Check*, or schedule it on FOSSweb **For the teacher** • *Performance Assessment Checklist* • *Assessment Record*
Prepare Material	• Hang the *FOSS Outdoor Safety* poster • Prepare solar cells **A** • Check for optimal lighting **B** • Test hand-crank generator **C**
Plan for Assessment	• Review Step 19, "What to Look For" in the performance assessment • Plan for benchmark assessment, Step 29, *I-Check 4*

Teaching slides, 4.2

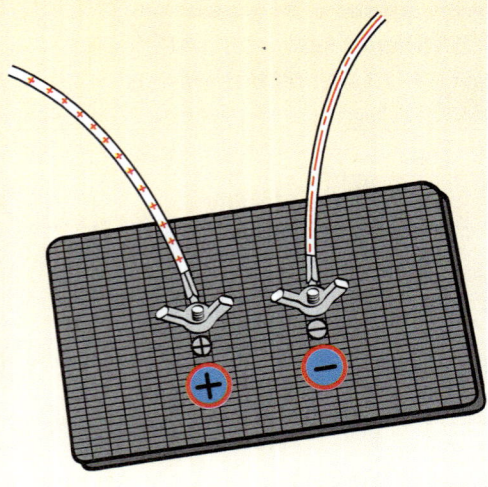

Preparation Details

A Prepare solar cells
The solar cells come with two sets of wires. Use the set that has two different ends: a metal ring and flat connector. You will not need the other set of wires.

Part 2: Electric Generators

Unscrew the wing nuts on the back of the solar cell. One of the wires is marked with dashes or tiny -- symbols and the other may be marked with tiny + symbols. Place the metal ring of the negative wire over the negative screw, and tighten the wing nut. Place the metal ring of the other wire over the positive screw, and tighten the wing nut. If the wires are attached, it is OK to separate them as needed.

B ▶ Check for optimal lighting

Test each solar cell in a circuit with a motor, sliding the wire ends of the motor into the metal connectors at the end of the solar-cell wires.

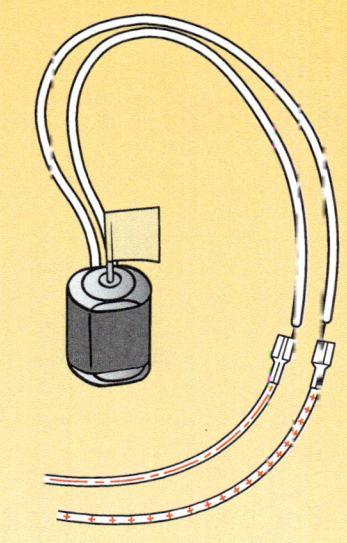

Test the solar cell in direct sunlight. You might need to twist the motor shaft to kick-start the motor. If there is not enough sunlight, you can test the solar cell under a bright lamp. Fluorescent bulbs typically are not bright enough. However, one incandescent bulb at close range (several inches from the cell) should work.

Consider how you will arrange the class activity. If a sunny day is forecast, you can take your classes outside. If that will not be an option, consider how to set up an incandescent bulb so that groups can take turns holding their solar cells under it.

C ▶ Test hand-crank generator

Practice turning the generator crank quickly to light up the installed lightbulb. A replacement lightbulb is in the box if you need it. You will want to turn it slowly at first, so that it doesn't light the bulb, so test that speed as well.

The generator comes with a wire that plugs into the generator below the lightbulb. Plug in that attachment, then clip the alligator clips at the end of the wires to a motor. When you turn the crank quickly, both the bulb and the motor will operate.

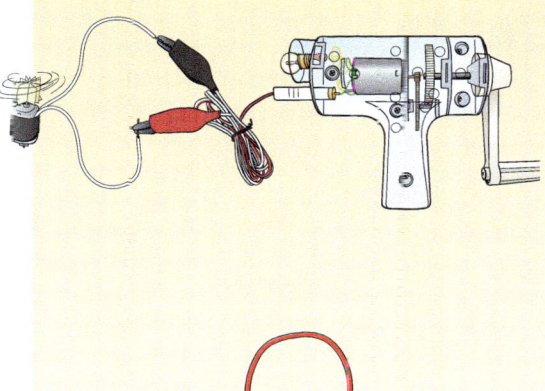

Test the wire attachment to run electricity back into the generator, effectively running it as a motor. Do this by disconnecting the motor and using the alligator clips to attach two D-cells in series.

Unscrew the lightbulb slightly so it won't drain energy from the circuit. The hand crank may start rotating due to the electric current. If it does not, push the crank with your hand to start the motion. The electric current will keep it moving. (If it does not, your batteries might be running low. New batteries or a third battery in series should get it working.) By supplying electrical energy to the generator, you have converted the generator into a motor, rotating the shaft upon which the handcrank is connected.

To prepare for your first class, screw the lightbulb back in and disconnect the wire attachment for the first part of the class activity.

Electromagnetic Force Course—FOSS Next Generation

INVESTIGATION 4 – Energy Transfer

FOCUS QUESTION

How can we generate electrical energy?

EL NOTE

Project or make a flow chart on the board, showing the transfer of energy.

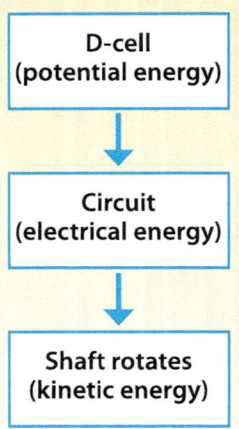

GUIDING the Investigation
Part 2: Electric Generators

SESSION 1

Students will . . .
- Think about how to generate electrical energy (Steps 1, 2)
- Explore a generator in terms of energy transfers (Steps 3–9)
- Discuss electric cars and their energy sources (Steps 10, 11)
- Consider human energy use and sources (Steps 12–14)
- Extend the investigation with homework (Step 15)

SESSION 2

Students will . . .
- Explore solar energy (Step 16–21)
- Think about environmental interactions (Step 22)
- Read about energy sources (Steps 23, 24)
- Record vocabulary and revisit focus question (Steps 25, 26)
- Answer the guiding question (Step 27)

SESSION 3

Students will . . .
- Have a sense-making discussion (Step 28)

SESSIONS 4–5

Students will . . .
- Demonstrate understanding on *I-Check 4* (Step 29)
- Review I-Check items throught next-step strategies (Step 30)

SESSION 1   45–50 minutes

1. **Consider energy transfer**
   Ask,

   ▶ *In the previous part of this investigation, what evidence did we see of energy transfer?* [Potential energy (battery) produced electrical energy to make a motor shaft turn (kinetic energy).]

   ▶ *Do you think it's possible to do the opposite, to transfer kinetic energy to generate electrical energy?*

   Tell students that will be the topic of exploration in this part.

284   Full Option Science System

Part 2: Electric Generators

2. **Focus question: How can we generate electrical energy?**
   Display the focus question and have students copy it into their notebooks.

   ➤ *How can we generate electrical energy?*

3. **Explore a *generator***
   Tell students that you have a tool that will help them investigate kinetic energy. Bring out the hand-crank generator and turn the crank very slowly, so that the lightbulb doesn't light. Ask students to describe evidence of kinetic energy that they can see (the crank is moving, and some gears inside the device are moving).

   Invite a student to turn the crank faster and faster until the lightbulb lights. Walk with the student and device to make sure that each student can see the light. Ask,

   ➤ *What evidence do you observe of energy besides kinetic energy in the system?* [Heat and light from the bulb; electrical energy must be present because the bulb is functioning.]

   Ask students to discuss the next question in their groups. Have Reporters share answers.

   ➤ *What energy transfers occurred to make the bulb light?* [Motion energy from the body turns the crank, and the crank does something inside the device to transfer energy to electrical energy to light the bulb, which in turn radiates light energy and heats up.]

4. **Analyze generator components**
   Project teacher master L, *Hand-Crank Generator*, or hold the device under a document camera so the class can see what is inside the clear plastic casing. Give students time to discuss the following question with a partner before discussing it as a class.

   ➤ *What might be happening inside the device?* [Cranking by hand turns a shaft inside. The shaft goes into a metal case. There are probably electromagnets in the metal case similar to the motor. Somehow turning the shaft generates electricity.]

   Tell students,

   *When the shaft turns, it moves coils of wire in a magnetic field that induces an electric current in the wires, like an electromagnet in reverse. That current travels through the circuit and lights the bulb. This system is called a **generator** because it generates electricity.*

   But it doesn't create energy out of nothing, and doesn't have stored energy like a battery. Generators transfer energy from one place to another, in this case from kinetic energy of the turning shaft to the electrical energy that lights the bulb.

EL NOTE
Use a flow chart to help students think about the energy transfers.

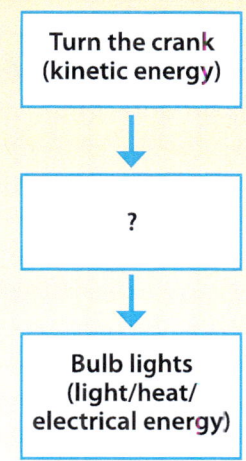

CROSSCUTTING CONCEPTS
Energy and matter

INVESTIGATION 4 – Energy Transfer

Generators used during power outages, at campsites, and for motor homes are often powered not by a hand crank, but by engines producing kinetic energy that are in turn fueled by gasoline, which is a form of potential energy.

Let students pass the generator from table to table to test it and see it up close as you begin the next step.

5. Observe other energy transfers

Project and distribute notebook sheet 13, *Energy Transfers*, and tell students they will see interactions involving energy transfer.

Plug in the wire to the generator, and hook up the motor to the alligator clips. Ask students to make predictions about what will happen now when you turn the crank. Encourage them to use reasoning and their prior experiences to explain why. Then turn the crank until the lightbulb lights and the motor turns on. Walk around so students can observe the system as you crank.

Ask students to work individually on question 1 from the notebook sheet. Ask them to share ideas with the class.

➤ *What energy transfers are happening to make the motor run?* [Kinetic energy from your hand transfers to the shaft. The kinetic energy of the shaft transfers energy to the electromagnet coils, generating electric current. The electrical energy travels through the circuit to the motor, turning on electromagnets that produce magnetic force that makes the shaft rotate (kinetic energy).]

6. Compare generators and motors

Distribute a copy of *FOSS Science Resources* to each student and have students open to "Generator Dissection." Give students a few moments to work on questions 2 and 3 on the notebook sheet while you project teacher master L. They can look back in their notebooks to find their notes on motors. Ask students to share ideas with the class.

Ask students to compare

- The energy transfers of a battery/motor system (chemical/electrical energy transfers to kinetic energy of the shaft) to the energy transfers of a generator (kinetic energy of the shaft generates electrical energy).

- The inner workings of the motor and generator (they both have a shaft connected to an electromagnet).

Point out that a motor and a generator can basically be considered the same component; it just depends on which way the energy transfers. Students should add information to their notebook-sheet responses.

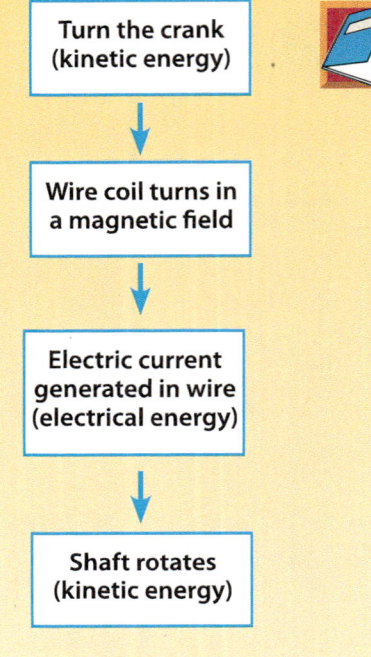

SCIENCE AND ENGINEERING PRACTICES

Analyzing and interpreting data

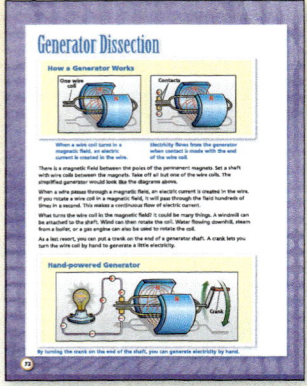

FOSS Science Resources

Part 2: Electric Generators

7. **View video: *Generator Dissection***
   Tell students that you are not going to let them take apart the class generator to learn more about its inner components, but you have a video of someone doing so. Ask students to review what they have written so far for item 3 on the notebook sheet. As they watch the video, they should add more information to their response.

   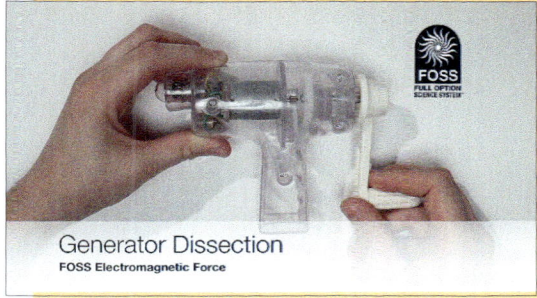

   Play the video, pausing or replaying if students request to see it in more detail. Allow a moment for students to update their notebooks, then lead a quick class discussion about what evidence they saw in the video that motors and generators can be considered the same component.

8. **Think about generator and batteries**
   Ask,

   ➤ *If a generator has essentially the same components as a motor, including magnets, coils of wire, and a shaft, what do you think will happen if I hook up a battery to the wires of this generator?*

   Let students speculate and give them time to respond to question 4 on the notebook sheet. Encourage them to use reasoning and their prior experiences to explain their answers.

   If students need help getting started, use this prompt: "Based on what I know about how energy transfers, I think _____ because _____."

9. **Use the generator as a motor**
   Hook up two batteries in series to the generator's auxiliary wires. Unscrew the lightbulb slightly so it won't drain energy from the circuit, and push lightly on the crank if needed to start it moving. Students will be able to see that the crank keeps moving, driven by the battery power. Give students time to record an answer to question 5 on the notebook sheet.

   Ask,

   ➤ *We are using the generator as a motor now, by transferring energy into the system. What is the source of energy?* [Chemical potential energy of the battery, or electrical energy.]

   ➤ *What does that energy transfer to?* [Kinetic energy.]

10. **Discuss electric cars**
    Ask students to raise their hands if they have seen or ridden in an electric car. Project or show images of electric cars and have students discuss what they know about them. Ask students what questions they have. Add the following questions if they don't come up, and let students share their thoughts,

> **TEACHING NOTE**
>
> Go to FOSSweb for Teacher Resources and look for the Science and Engineering Practices chapter for details on how to engage students with the practice of asking questions.

SCIENCE AND ENGINEERING PRACTICES
Asking questions

INVESTIGATION 4 – Energy Transfer

➤ *What makes an electric car move?* [An electric motor.]

➤ *Where does the energy come from to run an electric car?* [From a battery that gets recharged from being plugged into an electric outlet.]

Confirm that electric cars use rechargeable batteries that get plugged in to store electrical energy.

Tell students,

Electromagnets, electric motors, and generators are technologies that make electric cars work. When you apply the brakes in a traditional car, the brake pads heat up as they rub against the wheels and apply friction to slow the car. The kinetic energy of the car transfers to heat energy, so it transfers to the environment. It is lost.

In an electric car, this kinetic energy is not all lost. When you brake, the car's electric motors can work as generators. These generators can transfer some of the kinetic energy to electrical energy, which is then stored as potential energy in the car's battery. That battery can then be used to power the motor of the car. Engineers are always looking for ways like this to improve the energy efficiency of a car.

11. Discuss energy sources

Ask,

➤ *When an electric car is plugged in to charge the batteries, where does the energy come from?* [From the electricity in plugs, provided by utility companies.]

➤ *Where do utility companies get their electricity?*

Students might have an idea of how electricity is generated in their community. Often this local information can be determined by visiting the utility company's website, which makes an interesting follow-up project for students.

Tell students,

Utility companies that provide electricity to people, homes, and businesses can't create energy. They have to transfer some kind of energy to generate electricity, like the energy transfers in class with the hand-crank generator.

In many areas, the prime source of energy is chemical energy stored in **fossil fuels** *such as coal or natural gas. As fuel burns, its stored energy transfers to run electric generators. Fossil fuels are* **nonrenewable***, meaning that they were created by geological processes that take many millions of years. When they are all used up, other sources of electricity will become essential for us to have electricity. We'll discuss those shortly.*

EL NOTE
Use a simple diagram to explain these processes.

CROSSCUTTING CONCEPTS
Scale, proportion, and quantity
Energy and matter

Part 2: Electric Generators

12. Examine real-life applications
Ask,

➤ *Can you think of any real-life applications where environmental kinetic energy can be harnessed to generate electrical energy?*

Students may list steam, wind, water, or waves. They may also have seen a museum display or other instance where a human-powered bicycle can generate electrical energy (light a lightbulb, or power a phone charger).

13. Introduce renewable energy
Tell students,

Energy from the wind blowing, water flowing, ocean waves, and steam from volcanic vents are examples of natural kinetic energy sources that can be harnessed to generate electricity. That electricity can power factories or homes and do anything you might typically want from a source of electricity. This is called **renewable** *energy because the wind and water flow are not used up; they are constantly recurring.*

Ask students if they have any ideas of other naturally occurring energy that can potentially be harnessed to generate electricity. They might suggest capturing energy from Earth's heat (geothermal) or the Sun (solar).

14. Discuss energy transfer to the environment
Point out that another way to reduce use of nonrenewable energy sources is to reduce the amount of energy needed in the first place, by looking for places where it may be lost to the environment. For example, a lightbulb that transfers more heat energy to the environment (like an incandescent bulb) uses more energy than a lightbulb that transfers very little heat energy to the environment (like a fluorescent or LED bulb).

Similarly, engineers are looking for ways to reduce the amount of energy transferred to the environment as electricity makes its way to homes and businesses from a power plant.

CROSSCUTTING CONCEPTS

Energy and matter

INVESTIGATION 4 – Energy Transfer

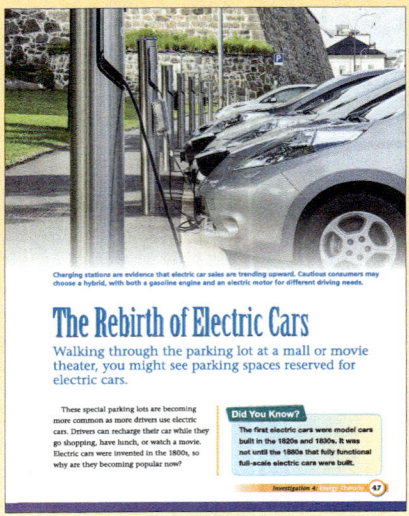

FOSS Science Resources

ELA CONNECTION

These suggested strategies address the Common Core State Standards for ELA for literacy.

WHST 9: Draw evidence from informational texts to support analysis, reflection, and research.

RST 2: Determine the central ideas or conclusions of a text.

SCIENCE AND ENGINEERING PRACTICES

Obtaining, evaluating, and communicating information

READING in Science Resources

15. Extend the investigation with homework

The article "The Rebirth of Electric Cars" can be assigned as homework to inform students about the practical application of the motor technology discussed in class.

To support reading comprehension, tell students,

Before reading, skim through the article to get a sense of what it is about. Analyze the diagrams and read the captions. There is a lot of information in this text. Reading with questions in mind can help you focus on some of the important ideas.

Suggest they set up their notebooks to take two-column notes, with one column for notes from the article that pertain to the Think Questions and one column for the Think Questions, with spaces in between for writing down their own thinking about the question based on the information from the text. Encourage them to include at least one new question they have for each section.

Notes (information related to the question)	Think Questions (plus my new ideas and questions)
	Why were gasoline-powered automobiles so popular for most of the 20th century?
	What are some technological limitations for electric cars?
	How do electric cars help reduce fossil-fuel use?

Have students answer the Think Questions using evidence from the text to support their answers.

➤ *Why were gasoline-powered automobiles so popular for most of the 20th century?* [Fuel (petroleum) was widely available, and the technology for electric cars was not advanced yet.]

➤ *What are some technological limitations for electric cars?* [To speed up quickly, you need a lot of energy at once, which drains the battery faster. An electric car is limited by how far it can travel before it recharges, but bigger batteries add weight to the car and reduce the travel range, too.]

➤ *How do electric cars help reduce fossil-fuel use?* [Electric cars lose less energy to the environment because they use regenerative braking, so they need less fuel overall. And, electric cars could be charged by renewable energy sources like wind or solar power.]

Part 2: Electric Generators

SESSION 2 45–50 minutes

16. Focus on solar energy
Hold up one of the solar cells and tell students,

*These **solar cells** take advantage of the properties of silicon, an element, to transfer light energy from the Sun into electrical energy. This energy can be used just like any other electric source.*

Ask students to share experiences with solar cells on their toys, calculators, homes, or other buildings in their neighborhoods, and give them a few moments to make connections to these experiences. Large solar panels are composed of many solar cells like the ones students are using in class.

> **EL NOTE**
> You might project or provide images or real examples of solar-powered devices.

17. Overview activity and model development
Show students how a solar cell can be attached to a motor. Describe the procedure the class will use to activate the solar cells: you will take the class outside, or they will take turns using an incandescent bulb in the room to illuminate the cells.

Tell students that while they are working with the materials, they should draw a diagram of the completed circuit in their science notebooks, and develop their model by labeling the diagram to show the energy source and energy transfers.

18. Go outdoors
Make sure students are dressed appropriately, and head to your outdoor gathering spot. This spot should be on a flat lawn or other open area. Have students help you carry the equipment outdoors.

- Solar cells
- Motors
- Notebooks
- *Performance Assessment Checklist*

Set up the boundaries for the session and make sure all students know where they are.

SCIENCE AND ENGINEERING PRACTICES

Developing and using models

Planning and carrying out investigations

Constructing explanations

19. Assess progress: performance assessment
Observe the groups as they assemble their systems, test them, and make diagrams that explain the energy transfers in the system. Ask questions to assess students' three-dimensional learning. Note their progress on *Performance Assessment Checklist*.

DISCIPLINARY CORE IDEAS

PS3.B: Conservation of energy and energy transfer

What to Look For
- Students assemble a working circuit, angling the cell toward the light source and connecting contact points between the motor and cell. (Planning and carrying out investigations; cause and effect.)

Electromagnetic Force Course—FOSS Next Generation

INVESTIGATION 4 – Energy Transfer

CROSSCUTTING CONCEPTS

Cause and effect
Systems and system models
Energy and matter

CROSSCUTTING CONCEPTS

Energy and matter
Stability and change

▶ **NOTE**
Go to FOSSweb for *Teacher Resources* and look for the Crosscutting Concepts and Integration chapter for details on how to engage students with the concept of stability and change to integrate content at this grade level.

- Students develop a model of the system that shows the components, the energy source, and the energy transfers: solar energy transferred to solar cell to generate electrical energy, and electrical energy running the motor transferred to kinetic energy. (Developing and using models; constructing explanations; PS3.B: Conservation of energy and energy transfer; systems and system models; energy and matter.)

20. **Return to class**
Return to the classroom and collect materials from groups.

21. **Share diagrams**
Ask a few groups to share their diagrams and discuss the energy transfers in the system. Encourage students who might have left out part of the diagram or an energy transfer to add it to their notebook entry.

22. **Think about environmental interactions**
Tell students,

Remember that we can't create energy, or destroy it. We can only move it around by transferring it. Finding ways to transfer energy from renewable energy sources like the Sun, wind, or water is a great challenge for humans because nonrenewable energy sources such as coal, natural gas, and oil will eventually be used up.

Ask students,

➤ *The human population on Earth is increasing. What could that mean for fossil fuel use?* [More humans will have more demand for energy sources. Fossil fuels may run out faster, or become more scarce.]

Tell students,

Before fossil fuels are completely gone, they will continue to get more expensive because they are a limited resource. Another problem with fossil fuels has to do with something you may have heard of: climate change. The gases released when fossil fuels are burned have long-term effects in Earth's atmosphere.

Ask students,

➤ *What does an increasing human population have to do with climate change?* [More humans using more fossil fuel means that the climate could change more quickly.]

This is another reason that scientists and engineers are eager to harness more renewable energy sources for human use.

Part 2: Electric Generators

READING *in Science Resources*

23. Read "Where We Get Energy"

Tell students that the article "Where We Get Energy" will give them a chance to think in more detail about human energy use and sources. Distribute a copy of *FOSS Science Resources* to each student. Have students preview the article by looking at and discussing the photographs and diagrams with a partner, reading the captions and subtitles, and noting the words in bold.

Next, distribute the black and white copies of the reading, notebook sheets 14–20, to students and have them affix the sheets in their notebooks. Suggest they leave a blank page next to each sheet for taking notes. (Left-handed students might want to glue their sheets on the right side.) Tell students,

As you read the article, have a pen, colored pencil, or highlighter ready. When you read an important point, highlight or underline it in the text. If you encounter a word you don't know, circle the word. And if you have a question about part of the reading, or an interesting idea related to the reading, take notes in the margin or on the adjacent blank notebook page.

24. Use a reading comprehension strategy

Students can jigsaw the article following this procedure.

a. Start by reading aloud or call on a volunteer to read the first page. Model how you would highlight the last sentence and say,

   This is what I think the rest of the article will be about.

b. To start the jigsaw, have students number off 1–6 and get into their numbered groups. They will be the "experts" for their section. Assign each group one of the sections of the reading and have them read it independently. When they finish, have them discuss their notes and agree on what are the important parts for that section. The Recorder for the group should write down the agreed-upon summary of the main idea.

c. Make new groups comprised of students from each of the numbered groups, (i.e., each group should have an expert for every section).

d. Assign a facilitator for each group to make sure every student shares his/her summary with the rest of the group. A Recorder can write down any new questions that come up.

Review any difficulties students had with the article and interesting questions that were generated. Use the following guide to lead a whole-group discussion of the article.

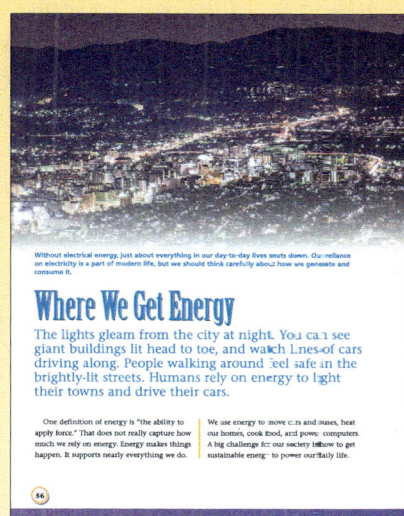

FOSS Science Resources

ELA CONNECTION

These suggested strategies address the Common Core State Standards for ELA for literacy.

RST 7: Integrate quantitative or technical information expressed in words in a text with a version of that information expressed visually.

RST 4: Determine the meaning of symbols, key terms, and other domain-specific words and phrases.

RST 10: Read and comprehend science texts independently and proficiently.

SCIENCE AND ENGINEERING PRACTICES

Asking questions

Obtaining, evaluating, and communicating information

INVESTIGATION 4 – Energy Transfer

Organize information:
Suggest that students set up the energy source table described in Think Question 3 so they can record the information as you discuss each energy source. They might also color code the advantages and disadvantages of each on their black and white copies using two different colored highlighters or pencils, or by using symbols such as (+ and -).

Without electrical energy, just about everything in our day-to-day lives shuts down. Our reliance on electricity is a part of modern life.

Where We Get Energy

The lights gleam from the city at night. You can see giant buildings lit head to toe, and watch lines of cars driving along. People walking around feel safe in the brightly-lit streets. Humans rely on energy to light their towns and drive their cars.

One definition of energy is "the ability to apply force over a distance." That does not really capture how much we rely on energy. Energy makes things happen. It supports nearly everything we do. We use energy to move cars and buses, heat our homes, cook food, and power computers. A big challenge for our society is how to get sustainable energy to power our daily life.

ELA CONNECTION

This suggested strategy addresses the Common Core State Standards for ELA for literacy.

WHST 9: Draw evidence from informational texts to support analysis, reflection, and research.

Part 2: Electric Generators

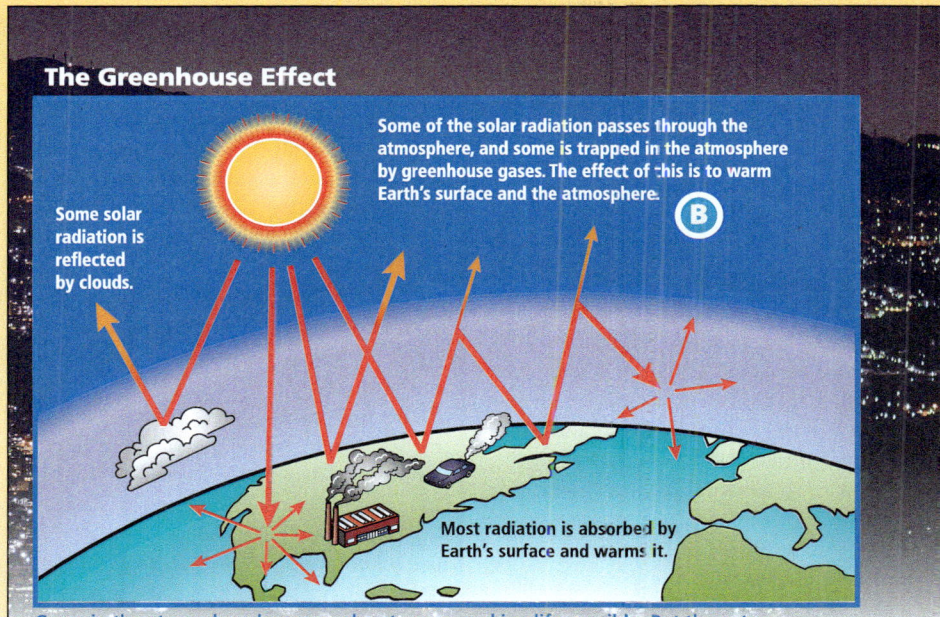

Gases in the atmosphere keep our planet warm, making life possible. But the extra greenhouse gases added by global human activity are changing Earth's climate.

The Fossil-Fuel Source

Fuel is a material that stores energy. Our ancestors were burning wood as fuel more than 400,000 years ago. Humans have been burning coal as fuel for over 5,000 years. In the past 100 years or so, humans have grown used to cheap energy from fossil fuels. Fuels such as coal, oil, and natural gas have been plentiful and inexpensive. Using fossil fuels, however, creates serious problems.

 When we burn fossil fuels to release energy, a chemical reaction occurs. The reaction uses the stored chemical energy of the fuel to generate thermal energy. Thermal energy can be transferred to mechanical energy and electrical energy. Mechanical energy powers the engines of cars, buses, and planes. Electrical energy travels from a power plant to our communities through the **power grid**. A power grid is a complex network of wires that delivers electricity to homes and other buildings.

Burning fossil fuels releases carbon dioxide and other pollutants into Earth's atmosphere. Carbon dioxide is a **greenhouse gas**. It helps the atmosphere "trap" thermal energy that would otherwise radiate into space.

As carbon dioxide builds up in the atmosphere, Earth becomes warmer. This is known as climate change. Human-induced climate change is driving global temperatures higher and altering climate all over Earth. Climate change leads to serious problems around the globe, like sea level rising, more severe droughts, more severe storms, and heat waves. Carbon dioxide emissions are also causing the ocean to become more acidic, endangering ocean life.

Investigation 4: Energy Transfer 57

Analyze diagram: Tell students to discuss the diagram with a partner.

▶ *What are the parts of this model?* [Sun, Earth, atmosphere, clouds, red arrows.]

▶ *What do the arrows represent?* [The arrows represent energy.]

▶ *What does it explain?* [Some energy comes from the Sun. Energy is then absorbed, radiated, or reflected by Earth and the atmosphere.]

Diagram energy transfers: Students might want to make a quick diagram to illustrate this process in their notebooks.

Consider language use: Pause at the word "trap." Ask student what they think that means and what the consequences are. Encourage them to cite evidence from the text to support their ideas.

ELA CONNECTION

These suggested strategies address the Common Core State Standards for ELA for literacy.

RST 7: Integrate quantitative or technical information expressed in words in a text with a version of that information expressed visually.

L 5: Demonstrate understanding of word relationships and nuances in word meaning.

RST 1: Cite evidence to support analysis of science texts.

Electromagnetic Force Course—FOSS Next Generation

INVESTIGATION 4 – Energy Transfer

Develop vocabulary: Point out the question-and-answer structure the author uses to present this information. Suggest students make a flow chart to show the process of generating electricity by burning fossil fuels.

Add to graphic organizer: Give students a few minutes to add information to the energy source table and discuss new questions.

ELA CONNECTION

These suggested strategies address the Common Core State Standards for ELA for literacy.

RST 6: Analyze the author's purpose in providing an explanation, describing a procedure, or discussing an experiment in a text.

RST 3: Follow precisely a multistep procedure.

Powering a Grid

Most of our electricity comes from power plants that burn fossil fuels. How does burning coal, oil, and natural gas make electricity?

Let's look at a power plant that burns coal to heat water. It creates high-temperature, high-pressure steam. That steam rushes through a **turbine** and spins it. A turbine is a machine that has many blades, like a highly engineered fan. Natural gas plants also use turbines. Instead of using steam, burning natural gas expands the gas, which spins the turbine.

The turbine turns a shaft that connects to an electric generator. The shaft is like the hand crank we used in class, only much, much larger. As the shaft rotates, coils of wire interact with permanent magnets to generate electricity. In some generators, this electricity passes through a **commutator** and **brushes**. They carry the electricity from the rotating coils to wires that connect to the power grid.

The power plant transforms the electricity for your home into a high voltage. It can travel a long way with very little energy loss in the wires.

That high-voltage electricity goes through high-voltage wires to a local transformer. The transformer lowers the voltage to 240 volts or 120 volts before delivering it to your home.

Burning fossil fuels produces about 67 percent of US electricity. Coal plants provide 33 percent, natural gas 33 percent, and petroleum about 1 percent.

Turbines are like giant pinwheels. They spin when steam, expanding gas, falling water, or wind turns their blades. A spinning turbine provides the kinetic energy for an electricity generator.

58

Part 2: Electric Generators

Alternative Energy Sources

Other sources of heat are used for generating electricity. About 20 percent of US electricity comes from nuclear power. In nuclear power plants, the radioactive decay of the element uranium heats water to make steam and turn turbines. Uranium is mined and is **nonrenewable**, like fossil fuels.

Nuclear power plants do not produce greenhouse gases that would contribute to global warming. But they do produce radioactive waste. That waste must be carefully contained and stored for thousands of years. These plants present a risk to nearby communities if their equipment breaks or is damaged by a natural disaster, like an earthquake.

Fossil fuels and nuclear fuel are not sustainable energy sources. Fossil fuels form over hundreds of millions of years and cannot be replaced as fast as we are using them up. The situation with nuclear fuel is similar.

Burning wood to make steam for turbines is also possible. About 0.4 percent of US electricity is produced that way. Is wood a sustainable energy source? That depends on whether trees are replanted and how fast they can grow.

Nuclear power plants generate electricity by using steam to turn turbines. The heat to make the steam is produced not by burning fuel but by splitting the nucleus of a uranium atom, a process called fission.

G

Connect to prior knowledge: Ask students to share their prior knowledge about nuclear power. Discuss the advantages and disadvantages. Encourage students to cite evidence from the text (and other sources they are familiar with) to support their ideas. Add information to the energy source chart.

ELA CONNECTION

This suggested strategy addresses the Common Core State Standards for ELA for literacy.

RST 9: Compare and contrast the information gained from experiments, simulations, video, or multimedia sources with that gained from reading a text on the same topic.

INVESTIGATION 4 – Energy Transfer

Connect to prior knowledge: Ask students to share their prior knowledge about geothermal and hydroelectric power. Discuss the advantages and disadvantages. Encourage students to cite evidence from the text (and other sources they are familiar with) to support their ideas. Add information to the energy source chart.

Hydropower, produced by the force of flowing or falling water, is the most widely used renewable energy source. Hydroelectric dams are nonpolluting, but they do have significant environmental impacts.

Iceland has lots of geothermal activity. About 25 percent of Iceland's electricity comes from geothermal energy.

Sustainable Energy Sources

One source of sustainable energy is Earth's heat. In some places, Earth's crust is quite thin. Water just beneath the surface can be very hot. Sometimes, geological features called geysers shoot steam and water out of the ground, or hot springs form. Geothermal power plants in these locations use high-pressure steam or very hot water from deep underground to run turbines. Geothermal power plants do not produce greenhouse gases. They produce only about 0.5 percent of US electricity.

A turbine can spin without needing to burn fuel or collect heated steam. Water flowing through a dam can turn turbines. The turbine connects to a generator to make electricity. This sustainable method, called hydroelectric power, produces no greenhouse gases. It produces about 6 percent of US electricity.

Hydroelectric power does create problems. Damming rivers and converting them into lakes has serious effects on surrounding ecosystems. As the lake behind the dam fills up with sediment, the water pressure drops. Lower water pressure reduces the efficiency of the power plant. Engineers are working to develop water turbines to harness power from rivers, ocean waves, and tides. These turbines are more efficient and do less harm to ecosystems than turbines in dams.

60

ELA CONNECTION

This suggested strategy addresses the Common Core State Standards for ELA for literacy.

RST 9: Compare and contrast the information gained from experiments, simulations, video, or multimedia sources with that gained from reading a text on the same topic.

Part 2: Electric Generators

Variable Energy Sources

Wind turbines can be connected to generators. This technology is simple, inexpensive, and sustainable. It produces about 5 percent of US electricity. One drawback of wind-electric power is that it varies, depending on wind speed. And when wind speeds are too high, wind turbines must stop to avoid damage. For this reason, wind-generated electricity is usually stored. It is just one source of electricity connected to a power grid.

Photovoltaic technology does not depend on electric generators at all. It uses solar panels made of flat arrays of **solar cells**. When sunlight shines on a solar cell, part of the energy in the light is converted directly into electricity.

You can find solar panels on the roofs of some schools, businesses, parking lots, and homes. Some very large power plants in deserts use solar cells to generate electricity for cities. Only about 0.7 percent of US electricity comes from solar panels. Solar installations are rapidly growing, so the percentage of US electricity that is solar could increase dramatically in years to come.

Like wind power, solar power is variable. It does not generate electricity at night or on dark stormy days. This energy source is sustainable in the long run, but must be stored or added to other sources of electricity. One relatively simple way to store electricity is in rechargeable batteries. Another is using the electricity to pump water uphill. Holding the water in that position stores **potential energy**. To produce electricity, the water flows through a turbine in a hydroelectric system when the stored energy is needed as electricity again.

Take Note
Ask your local electric company what energy sources and technologies provide your community's electricity.

Investigation 4: Energy Transfer **61**

ⓘ
Develop vocabulary: Read the section head, "Variable Energy Sources," and have students think about and share with a partner what "variable" means in terms of energy sources.

Ⓙ
Connect to prior knowledge: Encourage students to share their experiences with solar power and any prior knowledge they have about wind power. Discuss the advantages and disadvantages. Encourage students to cite evidence from the text (and other sources they are familiar with) to support their ideas. Add information to the energy source chart.

Ⓚ
Develop vocabulary: Pause to discuss the role of potential energy. Have students discuss and/or make a model to explain this concept in terms of producing energy in a hydroelectric system or in a battery.

ELA CONNECTION

These suggested strategies address the Common Core State Standards for ELA for literacy.

RST 1: Cite evidence to support analysis of science texts.

L 6: Acquire and use academic and domain-specific words and phrases.

SL 5: Integrate visual displays into presentations.

Electromagnetic Force Course—FOSS Next Generation

INVESTIGATION 4 – Energy Transfer

Share current technology information: If time permits, allow students to share their thoughts and other sources of innovations they are aware of. Students may want to research what other countries are doing or what is happening in your state.

Review Think Questions: Give students time to work on the Think Questions in their groups and then call on Reporters to share their groups' ideas.

➤ *Why is using fossil fuels considered unsustainable?* [Fossil fuels form over hundreds of millions of years, and when they are burned they are used up in a chemical reaction.]

➤ *What are some advantages of using sustainable energy sources?* [They do not have any chemical byproducts that could cause climate change, and they are constantly replenished by earth processes.]

➤ *Compare the energy sources described in this article.* [See table below.]

ELA CONNECTION

This suggested strategy addresses the Common Core State Standards for ELA for literacy.

RST 9: Compare and contrast the information gained from experiments, simulations, video, or multimedia sources with that gained from reading a text on the same topic.

The Future of Renewable Energy

As we start to experience the effects of climate change, countries around the world are working together to reduce carbon dioxide emissions. Renewable energy sources supply just 13 percent of US power, but it's a start. What are other countries doing?

- Sweden is becoming 100 percent fossil-fuel free. It is investing heavily in solar and wind power and energy storage.
- Germany has turned its attention to solar energy. Depending on weather conditions and time of year, it produces up to 78 percent of its electricity from renewable sources.
- China is committed to phasing out coal burning. It is also addressing its serious air pollution problems. It is the largest producer of renewable energy in the world, mostly from wind and solar power.

The United Nations brings countries together to use more sustainable energy sources. Each year, countries agree to goals that each country works to meet. These goals call on engineers to develop new technologies. They encourage all people to reduce energy use. We can all help reduce carbon emissions and try to slow climate change.

Solar energy is the cleanest and most abundant energy source available. These rooftop panels convert sunlight to electricity that can be stored and used to meet household power needs.

Think Questions

1. Why is using fossil fuels considered unsustainable?
2. What are some advantages of using sustainable energy sources?
3. Compare the different energy sources described in this article. In your notebook, draw a table like the one below. Mark with an X to show how each energy source works. The first row shows coal as an example.

Energy source	Uses steam	Uses turbine	Uses generator	Emits carbon dioxide	Sustainable in long term
Coal	X	X	X	X	

Energy source	Uses steam	Uses turbine	Uses generator	Emits carbon dioxide	Sustainable in long term
Coal/Oil/Natural Gas	X	X	X	X	
Uranium	X	X	X		
Wood	X	X	X	X	?
Earth's heat	X	X	X		X
Water flowing	X	X	X		X
Wind		X	X		X
Solar					X

Part 2: Electric Generators

25. Record vocabulary
Give students a few moments to review the vocabulary developed in this part and to update their vocabulary indexes if they haven't already done so.

26. Revisit the focus question
Ask students to return to the focus question.

➤ *How can we generate electrical energy?*

They should draw a line under their original response and add new thoughts below the line.

27. Answer the guiding question
Ask students to discuss the investigation guiding question.

➤ *How do humans use energy?*

You might use an image from the *FOSS Science Resources* book (such as the background image on pages 56 and 57) to connect their thinking to the real world. Students can also ask additional questions about energy and energy use.

SESSION 3   45–50 minutes

WRAP-UP

28. Have a sense-making discussion
Gather the class for a sense-making discussion, using this prompt.

➤ *When a battery is connected to a bulb and the bulb lights up, does the energy get used up? Explain.*

Encourage students to review their notebook entries to provide evidence for their explanation. Helpful entries may include their model of the motor, response to the focus questions, and responses to the article, "Where We Get Energy."

Students should first pair with a partner to discuss the prompt. After several minutes, have students switch partners so they are paired with someone from a different group to share ideas.

Bring the class together for whole-group discussion. Here are some ideas that may come out.

- Energy can be transferred and take different forms, but it cannot be created or destroyed.
- When a bulb lights up, electrical energy transfers from the battery to the bulb. The bulb transfers energy to the environment in the form of heat and light.
- When a battery "dies," it has no more chemical potential energy because it transferred the energy to other parts of the system.

When the discussion wraps up, students can use any remaining time to review additional notebook entries and prepare for the I-Check.

Electromagnetic Force Course—FOSS Next Generation

---

fossil fuel
generator
nonrenewable
renewable
solar cell

EL NOTE
For students who need support, give them a few minutes to discuss their response with a partner before writing. You can also provide a sentence frame such as:
We have been exploring ___.
One way to generate electrical energy is ___.
For example, ___.
Another way to generate electrical energy is ___.
It's important to remember ___
This investigation makes me think about ___.

TEACHING NOTE
Refer to the Sense-Making Discussions for Three-Dimensional Learning chapter in Teacher Resources on FOSSweb for more information about how to facilitate this with students.

SCIENCE AND ENGINEERING PRACTICES
Constructing explanations

Engaging in argument from evidence

Obtaining, evaluating, and communicating information

CROSSCUTTING CONCEPTS
Systems and system models

Energy and matter

INVESTIGATION 4 – Energy Transfer

SESSION 4   45–50 minutes

29. Assess progress: I-Check

Administer *Investigation 4 I-Check*, asking students to respond to the items on paper or online on FOSSmap. Students should independently answer the questions. When taking the I-Check, students should not use their notebooks, but the notebooks are a good tool to use when students later reflect on their answers.

SESSION 5   45–50 minutes

30. Discuss I-Check results

Code the I-Check items, but do not make any marks on student responses. Note that FOSSmap automatically codes most of the items and provides you with student and class reports. Coding guides can be found on FOSSweb. You can record student results on the *Assessment Record* or download spreadsheets from FOSSmap for recording. Note important points about the items to review with students.

Return the I-Checks to students. Use self-assessment strategies as described in the Assessment chapter for each item to facilitate reflection and clarify student thinking.

DISCIPLINARY CORE IDEAS

PS3.B: Conservation of energy and energy transfer

PS3.C: Relationship between energy and forces

ESS3.A: Natural resources

ESS3.C: Human impacts on Earth systems

TEACHING NOTE

During or after these next steps with the I-Check, you might ask students to make choices for possible derivative products based on their notebooks for inclusion in a summative portfolio. See the Assessment chapter for more information about creating and evaluating portfolios.

Part 3: Force and Energy

MATERIALS for
Part 3: *Force and Energy*

Teacher-supplied items
For each student
- 1 *Entry-Level Survey* (from Investigation 1)

For the class
- Chart paper (optional)

FOSSweb resources
For each student
- 1 *Posttest*

For the teacher
- *Assessment Record*
- Teaching slides, 4.3

INVESTIGATION 4 – Energy Transfer

GETTING READY for
Part 3: Force and Energy

Quick Start

Schedule	1 session review 1 session assessment
Preview	• Preview the FOSSweb Resources by Investigation for this part (such as printable masters, teaching slides, and online activities) • Plan for homework: prepare for *Posttest*, Step 7
Print or Copy	**For each student** • *Posttest,* or schedule it on FOSSmap
Plan for Assessment	• Plan for benchmark assessment, Step 8, *Posttest*

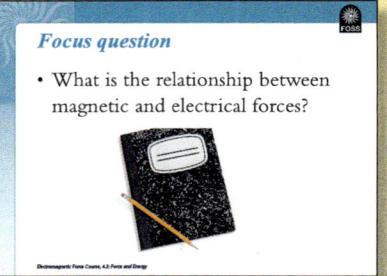

Teaching slides, 4.3

Part 3: Force and Energy

GUIDING the Investigation
Part 3: Force and Energy

SESSION 1

Students will . . .
- Review big ideas about energy and electromagnetic force (Steps 1–3)
- Review the *Entry-Level Survey* to prepare for *Posttest* (Step 4)
- Revisit the focus question and driving question and discuss *I-Check 4* results (Steps 5, 6)
- Extend the investigation with homework (Step 7)

SESSIONS 2–3

Students will . . .
- Demonstrate understanding on the *Posttest* (Step 8)
- Discuss *Posttest* results (Step 9)

FOCUS QUESTION
What is the relationship between magnetic and electrical forces?

SESSION 1 45–50 minutes

1. **Review force and energy**
   Ask students to think about the phenomena they have been exploring for the last couple of months in science class. Tell students,

   In this course, you've studied forces that you can easily observe, like a physical push or pull, and those that cannot be directly observed, the electromagnetic force. You learned about energy transfers as forces cause objects to move and affect other objects, including those within magnetic fields.

2. **Focus question: What is the relationship between magnetic and electrical forces?**
   Ask students to turn to the next clean page in their notebooks and write the focus question, which is also the driving question for the course.

   ➤ *What is the relationship between magnetic and electrical forces?*

   This question is similar to the guiding question for Investigation 3 so give students a moment to review that response before moving on to the wrap-up activity. Students will work to answer the question during the wrap-up activity.

INVESTIGATION 4 – Energy Transfer

WRAP-UP

3. Review notebook entries

Ask students to go through their notebook entries and select key points that summarize an important finding from the course. They should record these points in their notebooks.

Have students share their key points with their group, selecting one or two key points within the group to share with the class. Create a class chart of key points by recording each group's idea on a piece of chart paper, whiteboard, or document projected from the computer. You might need to help groups rephrase their key points for clarity.

Students should record the key points in their notebooks and reference the page numbers in their notebooks where additional information supports each key point. By using science and engineering practices and exploring core ideas through the lens of crosscutting concepts, students should come forward with these big ideas in the review discussions.

- A force is a push or a pull. (Developing and using models; planning and carrying out investigations; using mathematics and computational thinking; PS2.A: Forces and motion; cause and effect; systems and system models.)
- Magnets apply a force over distance throughout their magnetic field. (Developing and using models; planning and carrying out investigations; analyzing and interpreting data; using mathematics and computational thinking; PS2.A: Forces and motion; PS2.B: Types of interactions; patterns; cause and effect; scale, proportion, and quantity; systems and system models.)
- A completed circuit transfers electrical energy to components within the circuit. (Planning and carrying out investigations; PS2.B: Types of interactions; PS3.B: Conservation of energy and energy transfer; PS3.C: Relationship between energy and forces; cause and effect.)
- The electromagnetic force explains properties of electricity and magnetism. (Developing and using models; constructing explanations; PS2.A: Forces and motion; PS2.B: Types of interactions; PS3.C: Relationship between energy and forces; patterns; systems and system models.)
- Potential energy is energy stored in an object's position or chemical properties (as in a battery); kinetic energy is energy of motion. (Constructing explanations; PS3.A: Definitions of energy; systems and system models; energy and matter.)
- Energy can be transferred and take different forms, but it cannot be created or destroyed. (Constructing explanations; PS3.A: Definitions of energy; PS3.B: Conservation of energy and energy transfer; scale, proportion, and quantity; energy and matter; stability and change.)
- Engineers design components that use electromagnetism to achieve specific design goals. (Designing solutions; planning and carrying

---

SCIENCE AND ENGINEERING PRACTICES

Constructing explanations

Obtaining, evaluating, and communicating information

DISCIPLINARY CORE IDEAS

PS3.B: Conservation of energy and energy transfer

PS3.C: Relationship between energy and forces

ESS3.A: Natural resources

ESS3.C: Human impacts on Earth systems

CROSSCUTTING CONCEPTS

Cause and effect

Systems and system models

Energy and matter

Part 3: Force and Energy

out investigations; analyzing and interpreting data; engaging in argument from evidence; PS3.C: Relationship between energy and forces; ETS1.A: Defining and delimiting engineering problems; ETS1.B: Developing possible solutions; ETS1.C: Optimizing the design solution; cause and effect; structure and function.)

- Sources of energy used by humans may be renewable or nonrenewable. (PS3.B: Conservation of energy and energy transfer; ESS3.A: Natural resources; ESS3.C: Human impacts on Earth systems; cause and effect; energy and matter; stability and change.)

4. **Revisit *Entry-Level Survey***
   Return their *Entry-Level Survey* to students (if you haven't done so already). Ask students to read what they wrote before instruction and to construct a response to the questions now that they have learned about force and energy. Students will need 15–20 minutes for this process.

5. **Revisit the focus question and driving question for the course**
   Have students return to the page where they recorded the focus question and driving question for the course.

   ➤ *What is the relationship between magnetic and electrical forces?*

   Students should write a summary statement based on the key-points activity. If students finish early, they can begin to review their notebook entries and vocabulary index to prepare for the *Posttest*.

6. **Discuss I-Check results**
   Return *Investigation 4 I-Check* to students. Use self-assessment strategies as described in the Assessment chapter to facilitate reflection and clarify student thinking.

7. **Extend the investigation with homework**
   Students should review notebook entries to prepare for the *Posttest*.

   SESSION 2   *45–50 minutes*

8. **Assess progress: *Posttest***
   When students are ready, administer *Posttest* on paper or online on FOSSmap. They should work alone to answer the questions. Coding guides can be found on FOSSweb.

   SESSION 3   *45–50 minutes*

9. **Discuss *Posttest* results (optional)**
   Code the *Posttest* items, but do not make any marks on student responses. You can record student results on the *Assessment Record*. Note important points about the items to review with students.

Electromagnetic Force Course—FOSS Next Generation

INVESTIGATION 4 – Energy Transfer

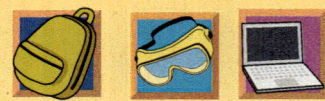

EXTENDING *the Investigation*

- **Dissect electronics**
  Students can bring in old, broken toys, doorbells, and speakers to take apart and check for internal components such as electromagnets and generators.

- **Research brushless motors**
  Students can conduct online research to learn how electronic controllers and sensors can replace brushes in motors, and how these designs can also provide stronger force and more continuous torque.

- **Research careers**
  Have students research science and engineering careers related to the content in this course using the Science and Engineering Careers Database on FOSSweb. The database includes information about various careers and features diverse scientists.

> **TEACHING NOTE**
>
> *Encourage students to use the Science and Engineering Careers Database on FOSSweb.*

Assessment

ELECTROMAGNETIC FORCE — *Assessment*

THE FOSS ASSESSMENT SYSTEM *for Middle School*

"Assessment is like science. …To assess our students, we plan and conduct investigations about student learning and then analyze and interpret data to develop models of what students are thinking. These models allow us to predict the effect of additional teaching addressing the patterns we notice in student understanding and misunderstanding. Assessment allows us to improve our teaching practice over time, spiraling upward" (*2016 Science Framework for California Public Schools, Kindergarten through Grade 12,* chapter 9, page 3).

An important rule of thumb in educational assessment is that assessments should be designed to meet specific purposes. One size does not fit all. The FOSS assessment system provides ample opportunities for both formative and summative assessment. Formative assessments provide short-term information about learning by making students' thinking visible in order to guide instructional decisions. Summative assessments provide valid, reliable, and fair measures of students' progress over a longer period of time, at the end of a course, or the end of the year. The purpose for the assessment determines the choice of instruments that you will use.

The FOSS assessment system is designed to assess students in cycles: short, medium, and long. The assessment tasks allow students to demonstrate their facility with three-dimensional understanding of science.

Short cycle. Embedded assessment opportunities are incorporated into each part of every investigation. These assessments use student-generated artifacts, including science notebook entries, answers to focus questions, response sheets, and **performance assessments**. Embedded assessments provide daily monitoring of students' learning and practices to help you make decisions about instructional next steps. Embedded assessments using science notebooks provide evidence of students' overall conceptual development. Performance assessments focus on science and engineering practices, crosscutting concepts, and disciplinary core ideas.

Contents

The FOSS Assessment System for Middle School	309
Assessment for the NGSS	311
Embedded Assessment	316
Benchmark Assessment	321
Next-Step Strategies	327
FOSSmap and Online Assessment	332
Sample Assessment Items	334

▶ **NOTE**
For the most up-to-date assessment masters, answer sheets, and coding guides, go to FOSSweb for this course.

FOSS Full Option Science System

ELECTROMAGNETIC FORCE — Assessment

I-Check opportunities occur at the end of one or two investigations. These assessments are hybrid tools that provide summative information about students' achievement, and have even more power when used for formative assessment. Daily embedded assessments provide a quick snapshot of students' immediate learning; I-Checks challenge students to put this learning into action in a broader context. Now students must think about the science and engineering practices, disciplinary core ideas, and crosscutting concepts they have been learning, and know when, where, and how to use them. I-Checks (short for "I check my own understanding") also provide opportunities for guided self-assessment, an important skill for future learning and development of a growth mindset. Properly executed feedback can help a student focus attention on areas that need strengthening. When a student responds to feedback, you can develop an even more precise understanding of the student's learning. A feedback/response dialogue can develop into a highly differentiated path of instruction tailored to the learning requirements of individual students.

Medium and long cycle. *Entry-Level Surveys*, *Posttests*, and portfolios are tools provided for medium- and long-cycle assessment. Students take the *Entry-Level Survey* before instruction begins. This entry-level assessment provides you with information about students' prior knowledge of disciplinary core ideas and science and engineering practices. What emerging conceptions do they have that you will be able to build upon as you move through the course? Students are encouraged to answer the questions as best they can, so you get the information you need to move instruction forward effectively.

The *Posttest* is given at the end of the course. It provides summative information about students' three-dimensional learning. It also lets students compare their *Entry-Level Survey* responses to those on the *Posttest* to see how their understanding has grown. You can also use the *Posttest* for formative instructional evaluation by making notes about things you might want to focus on or do differently next time you teach the course.

Students can also collect work samples in a portfolio as they work through the course. At the end of each investigation, they can create derivative products to document their three-dimensional learning.

See more about these assessments in the section "Benchmark Assessment."

ASSESSMENT *for the* NGSS

A Framework for K–12 Science Education (National Research Council, 2012), *Next Generation Science Standards* (National Academies Press, 2013), *Developing Assessment for the Next Generation Science Standards* (National Research Council, 2014), and many state frameworks provide a new vision for science education. These documents emphasize the idea that science education should resemble the way that scientists work. Students plan and conduct investigations, gather data to construct explanations, and engage in argumentation to build their understanding of the natural world. They apply that knowledge to engineering problems and design solutions. Students are expected to construct and discuss explanations and model systems in more and more sophisticated ways as they move through the grades. Assessment plays an important role in this new vision of science education—assessment is the bridge between teaching and learning.

Several key points in these foundational documents provide guidance for a well-designed assessment system. FOSS has followed these guidelines to ensure a robust assessment system that provides valuable diagnostic information about students' learning.

Assessment tasks should consist of multiple components in order to measure all three dimensions of science and engineering learning. The FOSS assessment system provides multiple tools and strategies to assess the three dimensions: (1) science and engineering practices, (2) disciplinary core ideas, and (3) crosscutting concepts. These tools and strategies provide evidence about what students can do, their developing conceptual understandings, and the connections that they are making among disciplines. Entry-level assessments, given before instruction begins, show what students can do and what they know before they begin a new course.

Assessment systems should include formative and summative tasks. Formative assessment tasks are embedded in the curriculum at key stages in instruction. These tasks are designed to support teachers in collecting and analyzing data about students' conceptual understanding and growing practice. Notebook entries, answers to focus questions, response sheets, performance assessments, and oral presentations/interviews provide the information you need to decide what students need to do next to move toward a learning goal. FOSS suggestions for next-step strategies help you address students' developing conceptions and provide information for differentiated instruction as needed.

> *"Assessment plays an important role in this vision—assessment is the bridge between teaching and learning."*

ELECTROMAGNETIC FORCE – Assessment

> *"When students take an active role in their learning, using these tools for self-assessment, achievement improves dramatically."*

Summative assessments are designed to provide valid, reliable, and fair measures of students' progress. The FOSS system includes three types of summative assessments: I-Checks, *Posttests*, and portfolios. These assessments include multicomponent tasks including open-ended constructed–response problems as well as some multiple-choice and short-answer items. *Posttests* are given at the end of a course. Coding guides, found on FOSSweb, provide teachers with guidance when evaluating these assessments. Students can also collect work products at the end of each investigation for inclusion in a portfolio. All written assessments are consistent with grade-level writing and mathematics in the Common Core State Standards for ELA/Literacy and for Mathematics.

Assessment systems should support classroom instruction. The main purpose of the FOSS assessment system is to support classroom instruction—to provide the bridge between teaching and learning. Teachers need information daily about what students have learned or may be confused about. FOSS has developed a technique in which teachers spend only 15 minutes at the end of the day, using a reflective–assessment practice (explained in detail later in this chapter), to gather data to determine instructional next steps. Are students ready to move on to the next lesson, or do they need some additional clarification? Our research has shown that the reflective-assessment practice provides evidence-based information that is crucial for differentiating instruction for all students—this practice can make a significant difference in students' overall achievement.

Assessment developers need to take a rigorous approach to the process of designing and validating assessments. The FOSS assessment system is based on a construct-modeling approach for assessment design. That means that we have done the research needed to describe a conceptual framework and learning performances that provide evidence of students' progressive learning (see the Framework and NGSS chapter), and we have done the technical work needed to ensure that assessment tasks provide valid, reliable, and fair evidence of students' learning. (See the Benchmark Assessment section for a more detailed description of the design behind the FOSS assessment system.)

Assessment systems should include an interpretive system and locate students along a sequence of progressively more complex understanding. FOSS provides extensive support for interpreting assessment information. For each embedded assessment, specific information in the Getting Ready Quick Start and Guiding the Investigation sections describes what students do and what to look for

Assessment for the NGSS

in student responses to assess progress. Common preconceptions (prior knowledge) and how the items will be connected to the investigations are described for survey items, and coding guides are provided for each item on benchmark assessments (I-Checks and the *Posttest*). Samples of student work, especially for open-response questions, are also available on FOSSweb. Resources in this chapter and on FOSSweb provide you with information about how to use the coding guides, as well as what to do for next steps when students need to spend more time on a practice or core idea, or to look at it from a different perspective to see more connections.

You can use FOSSmap to have students take assessments online and generate a number of diagnostic and summary reports (delivered as PDFs). Some of these reports provide information about class progress; others provide individual students and parents with information about what students know and what they still need to work on. (See the FOSSmap and Online Assessment section in this chapter.)

The FOSS assessment system was developed over a period of 5 years with data from more than 500 teachers and their students. We know that teachers can employ this assessment system for the benefit of their students, and we know students achieve more. Perhaps even more important is the change in classroom culture that occurs when assessment is thoughtfully employed as the bridge between teaching and learning. Assessment is no longer a stress factor for students or teachers. It encourages all to adopt a growth mindset—if I know where my strengths and weaknesses are and I continue to be thoughtful and work hard, I can make progress. It models what scientists do. Scientists use the information they have to argue for the best explanations, but they keep an open mind, so that when new evidence emerges, they can incorporate that into their thinking, too. That's also what good curriculum and assessment are all about.

> *"Assessment is no longer a stress factor for students or teachers. It encourages all to adopt a growth mindset—if I know where my strengths and weaknesses are and I continue to be thoughtful and work hard, I can make progress."*

ELECTROMAGNETIC FORCE — *Assessment*

NGSS Performance Expectations

"The NGSS are standards or goals, that reflect what a student should know and be able to do; they do not dictate the manner or methods by which the standards are taught.... Curriculum and assessment must be developed in a way that builds students' knowledge and ability toward the PEs [performance expectations]" (*Next Generation Science Standards*, 2013, page xiv). The chart displayed here shows the bundled performance expectations assessed in this course and where they are extended in other courses.

Middle School Physical Science NGSS Performance Expectations	FOSS Middle School Course
MS-PS1-1. Develop models to describe the atomic composition of simple molecules and extended structures.	Chemical Interactions
MS-PS1-2. Analyze and interpret data on the properties of substances before and after the substances interact to determine if a chemical reaction has occurred.	Chemical Interactions
MS-PS1-3. Gather and make sense of information to describe that synthetic materials come from natural resources and impact society.	Chemical Interactions Earth History *
MS-PS1-4. Develop a model that predicts and describes changes in particle motion, temperature, and state of a pure substance when thermal energy is added or removed.	Chemical Interactions Weather and Water
MS-PS1-5. Develop and use a model to describe how the total number of atoms does not change in a chemical reaction and thus mass is conserved.	Chemical Interactions
MS-PS1-6. Undertake a design project to construct, test, and modify a device that either releases or absorbs thermal energy by chemical processes.	Chemical Interactions
MS-PS2-1. Apply Newton's third law to design a solution to a problem involving the motion of two colliding objects.	Gravity and Kinetic Energy
MS-PS2-2. Plan an investigation to provide evidence that the change in an object's motion depends on the sum of the forces on the object and the mass of the object.	Electromagnetic Force Gravity and Kinetic Energy
MS-PS2-3. Ask questions about data to determine the factors that affect the strength of electrical and magnetic forces.	Electromagnetic Force
MS-PS2-4. Construct and present arguments using evidence to support the claim that gravitational interactions are attractive and depend on the masses of interacting objects.	Gravity and Kinetic Energy Planetary Science *

Assessment for the NGSS

Middle School Physical Science NGSS Performance Expectations	FOSS Middle School Course
MS-PS2-5. Conduct an investigation and evaluate the experimental design to provide evidence that fields exist between objects exerting forces on each other even though the objects are not in contact.	Electromagnetic Force Gravity and Kinetic Energy *
MS-PS3-1. Construct and interpret graphical displays of data to describe the relationships of kinetic energy to the mass of an object and to the speed of an object.	Gravity and Kinetic Energy
MS-PS3-2. Develop a model to describe that when the arrangement of objects interacting at a distance changes, different amounts of potential energy are stored in the system.	Electromagnetic Force Gravity and Kinetic Energy
MS-PS3-3. Apply scientific principles to design, construct, and test a device that either minimizes or maximizes thermal energy transfer.	Chemical Interactions Weather and Water
MS-PS3-4. Plan an investigation to determine the relationships among the energy transferred, the type of matter, the mass, and the change in the average kinetic energy of the particles as measured by the temperature of the sample.	Chemical Interactions Weather and Water
MS-PS3-5. Construct, use, and present arguments to support the claim that when the kinetic energy of an object changes, energy is transferred to or from the object.	Electromagnetic Force Variables and Design Chemical Interactions Weather and Water Gravity and Kinetic Energy
MS-PS4-1. Use mathematical representations to describe a simple model for waves that includes how the amplitude of a wave is related to the energy in a wave.	Waves
MS-PS4-2. Develop and use a model to describe that waves are reflected, absorbed, or transmitted through various materials.	Waves Planetary Science *
MS-PS4-3. Integrate qualitative scientific and technical information to support the claim that digitized signals are a more reliable way to encode and transmit information than analog signals.	Waves

* This course incorporates this performance expectation, but it is not the course's main focus.

Electromagnetic Force Course—FOSS Next Generation

ELECTROMAGNETIC FORCE – Assessment

EMBEDDED Assessment

In FOSS middle school, the unit of instruction is the course—a sequence of conceptually related learning experiences that leads to a set of learning outcomes. A science notebook gives students a place to record their thinking and develop deeper understanding of the course content by articulating relationships, patterns, and conclusions, as well as by asking questions that will guide further exploration. Science notebook entries give both you and your students opportunities to review and reflect on students' thinking.

From the assessment point of view, a science notebook is a collection of student-generated artifacts that exhibit student learning. You can informally assess student skills, such as the ability to use charts to record data, while students are working with materials. At other times, you collect the notebooks and review them for insights or errors in conceptual understanding. The displays of data and analytical work provide a measure of the quality and quantity of student learning.

As you progress through the course, you will see different strategies used throughout the *Investigations Guide*. These will be marked with the notebook or assessment icon. As you try these strategies, take note of the positive effect that keeping notebooks have on students' work, as students continually practice expressing their conceptual development in writing. Embedded assessments help you better understand and address students' misconceptions.

Assessment Opportunities

Notebook entries serve as assessment opportunities for learning. Each part of each investigation is driven by a **focus question**. Each part usually concludes with students writing or revising an answer to the focus question in their notebooks. Their answers reveal how well they have made sense of the investigation and whether they have focused on the relevant actions and discussions.

At times, students use prepared **notebook sheets** to help organize and think about data. You can note how carefully students are making and organizing observations and how they think about analyzing and interpreting the data. Sometimes students answer a specific question that provides additional insight into understanding. You will find answers for notebook sheets in the Notebook Answers chapter.

> **TEACHING NOTE**
>
> FOSS recommends that you do not grade notebook entries. This ensures a risk-free environment for students to write freely, knowing mistakes are part of learning. If you need to give a grade, have students complete a derivative product based on a notebook entry. Students might rewrite a focus-question answer, write up part of a lab, or revise a response sheet and turn it in, knowing that this product will be graded.

Embedded Assessment

Response sheets provide more formal embedded-assessment data. These are a specific kind of notebook sheet that assesses specific scientific knowledge that students often struggle with, giving you an additional opportunity to help students untangle concepts that they may be overgeneralizing or have difficulty differentiating.

Students also generate **free-form notebook entries** that can be used for assessing progress. These may occur when you choose to have students organize their own data, or when events in the classroom suggest a new aspect of students' learning that you want to know more about.

The *Entry-Level Survey* and **quick writes** (or quick draws) present questions that students answer before instruction, so you can analyze their prior knowledge and misconceptions. Knowing students' intuitive ideas (or prior knowledge) will help you know what parts of the investigations need the most attention. Make sure students date their entries for later reference. Quick writes can be done on a quarter sheet of paper or an index card. You collect them, review them, and return them to students to affix into their notebooks for self-assessment later in the investigation.

Performance assessments occur at times in the course as a way to specifically check students' three-dimensional progress, checking science and engineering practices, crosscutting concepts, and disciplinary core ideas. These assessments happen during class as you circulate among student groups during their investigations. Sometimes you will simply watch what students are doing; at other times prompts or interview questions will be suggested.

Time Management

In order to collect enough data from embedded assessment to adequately inform instruction, plan to spend 15 minutes after each part of an investigation is completed, reviewing student learning by examining student work. In middle school, you face the challenge of having a large number of students. This may mean collecting only a portion of students' notebooks at a time to keep your workload manageable. A sample of student notebooks across your classes should represent the general levels of conceptual understanding that students have. Some work, such as quick writes and notebook sheets, can first be completed on separate sheets of paper. These are easier to collect, read, and later return to students for their notebooks.

▶ **NOTE**
You need only 15 minutes after an investigation part to review student work and gather evidence of learning. See the reflective-assessment practice later in this chapter.

Electromagnetic Force Course—FOSS Next Generation

ELECTROMAGNETIC FORCE — Assessment

Planning for Embedded Assessment

Embedded assessments are suggested for each investigation part. The Getting Ready Quick Start tells you what copies to make and how to plan for assessment. Here is an example from the Quick Start chart for Investigation 1, Part 1.

Print or Copy	**For each student** • *Entry-Level Survey*, or schedule it on FOSSmap • Notebook sheets 1–3 **For the teacher** • *Embedded Assessment Notes*

Plan for Assessment	• Review Step 25, "What to Look For" in the notebook entry

During the lesson, a step in the **Guiding the Investigation** section tells you what to assess. It also suggests what to look for, including how students should be building and communicating disciplinary core ideas, science and engineering practices, and crosscutting concepts for the task.

> **25. Assess progress: notebook entry**
> After students have had a chance to respond, collect a sample of notebooks from each class to consider students' thinking about what makes things move. The sample you select should give you a snapshot of the range of student understanding at this point in time.
>
> **What to Look For**
>
> - *Students use academic vocabulary such as* force, action, lift, push, pull, *and* gravity *in their answers to explain what makes something move.*
> - *Students write that it takes force to move things.*
> - *Students understand that objects that appear to act on their own, such as by rolling down a hill, are still being acted upon by forces, even if the forces aren't seen.*

Embedded Assessment

Using the Reflective–Assessment Practice

Successful teachers incorporate a system of continuous formative assessment into their standard teaching practices. One of the keys to formative assessment is frequency. The more often you can gather evidence about students' progress, the more able you will be to guide each student's path to understanding. The **reflective-assessment practice** provides a proven method for gathering information, in a way that takes little time, but has a big impact on students' learning.

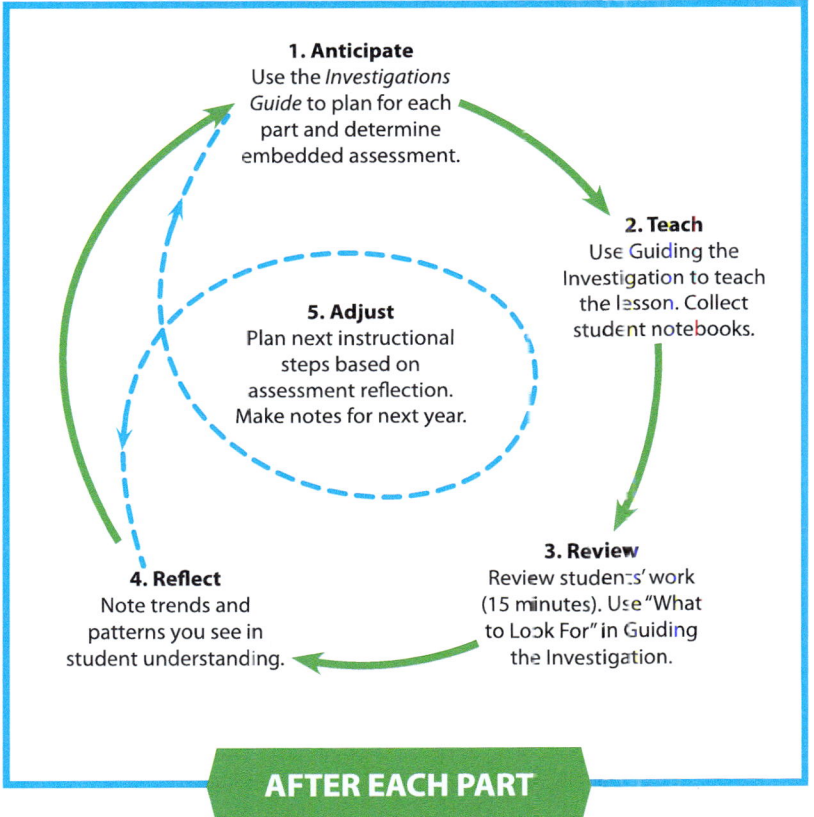

You can record notes for three lessons on each page.

Print or make copies of **Embedded Assessment Notes** to record students' progress with the embedded assessments in each part of an investigation (see the What to Look For bullets). If you have several classes doing the same course, choose a random sample across the classes to get the information you need, using the reflective-assessment practice. The important thing is that you are looking at student work as often as possible and looking for patterns that reveal strengths and areas that need additional support.

Electromagnetic Force Course—FOSS Next Generation

ELECTROMAGNETIC FORCE — *Assessment*

1. Anticipate. Check the Getting Ready Quick Start chart for the suggested embedded assessment for the part you are planning. Before class, fill in the investigation and part number along with the date on *Embedded Assessment Notes*. Check the assessment step in Guiding the Investigation, and fill in the things you are looking for in student thinking. Limit your assessment to one or two important ideas.

2. Teach. Follow the steps in Guiding the Investigation.

3. Review. At the end of class, have students hand in their notebooks *open to the page you will be reviewing.* (This may sound trivial, but it will save you a lot of time.) Collect a sample of student notebooks from each of your classes throughout the day. Try to represent students of all abilities within the sample, so you can fairly judge whether your classes are mastering the material. Use *Embedded Assessment Notes* to record what you observe. Make tally marks and write in names and notes under "misconceptions/incomplete ideas" for students who need help. Spend no more than 15 minutes on this review.

Mark tallies and make notes as you review student work.

Write reflections and next steps here after 15 minutes of review.

Embedded Assessment Notes — Electromagnetic Force

Investigation __2__, Part __2__   Date __2/20/20__

Concept: Students explain that a magnetic field induces magnetism in iron to turn it into a temporary magnet, which is attracted to the magnet.

Tally: Got it: ℍℍ //   Doesn't get it: ////

Misconceptions/incomplete ideas:
Confusion around what induced magnetism is; two students didn't mention it at all

Reflections/next steps:
Return to "Chair Demonstration" models and ask students to describe the changes to the paper clip when near the magnet

4. Reflect. Take 5 minutes to summarize the trends and patterns (highlights and challenges) you saw, and record notes in the "Reflections/Next Steps" section.

5. Adjust. Describe the next steps you plan to take in the next lesson. This is the key to formative assessment. You must take some action to help students improve their understanding. If you do this process frequently, the next steps should take only a few minutes of class time when the next part begins. A number of next-step strategies are listed later in this chapter.

BENCHMARK *Assessment*

Benchmark Assessment Design

The foundation of the FOSS assessment system rests on three pillars: a conceptual framework, a student-progress model, and the NGSS performance expectations. It is important to remember that the performance expectations are a sampling of expected student proficiencies and that a full curriculum will always necessarily include more. The **conceptual framework** for this module can be found in the Framework and NGSS chapter. It is a segment from a larger learning progression that FOSS has carefully engineered for grades K–8. The concepts you see in the framework span grades K–8, and the bullets designate learning that is important for middle schoolers. The **student-progress model** is displayed in the table on the next page. It describes in general terms how FOSS uses four levels to categorize student progress. The **NGSS performance expectations** also guide assessment design, providing a sampling of end goals and always reminding us that learning science is a three-dimensional enterprise that includes science and engineering practices, disciplinary core ideas, and crosscutting concepts.

Through our own research (ASK Project, 2003-2009) and that of others (most notably Dylan Wiliam and Carol Dweck), FOSS developers have concluded that the most important assessment goal is to support learning in a way that helps students develop a *growth mindset*. That means that the focus must be on formative assessment.

It also means that we don't use traditional scoring. Instead, we code student responses to categorize the level at which students have demonstrated competence. For instance, at first glance it looks as though students are being awarded a point for an incorrect answer. In fact, their work is in the level 1 category. They have attempted to answer the question, but the answer shows little influence of instruction. You will also notice that some items can be coded no higher than a level 2, even though the student-progress model has four levels. That particular item asks students only to demonstrate that they can perform a simple practice or have a piece of knowledge (a level 2 proficiency) essential to a broader understanding. When it is important to know what pieces students have or don't have in order to determine how to help them improve, a simpler question can help identify differentiated instruction that is necessary for some students.

ELECTROMAGNETIC FORCE – *Assessment*

Level	Description
Strategic (4)	Performance on an item or assessment shows exceptional understanding of three-dimensional learning. Students are able to apply their knowledge of practices, disciplinary core ideas, and crosscutting concepts to explain novel phenomena or solve new problems. Students at this level continue to build a network of knowledge, practice, and crosscutting concepts to bridge disciplines. They can apply all of those to real-world phenomena and design problems.
Conceptual (3) **(Minimum goal for all students)**	Performance on an item or assessment shows well-developed understanding of three-dimensional learning. Students are making connections among practices, core ideas, and crosscutting concepts in order to answer more complex questions and solve more complex problems. To get to the next level (strategic), students need to continue to build connections and be able to transfer this knowledge from the classroom to real-world phenomena.
Recognition (2)	Performance on an item or assessment shows developing understanding of three-dimensional learning. Students have built a foundational repertoire of pieces of knowledge and practices, and use academic language with greater facility. To get to the next level (conceptual), students need to continue to add knowledge about practices, core ideas, and crosscutting concepts, and then build connections among those pieces to form more complex understandings about phenomena.
Notions (1)	Performance on an item or assessment shows relatively little understanding of three-dimensional learning. Students may include some scientific vocabulary or recall of simple facts or procedures, but there is little evidence of the impact of instruction. To get to the next level (recognition), students need to develop practices, begin to incorporate academic language in their communication, and construct more pieces of knowledge that help explain phenomena.

Benchmark Assessment

Administering the Assessments

The FOSS benchmark assessments are intentionally designed to help you look at students' learning at the end of each investigation and at the end of the course. Each of these assessments includes items that incorporate the three dimentions described in the NRC Framework: science and engineering practices, disciplinary core ideas, and crosscuting concepts. Benchmark assessments provide a broader focus on students' learning than do the embedded assessments. Benchmark assessment require students to determine when and how practices, pieces of knowledge, and larger conceptual relationships need to be recalled or applied.

Entry-Level Survey

The **Entry-Level Survey** is administered before instruction begins. Students are often uneasy about having to take a "test" when they haven't yet had the instruction they need in order to do well. Help students view this survey as a tool for you to find out what they know before you begin instruction. It is important for them to know that the *Entry-Level Survey* will not be graded, but is a helpful way for you to get to know what they learned in earlier grades so you can build their knowledge accordingly.

When you administer the *Entry-Level Survey*, encourage students to answer the questions as best they can. Even if students think they do not know the answers, they should try to think about something related that they do know and apply that knowledge. Collect completed *Entry-Level Surveys*, and pull a random sample of students' responses from each of your classes. Review as many as you can for diagnostic purposes, but do not make any marks on them. You will find suggestions for what to look for on FOSSweb. Plan to use the *Entry-Level Surveys* to help students review for the *Posttest* at the end of the course.

I-Checks

At the end of many investigations, you will find a benchmark assessment called an **I-Check**. In some cases, content from two investigations is combined into one I-Check. This assessment serves as a checkpoint for student learning. To track achievement (a summative use of the I-Checks), use the coding guides found on FOSSweb to code the items.

> **NOTE**
> Always check FOSSweb for updates to the benchmark assessments before beginning the course.
>
> Students can take the *Entry-Level Survey* using FOSSmap. Although no reports are produced, it allows you to easily read through students' answers without shuffling papers.

> **TEACHING NOTE**
>
> *If you decide to have students take Entry-Level Surveys on paper, you can return them to the students to study for the Posttest, have them reflect on their original answers, then keep the answers they had or edit and add to them based on their new learning. It is important for students to know how their thinking changes based on new experiences and evidence.*

Electromagnetic Force Course—FOSS Next Generation

ELECTROMAGNETIC FORCE — Assessment

We recommend that you code one item at a time; that is, code item 1 for all students, then move on to item 2, and so on. Even though you have to shuffle papers more, you will find it actually takes less time overall to code the assessments. Coding tends to be more consistent across students when you use this method, and it allows you to think about the performance of the whole class for each item and the kind of next steps you might take to correct learning weaknesses.

I-Checks can also be used for formative assessment. Research has shown that students learn more when they reflect upon and evaluate their own responses. To do this, code students' tests but do not write on them. Learning tends to come to a halt when students see a grade on their work, especially if it is a poor grade. Instead, record marks in a grade book or computer spreadsheet. Use class discussion and **next-step strategies** to help students reflect on and refine their thinking. A good place to begin this process is by looking through the library of next-step strategies in the next section.

Choose three or four items from the I-Check that you want to discuss with students during class time. Determine the next steps you want to take. In the next session, start with these three or four items, using the strategies you chose. Then quickly go over other items, so that students can check the rest of their answers. When students check their own understanding, you are creating a class culture of assessment as a tool for the service of learning.

Posttest

Have students take the *Posttest* after all the investigations are completed. It can be administered in any of the ways described for the other benchmark assessments. Record student codes on a copy of the *Assessment Record* for the *Posttest*, or the downloadable spreadsheet.

Use the *Posttest* for formative evaluation of the course. Make notes about things you might want to focus on or do differently the next time you teach the course.

Benchmark Assessment

When Grades Are Required

"If we are always focusing on formative assessment, how do we give grades?" is a frequent question. Our recommendation is that you use derivative products for giving grades. That way students always know when they will be graded, and they always have a chance to improve their work before turning something in for a grade. For example, if you need to grade a notebook entry, have students rewrite that entry on a separate sheet of paper or provide an analytic summary of the notebook sheet to be turned in for the grade. In this process, they can work with other students or use a class discussion to improve their derivative product before turning it in.

When grading I-Checks, rather than figuring a percentage, choose three or four items that students reflect on through self-assessment strategies, then have the opportunity to rewrite before turning in for a grade. When you follow this process, students are always clear about when they will be graded and know that they always have the opportunity to make their work better, which helps develop a growth mindset.

If you must base grades on a percentage, first subtract 1 from each code (except zero, no negative numbers) to transform codes to points. Then you can add points and determine a percentage. We suggest 80% should be an A, rather than the traditional 90%. These assessments are designed for diagnostic purposes, not minimum mastery.

> **NOTE**
> If your students take the benchmark assessments online, FOSSmap does most of the coding for you. You only need to code open-response items and check codes for short-answer items. Then you can run a variety of class and individual diagnostic reports.

Portfolios

Students can choose work at the end of each investigation to include in a summative portfolio for end-of-course presenations or grades. Give students a *Portfolio Checklist* and a folder to hold the checklist and their work samples. At the end of each investigation, suggest an item or two that they might add to the portfolio to demonstrate their threedimensional learning. Students can photograph and print notebook pages, or create a derivative product from the notebook page to be included in the portfolio. As always, notebooks should not be graded—they should be a risk-free environment for students to record their thinking. If students are going to include something from their notebook, they should have a chance to improve it before adding it to the portfolio. A sample *Portfolio Checklist* can be found with the other FOSS assessment charts, or you could make your own with students. We suggest developing a scoring rubric with students, if the portfolio is to be graded.

ELECTROMAGNETIC FORCE — Assessment

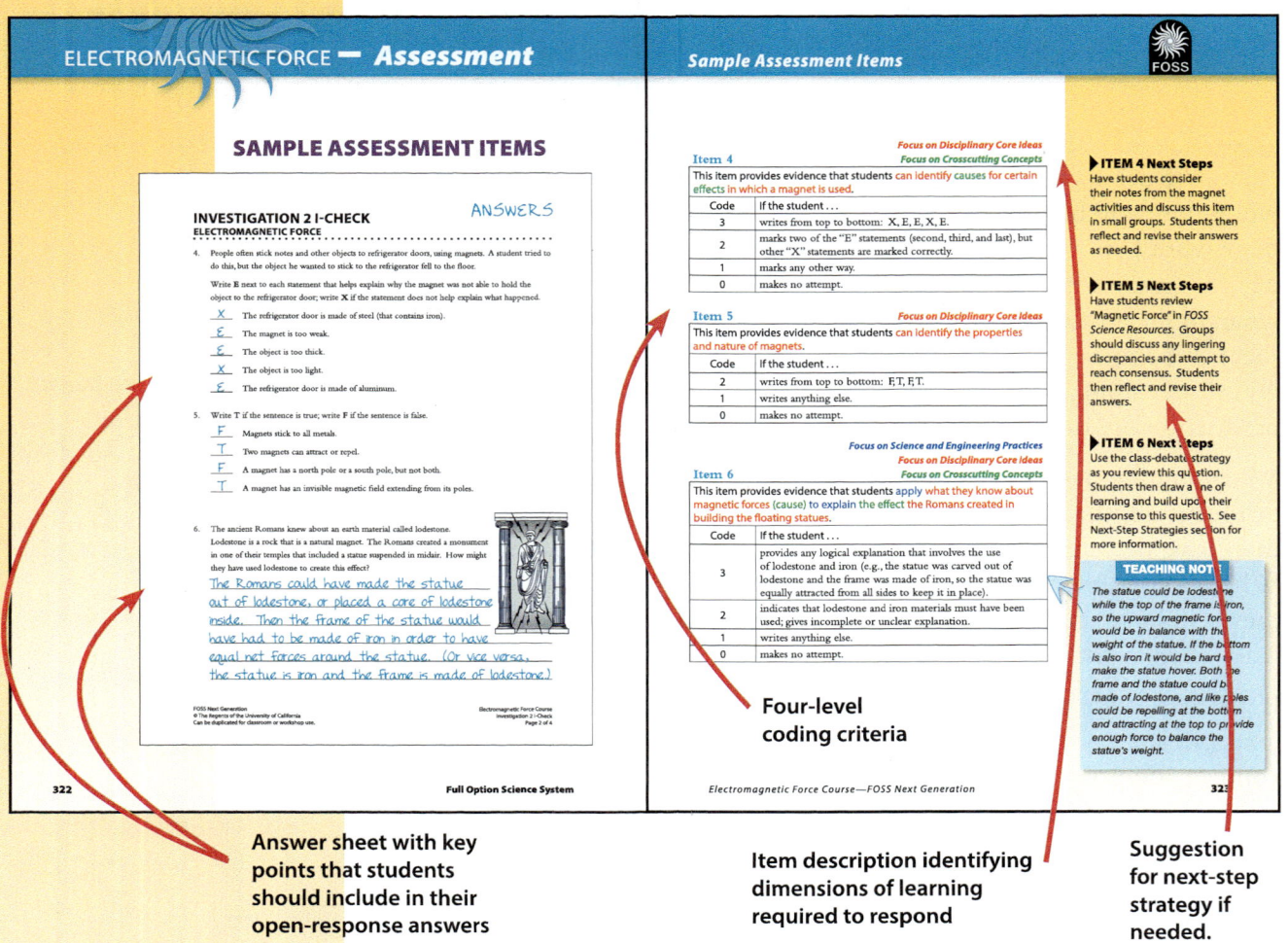

Answer sheet with key points that students should include in their open-response answers

Item description identifying dimensions of learning required to respond

Four-level coding criteria

Suggestion for next-step strategy if needed.

> **NOTE**
> Coding guides for all benchmark assessments are found on FOSSweb.

Coding Benchmark Assessments

Answer sheets and coding guides for all benchmark assessments are available on FOSSweb. A two-page spread has been dedicated to each page of each assessment. Here we show an example for coding a multiple-answer and an open-response question.

Record students' responses on a copy of the appropriate *Assessment Record* or on a spreadsheet. For multiple-choice, multiple-answer, and true-false items, record the letter(s) of the response rather than the code. (Later if you need a total score, you can replace the letter responses with numbers.) For short-answer questions, record the word or the code depending on the answer patterns you want to see. For open-response items, record the code as suggested in the coding guides. Remember not to make any marks on the students' papers. They will do that later during self-assessment activities.

326 Full Option Science System

Next-Step Strategies

NEXT-STEP Strategies

The ASK Project (Assessing Science Knowledge) was funded by the National Science Foundation in 2003. For 5 years, the FOSS development team worked with nine centers around the United States, including more than 500 teachers and their students as research partners. Based on the evidence provided by the assessments, we learned very quickly that assessment is worth doing only if follow-up action is taken to enhance understanding. Self-assessment provides students the opportunity to be responsible for their own learning and is a very effective tool for building students' scientific knowledge and practice.

Self-assessment is more than reading correct answers to the class and having students mark whether they got the right answer. Self-assessment must provide an opportunity for students to reflect on their current thinking and judge whether that thinking needs to change. This kind of reflective process also helps students develop a better understanding of what is expected in terms of well-constructed responses.

> **TEACHING NOTE**
>
> If students have taken an assessment online, print out their responses (the Student Responses Report) and use a projection system and the assessment masters or the PDF to show students the items under discussion.

The Importance of Feedback

Teacher feedback is important for students' understanding of how their conceptual thinking can advance. The science notebook provides an excellent medium for providing feedback to individual students or the class regarding their work. Productive feedback calls for students to listen to or read a teacher comment, think about the issue raised by the comment, and act on it. The feedback might ask for clarification, an example, additional information, precise vocabulary, or review of previous work in the notebook. In this way, you can determine whether the problem relates to flawed understanding of the science content or a breakdown in communication.

Your feedback will also encourage students to take the notebook more seriously and to write more clearly as they attempt to create a complete record of the course. When students use their notebooks as an integral part of their science studies, they think critically about their thinking.

Self-assessment with benchmark assessment items requires deep, thoughtful engagement with complex ideas. It involves students in whole-class or small-group discussion, followed by critical analysis of their own work. For this reason, we suggest that you focus your probing discussions on three or four questions from an I-Check, rather than on the entire assessment. The techniques described here are meant to give you a few strategies for entering the process of self-assessment.

ELECTROMAGNETIC FORCE — Assessment

There is no single right way to engage students in this process: it works best when you change the process from time to time to keep it fresh. The strategies listed here are sorted into two groups: strategies for whole-class feedback, and strategies for individual-student and small-group feedback.

Strategies for the Whole Class

Key points. Discuss the item in question. After it is clear that students understand what is intended by the item prompt, call on individuals or groups to suggest key points that should be included in a complete answer. Write the key points on the board as phrases or individual words that will scaffold students' revision, rather than complete sentences they might mindlessly copy. When students return to their responses, they can number each of the key points they originally included in their answers, then add anything they missed.

Multiple-choice discussions. Students sit in groups of three or four, depending on how many possible answers there were for a given question. You assign an answer to each student (not necessarily the answer they chose). Each student is responsible for explaining to the group whether the assigned answer is correct and why or why not.

Class debate. A student volunteers an answer to an item on an assessment (usually one that many students are having trouble with, or one that elicits a persistent misconception). That student is in charge of the debate. He or she puts forth an answer or explanation. Other students agree or disagree, but must provide evidence to back up their thinking. Students are allowed to disagree with themselves if they hear an argument during the discussion that leads them to change their thinking. You can ask questions to keep the discussion on track, but otherwise you should stay on the sidelines.

Multiple-choice corners. When the class is equally split on what students have chosen as the correct response or only a few students have gotten the correct answer, have them meet in different corners of the room. Those who chose *A* go to one corner, those who chose *B* go to another corner, and so on. Each corner group needs to come up with an argument to convince the other corners that their answer is correct. As in a class debate, students are allowed to disagree with themselves if they become convinced their position is flawed or the reasoning of another group is more convincing. They then move to that corner and continue by helping their new group shape their arguments. (Do not be surprised if you find all students migrating to one corner before the presentation of arguments even begins!)

Next-Step Strategies

Revision with color. Another way that students can revise their answers after a key-points discussion is to use colored pens or pencils and the three Cs. As they read over their responses, they confirm correct information by underlining with a green pen; complete their responses by adding information that was missing, using a blue pen; and correct wrong information, using a red pen.

Review and critique anonymous student work. Use examples of student work from another class, or fabricate student work samples that emulate the problems that students in your class are having. Project the work using an overhead projector, document camera, or interactive whiteboard. Have students discuss the strengths and weaknesses of the responses. This is a good strategy to use when first getting students to write in their notebooks. It helps them understand expectations about what and how much to write.

Line of learning. Many teachers have students use a line of learning to show how their thinking has changed. When students return to original work (embedded or benchmark) to revise their understanding of a concept, they start by drawing a line of learning under the original writing. The line delineates students' original, individual thinking from their thinking after a class or group discussion has helped them reconsider and revise their thoughts.

Group consensus/whiteboards. Have students in each group (or pairs in each group) work together to compare their answers on selected I-Check questions during a class review. First, they create a response that the group agrees is the best answer. Groups write their responses on a whiteboard. When you give a signal, everyone holds their whiteboard up and compares answers. The class discusses any discrepant answers.

Critical competitor. Use the critical-competitor strategy when you want students to attend to a specific detail. You need to present students with two things that are similar in all but one or two aspects. You can use any medium: two drawings, two pieces of writing, or a combination (such as a diagram compared to a description). The point is to compare two pieces of communication or representations in some way that will help students focus on an important detail they may be missing.

> **NOTE**
> You can make inexpensive whiteboards by using card stock and plastic sheet protectors. Students use whiteboard marking pens to write answers. Old socks make great erasers.

Electromagnetic Force Course—FOSS Next Generation

ELECTROMAGNETIC FORCE — **Assessment**

> **NOTE**
> You can also create feedback notes for embedded assessments using FOSSmap.

Sentence frames. After completing other self-assessment activities, have students consider all the items on the assessment and write a short reflection using sentence frames. This strategy allows students to choose one or two items that they would like to tell you more about.

I used to think _____, but now I think _____.

I should have gotten this one right, I just _____.

I know , but I'm still not sure about _____.

The most important thing to remember about _____ is _____.

Can you help me with _____ ?

I shouldn't have gotten this one wrong, because I know _____.

I'm still confused about _____.

Next time, I will remember to _____.

Now I know _____ .

Strategies for Individual Students and Small Groups

Self-stick note feedback. As you read through students' notebooks, add self-stick notes with comments or questions that help guide students to reflect on and improve their understanding.

Conferences. Use opportunities when students work independently, to confer with small groups or individual students.

Work in pairs. Have students work in pairs to continue to explore their ideas and refine their thinking. You might try to pair students so that a student who understands the concept well works with another student who needs some help.

Response log. Set up a response log at the back of students' science notebooks. Fold a notebook page in half, or draw a line down the center of the page. Write "Teacher Feedback" at the top of the left side of the page and "Student Comments" at the top of the right side of the page. When you want a student to think about something in his or her notebook, write your note in the "Teacher Feedback" column (or students can move a self-stick note from another page to the response log). Students then respond in the right-hand column, either addressing your comment there, or telling you which page to turn to in order to see how they have responded.

Next-Step Strategies

Response Log

Teacher Feedback	Student Comments
Response Sheet - Inv. 2 Yes, a magnetic field is at work. Now can you explain how it works? (Make sure you use the word "induce.")	Magnetism is induced in the nail when the permanent magnet comes close to the nail. Now the nail is a magnet, too, and they stick to each other.
Response Sheet - Inv. 3 I see why you agree with student 1. Can you explain your reasoning and why you disagree with student 2?	I disagree with student 2 because electricity can only move through materials that are conductors—not insulators like plastic. Magnetic fields can go through materials that are insulators or conductors as long as they're not steel or iron.

Electromagnetic Force Course—FOSS Next Generation

ELECTROMAGNETIC FORCE – *Assessment*

FOSSMAP *and Online Assessment*

FOSSmap (fossmap.com) is the assessment management program designed specifically for teachers using the FOSS Program in middle school. This user-friendly system allows you to open online assessments for students, to review codes for student responses, and to run reports to help you assess student learning. FOSSmap was developed at the Lawrence Hall of Science in conjunction with the Berkeley Evaluation and Assessment Research (BEAR) center at the University of California, as part of a 5-year research and development project funded by the National Science Foundation. It is based on the tools developed in the Assessing Science Knowledge (ASK) project.

Embedded-assessment data can be entered into FOSSmap to provide evidence of differentiated instruction, to run reports for formative analysis, and to print notes to provide feedback in student notebooks. It is also a tool for teacher reflection and instructional improvement from year to year.

FOSSmap allows you to give students access to the **online assessment** system (fossmap.com/icheck). Students log in to this system to take the benchmark assessments (I-Checks and *Posttest*). Responses are automatically sent to the FOSSmap teacher program, where most are automatically coded. You will need to check short answers (mainly for correct answers that include inventive spelling), and to code open-response items. Students can answer open-response items on the computer or using paper and pencil, depending on the resources you have available.

If you choose to have students take the *Entry-Level Survey* on FOSSmap, the answers will not be coded, but you will be able to look at all of the students' responses in one convenient place, and make notes about each item for use when you teach the different parts of the course.

Navigation page and a sample Embedded Assessment Report

FOSSmap and Online Assessment

FOSSmap Reports

The **Code Frequency Report** tells you at a glance which items were problems for the class. Each bar on the report represents how many students received a particular code. The colored bars indicate how many students received the highest (max) code possible for the item. Green bars indicate that 70% or more students got the highest code. Yellow bars indicate that 51% to 69% of students got the highest code. Red bars indicate that 50% or fewer of the students got the highest code on that item. So the quick and easy way to use this report is to look for the red bars. The red-bar items are the ones you want to take back to students for self-assessment activities.

Run the **Class by Item Report** to get the details on each item, especially the "red bar" problem items from the Code Frequency Report. This report displays students' names for each response, with a brief description of what each code means in terms of full or partial understanding. The report helps you decide what steps need to be taken next.

The **Student Responses Report** provides a printout of individual students' responses to all items answered online (including open-response items if they were typed into the system). This report is useful for student self-assessment activities. You can project the items for class discussion, and students can make notes in their notebooks, add to, or revise answers based on the discussions during the self-assessment activities.

The **Student by Item Report** (a good report to send home to parents) lists all the items on a test and shows how individual students responded to each item. It also provides the correct answer, or max code, and a description of what the student knows or needs to work on, based on the evidence inferred from each item.

The **Class All Codes Report** provides a spreadsheet that can be opened in any spreadsheet program. It gives you a list of the students, the maximum code for each item and the code each student received on each item. You can use this sheet if you want to convert codes into scores in order to determine percentage correct if that is needed for giving grades. To do that, you need to subtract 1 from each code, so that you are not actually awarding a point for wrong answers. Remember though, that FOSS assessments are designed to be diagnostic and not minimum mastery, so you may need to adjust your cut points for giving ABC grades. For example, instead of 90% being an A, you may decide that 80% is a better cut point for an A.

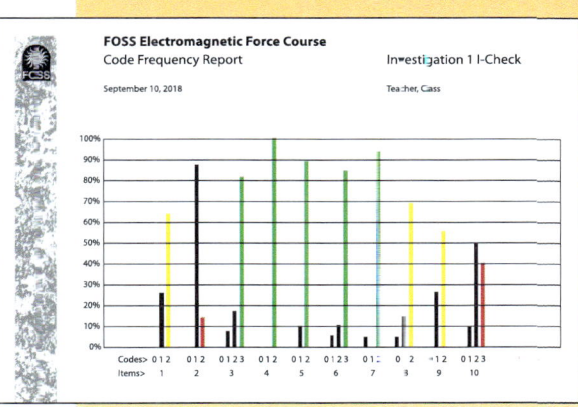

Code Frequency, Class by Item, and Student by Item Reports

Electromagnetic Force Course—FOSS Next Generation

SAMPLE ASSESSMENT ITEMS

INVESTIGATION 2 I-CHECK ANSWERS
ELECTROMAGNETIC FORCE

4. People often stick notes and other objects to refrigerator doors, using magnets. A student tried to do this, but the object he wanted to stick to the refrigerator fell to the floor.

   Write **E** next to each statement that helps explain why the magnet was not able to hold the object to the refrigerator door; write **X** if the statement does not help explain what happened.

   __X__ The refrigerator door is made of steel (that contains iron).
   __E__ The magnet is too weak.
   __E__ The object is too thick.
   __X__ The object is too light.
   __E__ The refrigerator door is made of aluminum.

5. Write **T** if the sentence is true; write **F** if the sentence is false.

   __F__ Magnets stick to all metals.
   __T__ Two magnets can attract or repel.
   __F__ A magnet has a north pole or a south pole, but not both.
   __T__ A magnet has an invisible magnetic field extending from its poles.

6. The ancient Romans knew about an earth material called lodestone. Lodestone is a rock that is a natural magnet. The Romans created a monument in one of their temples that included a statue suspended in midair. How might they have used lodestone to create this effect?

   The Romans could have made the statue out of lodestone, or placed a core of lodestone inside. Then the frame of the statue would have had to be made of iron in order to have equal net forces around the statue. (Or vice versa, the statue is iron and the frame is made of lodestone.)

Sample Assessment Items

Item 4

Focus on Disciplinary Core Ideas
Focus on Crosscutting Concepts

This item provides evidence that students can identify causes for certain effects in which a magnet is used.

Code	If the student . . .
3	writes from top to bottom: X, E, E, X, E.
2	marks two of the "E" statements (second, third, and last), but other "X" statements are marked correctly.
1	marks any other way.
0	makes no attempt.

Item 5

Focus on Disciplinary Core Ideas

This item provides evidence that students can identify the properties and nature of magnets.

Code	If the student . . .
2	writes from top to bottom: F, T, F, T.
1	writes anything else.
0	makes no attempt.

Item 6

Focus on Science and Engineering Practices
Focus on Disciplinary Core Ideas
Focus on Crosscutting Concepts

This item provides evidence that students apply what they know about magnetic forces (cause) to explain the effect the Romans created in building the floating statues.

Code	If the student . . .
3	provides any logical explanation that involves the use of lodestone and iron (e.g., the statue was carved out of lodestone and the frame was made of iron, so the statue was equally attracted from all sides to keep it in place).
2	indicates that lodestone and iron materials must have been used; gives incomplete or unclear explanation.
1	writes anything else.
0	makes no attempt.

▶ **ITEM 4 Next Steps**

Have students consider their notes from the magnet activities and discuss this item in small groups. Students then reflect and revise their answers as needed.

▶ **ITEM 5 Next Steps**

Have students review "Magnetic Force" in *FOSS Science Resources*. Groups should discuss any lingering discrepancies and attempt to reach consensus. Students then reflect and revise their answers.

▶ **ITEM 6 Next Steps**

Use the class-debate strategy as you review this question. Students then draw a line of learning and build upon their response to this question. See Next-Step Strategies section for more information.

TEACHING NOTE

The statue could be lodestone while the top of the frame is iron, so the upward magnetic force would be in balance with the weight of the statue. If the bottom is also iron it would be hard to make the statue hover. Both the frame and the statue could be made of lodestone, and like poles could be repelling at the bottom and attracting at the top to provide enough force to balance the statue's weight.

Electromagnetic Force Course—FOSS Next Generation

SAMPLE ASSESSMENT ITEMS

ANSWERS

INVESTIGATION 2 I-CHECK
ELECTROMAGNETIC FORCE

	Number of steel washers picked up		
Number of magnets	Trial 1	Trial 2	Trial 3
1	8	9	7
2	13	16	14
3	22	23	24

7. Study the data table.

a. What question was this student testing?

(Mark the one best answer.)

- ❍ **A** How many washers can you pick up with a magnet?
- ❍ **B** What is the average number of washers picked up by a magnet?
- ● **C** How does the number of magnets affect the number of washers picked up?
- ❍ **D** How many trials are needed to pick up the most washers?

b. What cause-and-effect relationship can be stated from the data in the table?

(Mark the one best answer.)

- ❍ **F** You can't say because something is wrong with the data; the student should have picked up the same number of washers for each trial.
- ❍ **G** The average number of washers picked up decreases as more magnets are used.
- ❍ **H** The average number of washers one magnet can pick up is 9.
- ● **J** The more magnets you use, the more washers you can pick up.

Sample Assessment Items

Focus on Science and Engineering Practices
Focus on Disciplinary Core Ideas
Focus on Crosscutting Concepts

Item 7

This item provides evidence that students can identify the appropriate question used to conduct an investigation that matches the data in a given table; can determine a cause and effect relationship based on interpretation of data in the table.

Item 7a

Code	If the student...
2	marks C.
1	marks any other way.
0	makes no attempt.

Item 7b

Code	If the student...
2	marks J.
1	marks any other way.
0	makes no attempt.

▶ **ITEM 7ab Next Steps**

If the class is equally divided in their answers, or only a few students have the correct answer, use the multiple-choice-corners strategy to reflect on this item. Or use the multiple-choice-discussion strategy. See the Next-Step Strategies section for more information.

▶ **NOTE**

Look for these resources in the Assessment section in *Teacher Resources* on FOSSweb.

- Assessment chapter
- Assessment masters
- Coding guides
- Assessment charts

Electromagnetic Force Course—FOSS Next Generation

ELECTROMAGNETIC FORCE — Assessment

TEACHER NOTES

TEACHER NOTES

TEACHER NOTES

TEACHER NOTES

TEACHER NOTES

TEACHER NOTES